Between science and philosophy

Consulting editor in philosophy •
V. C. Chappell • *University of Chicago*

Between science and philosophy

An introduction to
the philosophy of science

J. J. C. Smart

The University of Adelaide

Random House • New York

5-26-88

In memory of
Janet

preface

There are at least three types of textbook or treatise on the philosophy of science. First of all there is philosopher's philosophy of science. Such books may be full of rigor, may make use of the techniques of symbolic logic, and may be written at least partly for scientifically competent readers, but the argument is on an abstract level, dealing with certain high-level concepts, such as explanation, law of nature, and confirmation, and does not concern itself much with the actual state of the sciences. Secondly, there is what might be called "baby" philosophy of science: it tries to give a philosophical analysis of actual scientific methods which will be intelligible to students of philosophy who have had practically no scientific education. Thirdly, there is what might be called scientist's philosophy of science: it leans more heavily on actual science than does philosopher's philosophy of science and it assumes at least a little mathematical and scientific sophistication in the reader.

This book is an attempt at a not too technical scientist's philosophy of science in that it is written for readers who have at least something like freshman mathematics and physics in the United States, or A-level school mathematics in England, readers who enjoy such journals as the *Scientific American*. It is not meant to compete with some of the excellent treatises on philosopher's philosophy of science (as by Nagel, Hempel, and Scheffler) but is meant to supplement them. In the United States, more than in Britain or Australia, one finds many philosophy students who have *at least* this minimum of scientific sophistication. This is because the undergraduate colleges of arts and sciences are not broken down into separate "arts" and "science" faculties, as in Britain and Australia. However even in these latter countries one finds *some* undergraduates who manage to straddle the arts-science barrier. (Several of my own best students have come to philosophy only after completing a science or engineering degree.) This book is also written for scientists who are interested in philosophy. I think in particular of some of the scientists and technologists, working in or near Adelaide, who have attended philosophy courses at the university just for the fun of it. There must be many such philosophically interested scientists and technologists all over the world.

A philosophy book inevitably is written from a particular point of view. This is because nearly all philosophical questions are still subjects of controversy. However I have tried to compensate for personal bias by including suggestions for further reading at the end of each chapter. My own personal predilections also account for the selection of topics which are discussed. The reader will surely understand that there are many problems in the philosophy of science other than those which are discussed within this book. At least it is hoped that the reader will become interested in the questions discussed here, and that the book will give him an entry into some lively contemporary controversies and lead him on to interest himself in yet others. For those readers who are trained in science but who have not studied symbolic logic, Chapter 2 is intended as a summary of the leading ideas in the subject which may be needed in subsequent chapters. It is a summary only, and is not meant to be a substitute for a treatise on logic, of which there are many excellent ones. I have also included some discussion of probability in this chapter.

I should like to thank my colleague and former colleague, Mr. M. C. Bradley and Mr. I. C. Hinckfuss, and also Professor C. A. Hurst (of the mathematical physics department of the University of Adelaide) for reading an earlier draft of the book, and for making valuable comments. Professor H. G. Andrewartha, of the zoology department, University of Adelaide, Professor C. L. Hamblin, department of philosophy, University of New South Wales, and my colleague Mr. S. E. Hughes also have kindly commented on parts of the book. I should also like to thank Mrs. Angela Bartesaghi, who typed the manuscript, and Mr. Enrico Beretta, who helped with drawing some of the figures.

J. J. C. Smart
University of Adelaide

contents

1 · Introduction   3

Scope of philosophy of science   3
The scope of science   6
The theory of scientific structure   8
Science and metaphysics   11
Vindication of scientific method   16
Practical importance of philosophy   17
*Interaction between the two sorts of
    philosophy of science*   18
Suggestions for further reading   19

2 · Logic, semantics, and probability   23

Sentential logic   23
Predicate logic   26
Definite descriptions   31
Elementary number theory   32
Set theory   33   **xi**

Contents

Semantics and truth   36
Use and mention   37
Extensional and intensional contexts   39
Probability   40
The frequency interpretation of probability
  and the propensity interpretation   46
Suggestions for further reading   49

3 · Explanation, laws, and theories   53

Preliminary remarks on explanation   53
What is explanation?   56
The deductive-nomological pattern of
  explanation   58
Statistical explanation   65
Incomplete explanation   67
Explanation sketches   70
Explanation as analogy   71
Explanation as reduction to the familiar   74
Explanation as redescription   75
Feyerabend's criticism of the deductive model   76
Criticisms of Feyerabend's use of the concept
  of "meaning"   83
Theory-neutral concepts and common sense   85
Suggestions for further reading   88

4 · Explanation in biological sciences   91

Historical sciences   91
Natural history and taxonomy in biology   92
Explanation in biology   97
Teleological and evolutionary explanation in
  biology   100
Mathematics in ecology and evolutionary
  theory   107
Cosmic biology   108
Psychology   112
Suggestions for further reading   119

Contents

5 · Laws and theories in physics   121

Experimental laws, measurement, and approximation   121
Theories as pictures of reality   133
Instrumentalism and operationism   138
Metaphysical critique of instrumentalism and operationism   141
Methodological critique of instrumentalism   155
Quantum mechanics and instrumentalism   157
Laws, theories, and logic   163
Suggestions for further reading   171

6 · Induction and hypothesis   175

The philosophical problem of induction   175
Duhem's objection to the asymmetry between confirmation and refutation   200
Conclusion   202
Suggestions for further reading   203

7 · Space and time   207

Some philosophical theories about space   207
Newton's theory of space and time   209
Kant's example of the left hand and the right hand   217
Space-time in special relativity   218
The clock paradox   228
Space-time in general relativity   237
Geometry and physics   241
Suggestions for further reading   253

8 · Direction in time   255

The supposed passage of time   255
Temporal asymmetry and statistical mechanics   259
The principle of retarded waves   276

Temporal asymmetry and the expansion of   278
   the universe

Suggestions for further reading   288

9 · Determinism, free will, and intelligence   291

Determinism and indeterminism   291
Free will and determinism   298
Creativity and intelligence   306
Purposive mechanisms   321
Psycholinguistics and the Kantian problem   327

Suggestions for further reading   329

Reference notes   331

Index   349

Between science and philosophy

1

Introduction

Scope of philosophy of science

Since philosophers notoriously disagree among themselves about the scope and methodology of their subject, it is not possible to give a neat or universally acceptable definition of the field of philosophy of science. Disagreements about the scope of philosophy lead to disagreements about the scope of philosophy of science. But even if a neat delineation of the field of philosophy of science were possible, it would not be particularly desirable. Suppose that such a delineation were made, and a specialist in philosophy of science came across a problem which interested him, which he felt competent to investigate, and which lay just across the border of his field as thus delineated. Surely we would not want to discourage him from investigating this problem. It is important to prevent the rather rigid departmentalization which is typical of the administrative structure of universities from also partitioning too much our intellectual activities and interests. As the various sciences and philosophy, logic and mathematics, progress and develop, so the ways in which it is useful to classify the various intellectual activities change too. Consider for example the exciting field of modern structural linguistics and associated investigations into machine translation of languages. A \/orker in this field will find himself reading journals devoted to philology, psychology, mathematical logic, the theory of computability, electronics, and philosophy. Such a conjunction of disciplines would have looked very odd even a generation ago. Such new groupings of disciplines provide a hunting ground for the philosopher because conceptual problems which he recognizes as typically philosophical must inevitably arise when the specialized idiolects of previously unrelated, or hardly related, disciplines have to be brought together. In such a situation we find the philosopher learning about some specialities (such as structural linguistics or electronics) and we find the scientific specialists becoming interested in philosophy.

One way to indicate the field which in this book will be "philosophy of science" would be to say that we shall be concerned with the kinds of topics which are discussed in the American journal *Philosophy of Science* and *The British Journal for the Philosophy of Science*. Certainly if a non-philosopher were to ask "What is philosophy of science?" the simplest way to answer him would be to tell him to go to the library and have a look at a few copies of these two journals. If he were to do this he might notice that the questions dealt with are of two main kinds, or else are perhaps blends of these two main kinds. On the one hand we find discussions *about* science: among these are discussions of the patterns of scientific argument, the ways in which scientific theories are tested, the nature of laws and theories, the ways in which scientific concepts are defined or otherwise introduced, what makes a law or theory come to be regarded as more or less "simple" than another one, and whether scientific method in general can be defended against the skeptical arguments which have

4

been familiar since the days of David Hume. On the other hand we find philosophical discourse which is not so much *about* science but which *uses* science: it may turn out that the results of scientific investigation may help us to answer some of the questions about man and the universe with which philosophers have traditionally been concerned. For example, I should hold that scientific results either are or will be relevant to the question about whether space and time (or perhaps space-time) should be thought of as absolute or relational, and again that scientific theories enable us to understand why time appears to run one way. Further, to take another field of interest, the questions of the relation between mind and matter and of the freedom of the will are perhaps illuminated by modern neurophysiology, and by cybernetics (the theory of information and control, including the study of computers).

In short, philosophy of science can be conceived of as having two main components: (1) analytical and methodological talk *about* science, and (2) the use of science to help with the solution of problems generally recognized as philosophical. If it is objected that the use of science to attack a problem makes this problem automatically a scientific one, not a philosophical one, we may reiterate our objection to compartmentalizing academic disciplines, and may disclaim interest in whether someone else prefers to label the question "scientific" rather than "philosophical." There is no need for intellectual trade unionism, and if a member of a philosophical department feels both interested in a question and competent to answer it, it should not worry him that he does not wear a white coat or peer through a microscope or have "department of mathematical physics" written at the end of his corridor. Moreover, even though a scientific theory may be used to deal with questions which are commonly regarded as philosophical, it may not be possible to use it in a straightforward manner, since the question may be rather speculative

5

or may be full of the kinds of conceptual oddities and uncertainties which commonly bedevil philosophical discussions of any sort. Though scientific results and methods may be needed to deal with a question, scientific skills may not be so important as philosophical clear-headedness in disentangling concepts from one another and in applying the scientific results. This does not of course make a sharp distinction between philosophy and science, since scientists, in certain fields at least, have to do a good deal of conceptual innovation and clarification before getting on with the mathematics and chemistry. The difference is one of emphasis. Indeed as far as conceptual *innovation* is concerned it could well be argued that the metaphysicians have been far outstripped in versatility and subtlety by mathematicians and physicists. A further reason why certain applications of science are nevertheless felt to be philosophical is that they involve several different branches of science, and so are not the prerogative of any particular specialist anyway.

The scope of science

The scope of philosophy of science also depends on the scope of science. For example, some books on philosophy of science concern themselves with the analysis and methodology of explanation in general, and so their field covers not only the conceptual analysis and methodology of the physical and biological sciences but also that of sociology and history. In this book I shall exclude sociology and history and confine myself to the physical and biological sciences. Much of history is narrative, and insofar as it goes beyond narrative and gives explanations it normally uses fairly commonplace knowledge about men's desires, motives, and beliefs. Again, sociology deals with facts about particular groups of people, and like history it does not use much in the way of general principles other than those of a fairly commonsense sort. It is true that it supplements commonsense principles with some less obvious ones which are derived from statistical analyses of sets of particular observations, but these principles can be taken only as approximately valid of particular cultures and groups and are far from being laws of nature. Of course some fields of study which are commonly regarded as sciences, and which will be taken as such in this book, are historical in nature in that they deal with particular facts. Nevertheless they make use of the physical and biological sciences in a way in which history and sociology usually do not. Thus though geology and astronomy deal with particular facts, they use high-level theories of physics and chemistry in their explanations of these particular facts, and astronomical facts are often used in order to test physical theories. Again, the so-called theory of evolution is historical in nature, since it is concerned with a particular (though long-lasting) terrestrial process but it is closely tied in with biological sciences, such as genetics and biochemistry.

For the purposes of the present book, therefore, I shall take "science" to cover physics, chemistry, astronomy, geology, and the biological sciences, including experimental psychology, but not the social sciences and history. I have long been puzzled as to where to classify economics. I have been tempted to regard it not as descriptive but as an idealization comparable to the mathematical theory of games, but of course much of economics *is* meant to be descriptive, and deals with matters of historical fact and their explanations. It does not seem to contain laws of nature in the way in which physics does, and yet economists are often employed as professional purveyors of predictions in a way in which historians hardly ever are. So far there seems to be lacking a philosophy of economics which places it correctly and perspicuously on the intellectual map, and there is useful work to be done by philosophically minded economists and economically minded philoso-

7

phers. At any rate economics will not be regarded as coming within the purview of this book. Though we shall not be concerned with the philosophy of history as such, there will, however, have to be some discussion of the historical pattern of explanation, since there are arguments about biological evolution and in geology and astronomy which are from the logical point of view historical in nature, since they provide explanations of particular facts, even though they use general premises which are drawn from the sciences, and do not depend mainly on commonsense generalizations.[1]

The theory of scientific structure

There are some terms which are common to discourse about various different branches of science, though they do not occur essentially in discourse about the subject matters of these branches of science. Thus any scientist who talks about electrons or genes or stars may also want to say things about his statements *about* the electrons or genes or stars. He is then talking not about the subject matter of his science but about the statements of his science. For example he may want to say that they form part of a *theory* or *hypothesis*, that they express a *law* or report an *observation*, or that some of them are *evidence* for others. Consider, then, such words as "theory", "hypothesis", "law", "observation statement", "explain", "evidence". These terms occur in discourse about any science, no matter what its subject matter is. Israel Scheffler[2]* has called them "structural terms". They are used to describe the structure of scientific discourse. Though they occur within scientific books, we could nevertheless imagine all

[1]Of course even human history has in rare cases made use of sophisticated scientific theories. For example the failure of a fleet to depart from a port has been explained by an astronomical retrodiction of neap tides on the date in question.[1]* If this sort of thing were much more common, historians might be thought of as scientists more than they now are.

*Reference Notes appear at the end of the book, pp. 331–347.

scientific explanations being given without them. They occur only when the scientist stands back from his work and tells us what he is doing, instead of actually getting on with doing it. It is obvious, for example, that Newton's third law of motion could have been stated quite adequately even if it had never been flagged with the word "law", and the genetical explanation of the relative prevalence of sickle cell anemia in malarial countries could have been given without being flagged with the word "explanation".

Notice that these terms are structural in the sense that they are used to *describe* structure, but not to create structure themselves. That is, they are not structural in quite the same sense as that in which the terms of logic, such as "not", "or", "and", "if", "all", and "some" are sometimes called "structural". Notice also that though these latter terms do of course occur in all discourse about different sciences, they also occur within the sciences themselves. The logical expressions are structural elements *of* sentences, not descriptive terms *about* structure. For this reason it is perhaps wise to avoid referring to investigations of scientific structure in Scheffler's sense as "the logic of science", even though many philosophers, especially some of those influenced by Wittgenstein, may be tempted to do so. (Scheffler himself avoids this temptation.) After all, in the sense in which the word "logic" will be used in this book (and as it will be elucidated in Chapter 2) there is no special logic of science. Science uses the same logic as any other sort of discourse, for example mathematics, history, theology, ethics, political theory.

Scheffler conceives of a very general theory of scientific structure which is designed to give an understanding of the structural terms,[3] and since many such terms belong not only to discourse about the various sciences but also to parts of commonsense discourse (consider the detective's "hypothesis" or "explanation") there is no sharp line between the theory of scientific

9

structure and general epistemology (theory of knowledge). Scheffler therefore operates on a very high plane of abstraction. Following a suggestion of Noam Chomsky's, he compares the relation between, on the one hand, the theory of scientific structure and, on the other hand, the use of the structural terms in relation to particular sciences, with the relation between the general theory of structural linguistics[2] and the grammars of particular languages. Of course, just as the theories of structural linguistics have to be tested by considering their applicability to the various grammars of particular languages, so the theory of scientific structure has to be tested by seeing how it works out in relation to more particular discourse about the structures of the various sciences, as well as in relation to discourse about commonsense explanatory talk. Nevertheless the fact that Scheffler works in considerable abstraction from actual scientific discourse is emphasized by the fact that the names "Einstein", "Newton", "Darwin", and "Mendel" are absent from the index to his book. His book is of course none the worse for that: indeed in the light of his aims and his philosophical methods this abstraction is a virtue. However a more concrete approach also has its virtues, since there are many problems which depend on an appreciation of *differences* among the various sciences and parts of science, and these differences in structure may be traceable to empirical differences in the objects which are discussed in these sciences or parts of science. Thus, as I shall try to show in Chapter 4, there are structural and methodological differences between physics and biology which depend on some very general facts about the world. It may even be the case that the differences between explanations and hypotheses in the various sciences (or groups of sciences) may be of as much philosophical consequence as are the similarities. In which case a more concrete

[2]A field to which Chomsky has of course made outstanding contributions.[4]

approach, with a closer eye to actual scientific theories, may be of some value.

Science and metaphysics

As was noted earlier, besides philosophy of science conceived of as the analysis of the structure and methods of science, there is philosophy of science conceived of as the application of scientific knowledge to the solution of philosophical problems. Chapters 7-9 will be mostly concerned with philosophy of science of this second kind. If it is agreed that it is science which fashions our world view, surely it must be agreed that science has something to tell us about some of the large questions about man and the rest of the universe with which metaphysicians have traditionally been concerned. Of course these questions can sometimes be discussed only very tentatively and may depend on rather speculative branches of science, such as cosmology. They may also depend on some sort of synthesis of the special sciences.

Since Ludwig Wittgenstein, a climate of philosophical opinion has arisen according to which science is irrelevant to the solving of philosophical problems. Let us therefore pause to discuss the sort of objection which many philosophers would make against the remarks of the previous paragraph. It will be convenient to fasten on some trenchant remarks of W. H. Watson in his book *On Understanding Science*.[5] Watson is a physicist who attended lectures by Wittgenstein in 1929-1931 and was much influenced by Wittgenstein's philosophy. His first criticism of synthetic philosophy is that if philosophy were some sort of synthesis of the special sciences then it would decide nothing: it would be based on particular scientific theories, and it would be the scientists who would decide whether these theories should be accepted or whether they should be discarded as a

11

result of new experiments and observations.[6] The answer to this criticism is surely a fairly simple one, namely that the synthetic philosopher does not claim to "decide things" in this sense. He is concerned with relating the various sciences to one another, and he takes his raw material (the various extant scientific theories) from the scientific specialists. He does not decide what these theories are, but he does claim to decide what is the best unified conceptual scheme whereby they might be synthesized. Curiously enough the synthetic philosopher may find himself involved in the very activities which are commended by those "analytic" philosophers who are hostile to the idea of a synoptic philosophy. For the synthetic philosopher will have to clear away the conceptual confusions which often arise on the borders between different disciplines (where different sciences tend to use different types of concepts in order to deal with the same subject matter). That is, the synthetic philosopher will be engaged in much of the same general sort of activity which is described and carried out by Gilbert Ryle in his book *Dilemmas*,[7] namely the investigation and adjudication of borderline disputes. For example it will be argued in Chapter 9 that it is conceptual confusion in relating different realms of discourse which leads many physicists to think that Heisenberg's uncertainty principle has anything to do with the problem of free will. This is the negative part of synthetic philosophy. The positive part, which the Wittgensteinian or analytic philosophers deny to be part of philosophy, is the use of *other* scientific results to bear on the problem. Even though we may argue that some scientific results (Heisenberg's uncertainty principle, for example) do *not* bear on the problem of free will, it can also be argued that other scientific results *do* bear on this problem.

The above considerations suggest a further defense of the idea of synthetic philosophy. Since specialists in the various sciences do not commonly think much about other sciences, there does seem to be a place in the intellectual world for a man who tries to keep an eye, however inexpertly, on all of them, and to see how they are related to one another. To say that such a man "decides nothing" is no more sensible than it would be to say that a theoretical physicist "decides nothing" because it is the experimentalist who provides the crucial data. I would indeed concede that the synthetic philosopher is a less important person than the physicist. Certainly it seems to me that theoretical physicists have far outstripped philosophers in their imaginativeness and in their powers of conceptual innovation and analysis. But to concede this much is not to deny that there is a place for the synthetic philosopher: to try to see the world not as a physicist or chemist or biologist or psychologist but as a complete whole is surely something which is worth doing for its own sake.

We must not think that all we need to do in order to achieve a philosophical synthesis is to be encyclopedic: simply to conjoin summaries of the various sciences. If this were so, then there would be no great difference between the synthetic philosopher and the all-round popularizer of science. Such a merely encyclopedic activity is not good enough, however, because of the conceptual troubles which, as we have noted, lie on the borderlines between different sciences. It needs someone like a philosopher to bring things together. We may recall Ryle's conception of the philosopher as concerned with the adjudication of borderline disputes between different sciences. According to Ryle, when two fields appear to conflict, we generally find that the conflict is not a real one, and that when sufficient clarification has been achieved both sides can be satisfied. As against this, I think that we should be much more willing to suppose that one of the disputants may simply turn out to be wrong. This is especially so when the conflict is between a science and a commonsense or traditional belief. At the other extreme, borderline disputes can occur even between conceptual schemes within a single science. We shall subsequently be discussing some of the difficulties which seem to arise in relating phenomenological and statistical thermodynamics.[3] Some scientists and philosophers would wish to hold that both forms of thermodynamics can be retained, and that the apparent conflicts between them can be resolved, whereas others would say that statistical thermodynamics simply shows the falsity of phenomenological thermodynamics.

However, Watson has a second criticism of the idea of synthetic philosophy, which is stronger than his first criticism because if it is accepted then the previous one becomes unnecessary. Watson says that any statement either is "on the same level" as a statement of scientific fact or it is nonsense. Here Watson is apparently influenced by the view expressed in Wittgenstein's *Tractatus Logico-Philosophicus*.[8] In the *Tractatus* Wittgenstein held that all meaningful sentences are pictures of facts or complexes (truth functions[4]) of pictures of facts. This ties in with a view of science as an accumulation of pictures, and of a synthesis of the sciences as just an accumulation of accumulations of pictures, that is, just one big accumulation. According to the picture theory a scientific innovation would consist in the reallocation of the truth values ("true" or "false") which we had previously assigned to sentences, or perhaps in assigning truth values to sentences which had previously not been considered or which had not been assigned truth values. However, we shall see that the development of science does not fit this accumulative or reallocatory pattern and that typically it involves radical changes in conceptual schemes. (It should be noted that Wittgenstein himself came to give up his *Tractatus* view of language and his later views do not support the dichotomy "either statement of scientific fact or nonsense".) The

[3]See pp. 77–83 below.
[4]See pp. 23–26 below.

fitting together of the diverse conceptual schemes of science involves a standing back from the concepts, a looking at them, or to revert to Watson's metaphor of level, an ascent to a higher linguistic level where temporarily we have to talk about the theories of physics, biology, etc., rather than about the objects of these sciences. A good example of a philosopher who makes masterly use of such temporary linguistic ascent is W. V. Quine.[9] He thinks that a major aim of philosophy is the discovery of the language which is most economical in its ontological commitments and which is yet capable of expressing total science. This comes very near to trying to find the simplest possible synoptic theory about the world.

In insisting upon the atomic (or at least discrete) nature of facts Watson opposes a writer in the *Encyclopaedia Britannica*,[10] who in the spirit of idealist philosophy insists that the world is not a collection of individual facts "existing side by side and capable of being known separately". According to this writer, a fact "is nothing except in its relation to other facts; and as these relations are multiplied in the progress of knowledge, the nature of the so-called fact is indefinitely modified". Divesting this of the terminology of idealist philosophy, what it comes to is that even observation sentences are theory laden and can not be understood apart from the theoretical conceptions with which they are laden. If we pursue this line of thought further it does not seem so obviously absurd that the facts of the special sciences might be seen differently when they are looked at from the point of view of a philosophical synopsis, or that a synthetic philosophy might react back on the special sciences with which it starts, albeit in a way which might be of little *practical* importance to specialists. The suggestion is not so absurd as it looks from the perspective of a "picture" theory of how our language represents the world. We need not be idealists to recognize some good insights in the writings of idealist philosophers. Watson's criticism loses its force once we give up the picture theory of language on which it seems to be based.

Vindication of scientific method

In the previous section I have tried to show how the view that philosophy can be some sort of *superstructure* on the sciences might be defended against the kind of objection put forward by Watson. Let us now look at the view that philosophy might also provide some sort of *substructure* or foundation for science. This view is surely absurd if it means that a physicist or a geneticist, say, should feel insecure until he had laid a philosophical foundation. There is no reason why we should expect him to solve the problems raised by skeptical philosophers. Indeed, unless he is going to divert his energies, he would be well advised to ignore the philosophical skeptic. Nevertheless this does not contradict the fact that a philosopher may be interested in asking why it is (as he surely believes that it is) that science is better than magic or witchcraft. Of course it is pretty obvious that there are good scientific reasons for preferring science to magic, but then, presumably, there would be good magical reasons for preferring magic to science. Can science be justified against magic only in a patently circular way? In Chapter 6 we shall come across two possible ways of justifying scientific method, "validation" and "vindication". (This distinction between validation and vindication was made by Herbert Feigl. [11]) It is generally agreed that the validation of scientific method is impossible, but many philosophers hold that the other and weaker sort of justification, namely vindication, can be achieved. The question of whether or not this is so is surely an important topic for the philosopher to study.

Practical importance of philosophy

No one can deny the practical importance of the sciences, since so many of their exciting technological applications are familiar to us. By comparison philosophy (including philosophy of science) would seem to have little practical importance. Nevertheless it would be unwise to think that philosophy is exclusively a subject for inhabitants of ivory towers, and that it does not in its own way possess practical value. The practical importance of philosophy is three-fold: (1) Insofar as it is the art of conceptual clarification, it provides a training in thinking clearly about unclear matters. This obviously will be of value if this ability can be transferred to ethical, political, and religious thinking, all of which clearly affect men in a practical way. (2) Insofar as some, at least, of the conceptual clarifications determined by the philosopher of science help the scientist to formulate better theories, this philosophical thinking has indirect practical value via the practical value of the scientific theories in question. (3) Insofar as philosophy is synoptic and speculative, it can have practical effects in suggesting the scientific theories of the future. Consider the way in which Democritus' metaphysical atomic theory must have infected the cultures of later ages, thus facilitating the invention of fruitful and testable scientific theories. Modern speculations about possible alternatives to the Copenhagen interpretation of quantum mechanics[5] possibly fall into this category of untestable and as yet metaphysical hypotheses which may nevertheless help to bring about scientifically fruitful theories. However, we must not forget the harm that can be done to science if we allow ourselves to be fascinated too much by any one speculative philosophical system, since it may prevent our thinking from breaking

[5]See pp. 157–163 below.   17

out of an unproductive mold. For example, before mathematicians could get non-Euclidean geometries to be taken seriously, they had to overcome prejudices derived from Kantian philosophy. Albert Einstein, in his "Autobiographical Notes",[12] says that in inventing the special theory of relativity "The type of critical reasoning which was required for the discovery of this central point was decisively furthered . . . especially by the reading of David Hume's and Ernst Mach's philosophical writings". It could be argued, however, that the influence of Hume and Mach was not altogether beneficial, since Einstein's early papers on relativity are couched in an unnecessarily operationist[6] form which is misleading and inconsistent with Einstein's later philosophical outlook, and indeed with Einstein's own scientific practice.

Interaction between the two sorts of philosophy of science

In this chapter I have distinguished two sorts of philosophy of science: (1) conceptual and methodological analysis of science, and (2) application of scientific knowledge towards the solution of problems which have been regarded as philosophical. It might be thought that there is little connection between these two sorts of activities other than the fact that they are both pursued by philosophers who are interested in science and hence that they both tend to appear within journals such as *Philosophy of Science*. However the connection is closer than this, since many activities in philosophy of science are neither (1) in a pure form nor (2) in a pure form, but are a blend of the two. For this reason it might be better to describe (1) and (2) as two *components*[7] in the philosophy of science. That is, we shall often get (1) and (2) together. We may get (1) in a

---

[6]On operationism see Chapter 5 below.
[7]Analogous to components of a vector.

pure form, but not, I think, (2) in a pure form. This is because a problem which is felt to be philosophical, but for
which scientific knowledge is relevant, can hardly be a
straightforward scientific problem. It must involve elements of conceptual confusion as well as of scientific
problematics, since otherwise it would presumably have
been recognized as a scientific question, not a philosophical one. Even if a problem were of great human
emotional interest, like the problems of free will and
immortality, it would presumably not be felt to be philosophical if it were obviously one to be decided within a
special science. After all, the questions raised by biologists about the possible causes of cancer are certainly of
great human interest, but no one thinks of them as
philosophical. The salient point is that conceptual clarification is needed before purely scientific method can
be applied to the solution of the sort of problem which
we feel to be philosophical. There can also be a feed-
back from scientific knowledge to methodology. For
example in Chapter 4 we shall see that empirical facts
about organisms imply certain conclusions about the
conceptual structure and methodology of the biological
sciences, which makes them differ importantly from the
sciences of physics and chemistry.

SUGGESTIONS FOR FURTHER READING

In the text, reference has been made to Israel Scheffler, *The Anatomy of Inquiry* (New York: Alfred A. Knopf, 1963), and W. H. Watson,
On Understanding Physics (London: Cambridge University Press,
1938). Scheffler's book is a valuable treatise concerning the nature of
explanation, the criteria of significance of scientific language, and the
theory of confirmation. Watson's book is a difficult and original application of some of Wittgenstein's ideas to the conceptual clarification
of physics. A sequel (or "remote descendant" as the author calls it), is
W. H. Watson, *Understanding Physics Today* (London: Cambridge
University Press, 1963). Excellent treatises on philosophy of science
from the point of view of empiricist and analytic philosophy are R. B.
Braithwaite, *Scientific Explanation* (London: Cambridge University

19

Press, 1953, and paperback, New York: Harper and Row, 1960), and Ernest Nagel, *The Structure of Science* (New York: Harcourt, Brace and World, 1961). More elementary introductions are C. G. Hempel, *Philosophy of Natural Science* (Englewood Cliffs, N. J.: Prentice-Hall, 1966), A. Pap, *An Introduction to the Philosophy of Science* (New York: Free Press, 1962), and Rudolf Carnap (Martin Gardner, ed.), *Philosophical Foundations of Physics, An Introduction to the Philosophy of Science* (New York: Basic Books, 1966). An elementary introduction from a neo-Wittgensteinian standpoint is Stephen Toulmin, *Philosophy of Science* (London: Hutchinson, 1953, and paperback, New York: Harper and Row, 1960). Toulmin is writing for nonscientific readers and makes ingenious use of very simple illustrative examples. Another much more difficult book, which is also written from a neo-Wittgensteinian point of view and which requires more scientific competence from the reader, is N. R. Hanson, *Patterns of Discovery* (London: Cambridge University Press, 1958, and paperback, New York: Cambridge University Press, 1965). K. R. Popper, *The Logic of Scientific Discovery* (London: Hutchinson, 1959, and paperback, rev. ed., New York: Harper and Row, 1965) is one of the most controversial and influential treatises on the philosophy of science written in the present century.

A number of useful articles on the philosophy of science have been collected in H. Feigl and M. Brodbeck (eds.), *Readings in the Philosophy of Science* (New York: Appleton-Century-Crofts, 1953), and in A. Danto and S. Morgenbesser (eds.), *Philosophy of Science* (New York: Meridian Books, 1960).

Particularly good examples of philosophy of science in the sense of an application of scientific results to philosophical questions can be found in H. Reichenbach, *The Direction of Time* (Berkeley: University of California Press, 1956), and A. Grünbaum, *Philosophical Problems of Space and Time* (New York: Alfred A. Knopf, 1964).

My own philosophical approach has changed considerably over the past ten years or so. At one time I wrote an article, which was written much in the spirit of a Wittgensteinian point of view similar to that of W. H. Watson, and with which I now thoroughly disagree. See J. J. C. Smart, "The Relevance of Modern Analytic Philosophy for Science", *Australian Journal of Science*, XVI (1954), 165–170 and 215–218. For my present views see J. J. C. Smart, "Philosophy and Scientific Plausibility", in Paul K. Feyerabend and Grover Maxwell (eds.), *Mind, Matter and Method, Essays in Honor of Herbert Feigl* (Minneapolis: University of Minnesota Press, 1966), pp. 377–390. An interesting critique of the modern analytic and neo-Wittgensteinian approach to the philosophy of science is given by P. K. Feyerabend in his provocative paper "Problems of Empiricism", in R. G. Colodny (ed.), *Beyond the Edge of Certainty* (Englewood Cliffs, N. J.: Prentice-Hall, 1965) pp. 145–260. Wittgenstein did not write much explicitly on the philosophy of science, but his earlier position is that of his *Tractatus Logico-Philosophicus* and his later position is best exemplified by his posthumously published *Philosophical Investigations* (Oxford: Blackwell, 1953). Before his death his ideas had come to permeate much of

20

British and American philosophy, through his lectures and the influence of his pupils. An interesting recent paper on the relations between philosophy and science, which is written from a point of view which is in some respects different from any considered in the present book, is S. Körner, "Some Relations between Philosophical and Scientific Theories", *British Journal for the Philosophy of Science,* XVII (1966–67), 265–278.

2
Logic, semantics and probability[1]

Sentential logic

Consider the sentences "Jim is tall" and "Jill is freckled". Out of these we can make complex sentences such as "Jim is tall or Jill is freckled", "Jim is tall and Jill is freckled", and "if Jim is tall then Jill is freckled". We can also use "not" to make a new sentence out of a single one: e.g., "not (Jim is tall)" or more colloquially "it is not the case that Jim is tall". Instead of "not (Jim is tall)" in colloquial language we say "Jim is not tall", but in logic we put the "not" outside the sentence. That is, "not" in logic should be read as "it is not the case that". It should be noticed that putting "not" outside a sen-

---

[1]Much of this chapter consists of a summary of certain technicalities in logic, proof theory, and semantics which will be needed as background for the rest of the book. It is written partly for scientific readers who lack this background. It must be emphasized that it is merely a summary of concepts and results which are relevant to subsequent parts of the book. For details and proofs the interested reader is asked to consult the relevant treatises, some of which are mentioned in the Suggestions for Further Reading at the end of the chapter. Philosophers or students of philosophy to whom this material is already familiar may wish to skip it. The concluding part of the chapter on probability is more controversial.

tence may sometimes involve the recasting of the sentence itself. Thus though "Jim is not tall" means the same as "not (Jim is tall)", the colloquial English "some men are not tall" can not be rendered by "not (some men are tall)" (which could be true if there were no men at all), and must be rendered by the more complicated "there are some men and not (all men are tall)".

The words "or", "and", and "if ... then ..." to which we can add "... if and only if ...", are binary sentence connectives. "Not" can be thought of as a unary sentence connective. These sentence connectives are written in logical symbolism as "•" for "and", "∨" for "or", "⊃" for "if ... then ...", "≡" for "... if and only if ...", and "∼" for "not". They can be defined by means of the following truth tables. Thus the truth table for "⊃" gives the truth values (*true* or *false*) of "$p \supset q$" for the various combinations of truth values of "p" and "q". (We can think of "p", "q", etc., as dummy sentences, and "$p \supset q$", for example, is a "sentence schema" which becomes a sentence if "p" and "q" are replaced by appropriate sentences.)

TABLE 1

p	q	∼p	p • q	p ∨ q	p ⊃ q	p ≡ q
T	T	F	T	T	T	T
F	T	T	F	T	T	F
T	F	F	F	T	F	F
F	F	T	F	F	T	T

Thus the table for "$p \supset q$" shows that the compound sentence is true in every case except that in which the left hand component is true and the right hand component is false. Some philosophers doubt whether "⊃" means the same as "if ... then ..." in ordinary language. Certainly we may agree that it is odd to say "if $2 + 2 = 5$ then there is a satellite of the earth". Nevertheless the oddness of saying this does not prove that it has a different meaning from "$2 + 2 = 5 \supset$ there is a satellite of the earth" (which is clearly true). The oddness may simply arise from the fact that it is rather pointless to assert such an obvious and useless truth as "$2 + 2 = 5 \supset$ there is a satellite of the earth". In any case the question of whether the logical connectives mean exactly the same as the corresponding ordinary language ones is rather profitless. They do most, and perhaps all, the jobs that a mathematician or scientist requires of the connectives, and they are clearly defined and free from ambiguity.

We can build up more and more complex sentence schemata by iterating applications of the sentence connectives. Thus consider the schema:

$$[\sim (p \bullet q) \lor (p \lor r)] \supset (q \supset \sim s)$$

This becomes a determinate sentence if the sentence letters are replaced by sentences. Some sentence schemata must take the value "true" no matter what the truth values of the sentences which replace the sentence letters. Thus whether we replace the "p" in "$p \lor \sim p$" with a true sentence like "$2 + 2 = 4$" or a false one like "$2 + 2 = 5$" the combination "$p \lor \sim p$" must be true. (The truth of "it is raining or it is not raining" does not depend upon the weather.) Sentence schemata which come out true no matter what truth values we assign to the sentence letters are called *tautologous* or *valid* sentence schemata.

More complex examples of valid sentence schemata are:

(1) $\sim (p \bullet q) \equiv (\sim p \lor \sim q)$
(2) $[(p \supset q) \lor (p \supset r)] \supset [p \supset (q \lor r)]$

There is a mechanical method (the method of truth tables) whereby we can tell whether or not a sentence schema of propositional logic is a valid one. We simply consider all the possible combinations of truth values for the sentence letters in our schemata. There are 4 combinations in the case of (1) above and 8 in the case of (2). If we have n sentence letters there will be 2^n combinations to be considered. By reiterating applications of the truth table definitions of the sentence connectives, for each of these combinations, we find out the truth value of the complex formula for each of the combinations. Usually we will get a mixture of T's and F's but if we get T in every case then the schema is valid.

Predicate logic

Consider the sentences "Tom is tall", "Tom likes Mary", and "Tom is between Adelaide and Melbourne". Here "... is tall", "... likes ...", and "... is between ... and ..." are respectively monadic, dyadic, and triadic predicates. A predicate, then, is a linguistic expression with gaps in it such that it yields a determinate sentence when the gaps are replaced by names. Another way to convert a predicate into a determinate sentence is to use the *quantifiers* "something" and "everything". Thus from "... is tall" and "something" we get "something is tall". In logical symbolism this is written as "$(\exists x)$ x is tall". "Everything is tall" is written as "(x) x is tall". Then we can express "Everything likes something" as "(x) $(\exists y)$ x likes y". "Something likes everything" would be written "$(\exists x)$ (y) x likes y". "Something likes itself" would be "$(\exists x)$ x likes x". "Everything is between something and something" would be "(x) $(\exists y)$ $(\exists z)$ x is between y and z".

In "(x) x is tall" or "$(\exists x)$ x is tall" the variable "x" is said to be "bound" by the quantifier "(x)" or "$(\exists x)$". A variable which is not bound by any quantifier (as "x" in "x is tall") is called a "free variable". It can be thought of as a dummy name. For example, notice that "($\exists x$) x is tall" and "(x) ($\exists y$) x likes y" are only notationally different from "($\exists y$) y is tall" and "(z) ($\exists w$) z likes w" —or for that matter, "(y) ($\exists x$) y likes x". On the other hand "x is tall" and "y is tall" are not merely notationally different. We can not always replace the "x" with a "y" with impunity. For example "x is tall $\supset$ x is tall" obviously yields a true sentence whatever we replace "x" with (and so it is a valid schema) but "x is tall $\supset$ y is tall" is not a valid schema since it yields a falsehood if we replace "x" by the name of something tall and "y" by the name of something short. It should be noted that some method of bracketing is clearly needed to indicate the "scope" of a quantifier. "(x) ($Fx \supset Gx$)" clearly has a different meaning from "$[(x)$ $Fx] \supset Gx$", in which the latter occurrence of "x" is a free one. The latter schema is only notationally different from "$[(y)$ $Fy] \supset Gx$" whereas "(x) ($Fx \supset Gx$)" is by no means equivalent to "(y) ($Fy \supset Gx$)".

Now let us replace the predicates "... is tall", "... likes ...", "... is between ... and ..." by predicate letters "F", "G", "H", etc. Thus we can form expressions like "Fx", "Fxy", "$Fxyz$". With iterated applications of quantifiers and predicate letters we can form such an expression as, for example, "($\exists x$) (y) $[(Fxy \supset Gz) \bullet Hxyz] \supset$ ($\exists w$) Gw". (This contains a free variable "z" and the other variables are bound variables.) We can give an *interpretation* of this schema by replacing any free variables with names and any predicates letters by appropriate predicates. Thus "G" could be interpreted as "... is tall" and "F" as "... likes ...". Now let us suppose, for example, that all the ordered pairs of things in the world such that the first likes the second are exactly the same ordered pairs which are such that the first sees the second. If this were the case, the predicates "... likes ..." and "... sees ..." would be extensionally equivalent: they would be "true of" exactly the same ordered pairs of things. In predicate logic we consider extensionally   **27** equivalent predicates to be the same predicate, and we can specify a predicate simply by specifying what things in the universe it is true of (or of what ordered pairs of things, ordered triples of things, etc., in the case of dyadic, triadic, etc., predicates). Notice that while sentences are "true" or "false", predicates are "true of" and "false of". The class of things of which a predicate is true is sometimes called the "denotation" or "extension" of that predicate.

We can now define validity in predicate logic. A formula of predicate logic is said to be valid if it comes out true in every non-empty universe for all interpretations of its predicate letters. For example the formula "(x) $(\exists y)$ $Fxy \supset (\exists x)$ (y) Fxy" is not valid. Consider a universe consisting of individuals a and b such that "F" is true of the ordered pairs (a, b) and (b, b) and false of the ordered pairs (b, a) and (a, a). (To grasp this intuitively note that "someone loves everyone" does not follow from "everyone loves someone".) On the other hand there is no universe and interpretation of predicate letters which makes

$$"(x) \quad (Fx \supset Gx) \supset (y) \quad [(\exists x) \quad (Fx \cdot Hyx) \supset (\exists x) \quad (Gx \cdot Hyx)]"$$

come out false.[2]

It is possible to specify certain axioms and rules from which *all* valid schemata of predicate logic can be derived. Such sets of axioms and rules are said to be *complete*. The completeness of a set of axioms and rules for predicate logic was proved by Kurt Gödel in 1930.[1] When one system of axioms and rules has been shown to be complete it is usually easy to prove the same thing for certain other systems by showing that the former system can be derived from the latter ones.

On the other hand predicate logic differs importantly

[2]A sentence which has the form of the last schema is "If all kangaroos are marsupials then all heads of kangaroos are heads of marsupials". We do not need to know any zoology or anatomy to assure ourselves of the truth of this sentence: its truth is assured by logic alone.

from sentential logic in that there is no routine or "effective" method whereby we can calculate whether or not an arbitrary schema is valid. If we are lucky (or clever) we may hit upon a proof of validity or invalidity but there is no algorithm which will ensure success for us. (Compare the difference between devising a geometrical proof and carrying out a piece of long division. The former requires luck and intelligence whereas the latter requires mere application of a routine.) It is true that there is a routine method for constructing a sequence of valid formulae of predicate logic, so that if we apply the method long enough any valid formula will eventually turn up. On the other hand there is no similar routine method for constructing a sequence whereby eventually any invalid formula will turn up. Hence there is a routine method which will eventually give us the answer "Yes" to the question "Is this a valid formula?" provided that the answer *is* "Yes". On the other hand, if a formula has not yet turned up, we do not know whether the failure to construct our formula is due to the fact that we have not applied our method long enough, or whether it is that however long we apply our method we shall never construct our formula. We could answer our question in a routine way only if there were a method of constructing, one after the other, all invalid formulae. However it is mathematically impossible that there should be such a method, just as it is mathematically impossible to square the circle. In other words, predicate logic is unlike sentential logic in that it has no decision procedure. Not only do we not know any such decision procedure, but no decision procedure exists at all.[3]

The impossibility of a decision procedure for predicate logic was proved by Alonzo Church in 1936.[2] This has an important consequence for mathematics

[3]Certain *fragments* of predicate logic do have decision procedures. Thus monadic predicate logic (which contains only monadic predicate formulas) has a decision procedure. So also does the set of sentences of predicate logic in which all the universal quantifiers precede all the existential ones.

and science. Predicate logic (unlike, for example, sentential logic, which it contains as a proper part) contains within itself all the resources needed for expressing *any* mathematical or scientific argument. That is, any fully axiomatized scientific theory can be expressed in the notation of predicate logic, provided that predicate letters are replaced by suitable constant predicates. We simply add the axioms, as thus expressed, of the science in question to the axioms and rules of predicate logic itself. To take a very simple example, the theory of identity can be expressed by adding on the axioms:

(1) $x = x$
(2) $(x = y) \supset (y = x)$
(3) $(Fx \cdot x = y) \supset Fy$

Here "=" is a constant dyadic predicate meaning "is identical with". Now since any finite axiomatizable mathematical or scientific theory can be expressed within predicate logic in the above manner, a decision procedure for predicate logic would lead to a mechanical way of deciding whether or not some sentence of the theory was or was not a theorem. One would simply have to test for validity the formula $A \supset T$ where A is the conjunction of the axioms and T is the putative theorem. Any mathematical or scientific theory appears to be axiomatizable (even though the process of axiomatizing most theories has not been carried out and in some cases could be done only after a lot of hard work) and so proof of a decision procedure for predicate logic would in a sense[4] trivialize all problem solving in mathematics. Church's theorem shows that this trivialization will never come about.

It is the case, however, that some fragments of logic and mathematics do admit of a decision procedure. For example Tarski[3] showed that real number algebra

---

[4]Problem solving methods might of course still have been needed *in practice* if there had been a decision procedure but it had been too longwinded or clumsy to use in real life.

has a decision procedure.[5] (In real number algebra the variables are dummies for names of real numbers and there are no quantifiers. Nor do we need to mention *classes* of real numbers as in analysis.)

Definite descriptions

Predicate logic with identity enables us to do without names or uniquely referring expressions. That is, we may replace a sentence such as "the natural satellite of the earth is spherical" by a sentence which does not contain any such expression as "the natural satellite of the earth". We write instead:

($\exists x$) [x is spherical and (y) {y is a natural satellite of the earth $\equiv (x = y)$}]

A little reflection will show that the above sentence states that one and only one thing is a natural satellite of the earth and that this thing is spherical. In general we write:

$$F\,[(\imath x)\,Gx] = \text{def.}\ (\exists x)\,[(y)\,Gy \equiv (x = y)\ \bullet\ Fx]$$

A phrase of the form "($\imath x$) Gx" is called a definite description and can be read "the G-er". (Whether it exactly captures the meaning of phrases of the form "the so-and-so" in colloquial English does not matter, but it comes near to it at least.) A device due to W. V. Quine enables us always to replace names by definite descriptions. We simply read "Socrates" as "the socratizer", where to socratize is to possess that set of properties which enables us to single out Socrates. "The socratizer" sounds artificial, but it is no different in principle from replacing "Moon" by "the natural satellite of the earth".

---

[5]The procedure is not fast enough to use on real computers. My friend C. L. Hamblin is working on the problem of adapting Tarski's method for practical use.

Elementary number theory

Elementary number theory is the theory of the integers 0, 1, 2, 3, ... Fractions and real numbers do not come into it, nor do classes of the integers. Elementary number theory can be formalized within predicate logic by means of the addition of suitable axioms. Now the syntax of a formalized theory, which deals with such notions as "well-formed formula" and "deducible from" (and hence "provable", since this means "deducible from the axioms") can be mapped onto elementary number theory. That is, there is a way of assigning natural numbers to the symbols of the system, to sequences of symbols of the system, and to sequences of sequences of symbols of the system, such that various arithmetical relations hold among these numbers if and only if corresponding syntactical relations hold among the expressions corresponding to these numbers. The method of correlating numbers to expressions, sequences of expressions, and sequences of sequences of expressions, is called Gödel numbering. Elementary number theory is the weakest mathematical theory on which syntax can be mapped. Notice that syntax deals only with symbols and the ways of manipulating them, and does not deal at all with their interpretations. By taking advantage of this, and by mapping the syntax of number theory onto number theory itself, Gödel showed how to construct a sentence G, of a formalized system of number theory, which is the arithmetical sentence which corresponds to the syntactical assertion that the sentence in question is unprovable in the system, if the system is consistent. Of course if the system is inconsistent any formula must be provable, as must its negation. For the rules of sentential logic enable us to get from "p" and "$\sim p$" to "q", and hence by substitution any proposition whatever. (Proof: from "p" we get

"$p \lor q$" which together with "$\sim p$" yields "q".) Also as-suming consistency[6] it can be shown that the negation of G is not provable either. It can also be shown (in an argu-ment within the *semantics* of the system in question — see p. 36) that though G is unprovable it is never-theless true.

Of course the axioms of number theory could be aug-mented so that G became provable. (Trivially this could be done by adding G as an axiom.) But then it could be shown with reference to the augmented axiom set that if it is consistent there would be a sentence of elemen-tary number theory G' which was neither provable nor disprovable. And so on. The axioms of elementary num-ber theory are incompletable, at least if elementary number theory is consistent. Furthermore any stronger formalized theory, such as set theory, which is powerful enough for number theory to be derived from it, must also, if it is consistent, be incompletable. Since syntax can be mapped onto number theory, *a fortiori* it can be mapped on to this stronger theory, and so the Gödel argument can be carried out with respect to it.

Set theory

Set theory can be axiomatized within predicate logic by incorporating the constant dyadic predicate "ϵ" ("is a member of") and suitable axioms. The predicate "is identical with" and the notion of equivalence between sets can quickly be defined. Two sets are equivalent if their elements stand in a one-one relation to one another. (In spite of etymology, the notion of "one-one" relation can be defined *before* the natural number one is defined.) For example the set of natural numbers and the set of even numbers are equivalent, since there is a one-one relation which pairs off x and $2x$. Relations are them-

[6]Actually Gödel assumed a stronger requirement than consistency, called ω-consistency. Rosser proved a form of Gödel's theorem using only the weaker requirement of simple consistency.

33

selves sets, since they are defined as ordered pairs, and ordered pairs are themselves identified with sets. Thus the ordered pair (x, y) can be identified with $\{\{x\}, \{x, y\}\}$, i.e., the set which contains the set whose only member is x and the set whose members are x and y.

It turns out that the whole of mathematics, including analysis, can be mapped onto set theory, or to put it more loosely, "can be expressed" in set theory. For example, in one version of set theory (Zermelo's) the natural numbers are identified with Λ, $\{\Lambda\}$, $\{\{\Lambda\}\}$, etc., where Λ is the empty set. In another (von Neumann's) the numbers are Λ, $\{\Lambda\}$, $\{\Lambda, \{\Lambda\}\}$, etc., so that the number n is the set of all numbers less than n. There are yet other versions. It is clearly meaningless to ask whether the number 2 "really is" $\{\{\Lambda\}\}$ or $\{\Lambda, \{\Lambda\}\}$ or else some other entity again. Any sequence of set theoretic objects which form a progression will do the job as far as the mathematician is concerned.

It should be remembered that even if the natural numbers are *not* identified with set theoretic entities, set theory has an essential part to play in mathematics, since analysis requires the consideration of infinite sets of real numbers.

If all members of a set A are members of a set B, then A is said to be a subset of B. Note that a set is a subset of itself. It is easily shown that the set of subsets of a given set (whether finite or infinite) can not be put in one-one correspondence with that set. This is of course very obvious in the case of finite sets: for example the set of subsets of the two membered set $\{a, b\}$ has four members: Λ, $\{a\}$, $\{b\}$, $\{a, b\}$. If two sets are such that one is equivalent to a subset of the other, but not vice versa, the first is said to be smaller than the second. So the set of natural numbers is smaller than the set of subsets of the set of natural numbers. This last set is smaller than the set of subsets of itself. The set of natural numbers has a number $\aleph_0$. It can be shown easily that the set of subsets of the set of natural numbers is equivalent to the set of real numbers. So the number of this set, $2^{\aleph_0}$, is the number of the continuum. Is $2^{\aleph_0}$ the smallest transfinite number after $\aleph_0$? That is, is there a transfinite number, other than $\aleph_0$, which is less than $2^{\aleph_0}$? The *continuum* hypothesis is that there is not: i.e., that the transfinite number of the continuum is the first one after $\aleph_0$. Gödel showed that the continuum hypothesis is consistent with the other axioms of set theory.[4] More recently Paul J. Cohen[5] showed that its denial is consistent too. This provides another illustration of the fact that the question as to what set theory we adopt is to a great extent a matter of taste: there seem to be alternative and equally good set theories in a way in which there are not alternative and equally acceptable logics, or for that matter alternative and equally acceptable physical hypotheses.

Some of these matters are rather far removed from problems in the philosophy of science, but on p. 245 we shall at least need the distinction between $\aleph_0$ and $2^{\aleph_0}$. Set theory will always be of *some* interest to philosophers of science, since physics needs the theory of the real variable (analysis), and this can only be discussed with the help of discourse about infinite sets of real numbers.

Finally, the statement that set theory can be axiomatized by adding onto predicate logic certain axioms and the constant predicate "ϵ" needs a slight qualification. In some versions of set theory additional formation rules, (type rules in Russell; stratification rules in Quine), are needed. These rules prevent us from constructing expressions which would otherwise lead us into inconsistency. Consider Russell's paradox "the set of all sets not members of themselves is a member of itself". If we are allowed to suppose that there is such a set, then we get a paradox, because, if it is a member of itself, it isn't and if it isn't, it is. Type or stratification rules prevent us from constructing the offending sentence because it becomes "ungrammatical". In other systems the axioms themselves ensure the non-existence of the offending set, without the need for additional formation rules.

Semantics and truth

It has been mentioned that the syntax of a theory can be mapped onto that theory itself, provided that the theory is at least as strong as elementary number theory. However this is not true of semantics, which deals not only with such notions as "well formed formula", "provable", and "consistent", but also with such notions as "denotes", "is true of", and "true". Whether a sentence is true depends in general both on the way the world is and on the rules of the language. Thus "snow is black" would be true provided that "black" was used with the interpretation we at present give to "white". So we must not say that a string of symbols is true *simpliciter* but that it is true in some language L. "Snow is white" is true in English if and only if snow is white. One is tempted to generalize this by saying that in general " 'p' is true" if and only if p. However this is incorrect, since " 'p' " is not a variable name of a sentence but is the name of the letter "p". In order to overcome this difficulty Alfred Tarski[6] has in effect defined "true" in terms of "true of". A predicate "F" is true of x if and only if Fx. Then by considering the way in which a sentence in a given formalized language is built up out of its predicates, together with quantifiers and sentence connectives, Tarski was able to define "true in L" where L is a formalized language. It should be noted that since the formal apparatus of the theory has to be specifically considered in the construction of the definition of truth, this gives a mathematical reason why what is to be defined is not "true" but "true in L". Tarski also showed that "true in L" can be defined only in a language with more powerful means of expression than L. In particular, set theory is needed to define "true in L" when L is a formalized system of elementary number theory. In using "true" and "false" as predicates of *sentences*, we are assuming that the sentences are used independently of context. In colloquial language, of course, we often use context-dependent sentences. Thus if one person says "I am tall" he may say something true, whereas another person may use the very same sentence to say something false. In these cases we may wish to talk of the truth and falsity of *utterances* or *inscriptions* of sentences rather than of the sentences themselves. However for the purposes of this book we shall assume that the sentences of a scientific theory are expressed in context-independent terms.

Proof theory in general requires both syntax and semantics. Thus whether a theorem is provable or not from the axioms of a formal system is a question of whether certain strings of symbols can be transformed into others according to certain rules. One can think of the symbols simply as though they were chess pieces to be moved according to the rules of a game. So far we are within the realm of syntax. However when we ask whether all *true* or *valid* formulae are provable we are clearly using concepts of semantics.

Use and mention

Syntax and semantics, it will be noticed, are disciplines in which we talk *about* the symbolism of a system. The distinction between *using* a symbol or string of symbols and *mentioning* it is one which philosophers and logicians must always bear carefully in mind. For example in sentential logic we might use "p", "q", "r" ... as sentence letters, and use "$A \supset B$" to be a dummy (or variable) *name* of a string of symbols which consists of (1) some expression made up out of "p", "q", "r" ... and the connectives "$\sim$", "$\bullet$", "$\supset$", etc., followed by (2) the symbol "$\supset$", followed by (3) some expression made up out of "p", "q", "r" ... and the sentence connectives. In philosophy, too, it is important to be continually aware of the distinction between using a linguistic expression and mentioning it. For example in philosophy of mathematics one must remember to distinguish between *numerals* and *numbers*. The former are linguistic expressions whereas the latter are non-linguistic mathematical entities. Connoisseurs of logic may like to notice that to have been quite rigorous I should have used appropriate metalinguistic letters (such as "A" and "B" earlier in this paragraph) instead of "p" and "q" in the truth table on p. 24 above, since the table was meant to show how the sentence connectives function between any well formed combination of sentence letters and sentence connectives, and not just between the letters "p" and "q" themselves. However I have there followed the less rigorous (but common) practice of using "p" and "q", thus sacrificing rigor in the interests of simplicity in exposition.

The common mistake of reading "$\supset$" as "implies" arises out of a confusion of use and mention.[7] "$\supset$" is a sentence connective: it joins two sentences to form a compound sentence, and is on the same level as "and" and "or". "Implies" is not a connective but a binary predicate, which joins *names* of sentences. Notice that "Socrates is a man implies Socrates is mortal" is not even good English grammar since no sentence with just these words in it can contain three verbs. We must say "'Socrates is a man' implies 'Socrates is mortal'" or "the proposition *that* Socrates is a man implies the proposition *that* Socrates is mortal".[7]

What "implication" ordinarily means is obscure: possibly "'—' implies '...'" should best be construed as saying that the sentence "..." is deducible (perhaps in

---

[7] We sometimes talk of two sentences expressing the same proposition, so that a proposition can be thought of as something to which all these sentences stand in a certain relation. Some philosophers, such as Quine, find the notion of expressing the same proposition obscure and therefore prefer to talk only of sentences and inscriptions or utterances of sentences.

conjunction with some theory or body of background information) from "$-$", or perhaps it should be construed as asserting the *validity* of "$- \quad \supset \quad ...$". But "'$-$' materially implies '...'" is perfectly clear: it simply asserts the *truth* of "$- \quad \supset \quad ...$". It is a statement of semantics about the sentences "$-$" and "$...$", namely that when they are conjoined by "$\supset$", with the former occurring first, they yield a true sentence. The proposition "(x) (x is a madman $\supset$ x has some biochemical deficiency in his neurons)" is true or false according to whether or not the extension of the predicate "is a madman" is included in the extension of the predicate "has some biochemical deficiency in his neurons". It can be seen that the question of whether or not semantical terms like "true" and "denotes" are correctly applied in a particular case can turn on questions of empirical fact about the world.

Extensional and intensional contexts

Consider the expression "it is not the case that" or "$\sim$". If we replace A in $\sim A$ by some other sentence B whose truth value is the same as that of A (or, when A is a sentence schema containing free variables, if we replace A by some sentence schema B which is true of exactly the same objects as A is true of) then the truth value of $\sim A$ is the same as that of $\sim B$. We can call "$\sim$" an "extensional context" of the expression it operates on. Now consider the context "it is a matter of pure mathematics that ...". It is a matter of pure mathematics that $2 + 2 = 4$ but it is not a matter of pure mathematics that the earth has exactly one natural satellite, even though the sentences "$2 + 2 = 4$" and "the earth has exactly one natural satellite" have the same truth value. We say that "it is a matter of pure mathematics that" is an intensional, not an extensional, operator or sentence connective.

Again let A be a sentence containing one or more names or uniquely referring expressions. Let these names or uniquely referring expressions be replaced by others which single out the same objects, so as to yield a sentence *B*. Then in an extensional language *A* will be true if and only if *B* is. For example "it is not the case that the number of visible planets is less than ten" is true if and only if it is not the case that five is less than ten (since the number of visible planets is in fact five). However "it is a matter of pure mathematics that the number of visible planets is less than ten" is false whereas "it is a matter of pure mathematics that five is less than ten" is true. So "it is not the case that ..." is an extensional context and "it is a matter of pure mathematics that" is an intensional or modal one.

I have used "it is a matter of pure mathematics that ..." in my example in order to avoid expressions like "logically necessary" or "logically possible", or even "necessary" or "possible" on their own, since there are philosophical controversies connected with these words. However "necessarily" and "possibly" are indeed typical intensional contexts. Sometimes intensional talk can be replaced by extensional talk in the metalanguage: for example the intensional *operator* "necessarily" in "necessarily 2 + 2 = 4" can be replaced by the extensional *predicate* "is necessary" applied to the sentence "2 + 2 = 4", as in "'2 + 2 = 4' is necessary". Technical and philosophical difficulties arise when intensional operators are combined with quantificational logic. Fortunately if any scientific theory can be formalized it can be formalized in an extensional language. (I shall try to defend this point of view to some extent in this book, but for the most part the reader should take this as an assumption on which this book is based.)

Probability

Some philosophers appear to think of the theory of probability as a branch of logic which studies a relation which is weaker than that of implication (or perhaps deducibility). If so they make the mistake of confusing logic with its metatheory (syntax or semantics). The symbolism in which the theory of probability is sometimes expressed can bear witness to this confusion. Suppose, as is sometimes done, that a typical formula of the theory of probability is written somewhat as follows:

$$P(p \bullet q, r) = P(p, r) \times P(q, p \bullet r)$$

How could we read this formula? Suppose we read it as saying that the probability of both p and q being true, given that r is true, is equal to the probability of p given r multiplied by the probability of q given p and r. Notice that this makes sense only if we take "p", "q", and "r" to be dummy *names* of sentences, and not as sentences themselves, as in sentential logic. In other words, the theory of probability would be interpreted not as analogous to logic, but as analogous to metalogic.

To prevent confusion, therefore, let us replace "p", "q", "r", etc., by the letters "a", "b", "c", etc., and let it be understood that one possible interpretation for the formula

$$P(a \bullet b, c) = P(a, c) \times P(b, a \bullet c)$$

is a metalinguistic one, where a, b, c are dummy *names* of sentences. And we shall avoid the confusion which could arise from calling this a "logical" interpretation, by calling it the "*metalinguistic*" interpretation.

In science, however, the word "probability" is used to talk not about sentences but about events in the world. Thus the previous formula would be interpreted as: "The probability of an event which is of the sort c being an event which is both of the sort a and the sort b is equal to the probability of a c event being an a event multiplied by the probability of a b event being both an a event and a c event."

Let c be the class of undergrades in a university. Let a be the class of science students and let b be the class of females. Then the formula $P(a \bullet b, c) = P(a, c)$ **41**

$\times P\ (b, a \bullet c)$ can be interpreted as saying that the proportion of undergraduates who are both female and students of science is equal to the proportion of undergraduates who are science students multiplied by the proportion of undergraduate science students who are female.

It would be possible in the case of the university to examine all the students and count up how many were male, female, scientists, and non-scientists. In science we are normally concerned with sets of events, or of things, such that only a sample can ever be observed. Consider tosses of a penny. An indefinite number of tosses can be made, and if a long sequence of tosses is made, it will be found that the proportion of pennies which fall "heads" gets near to $\frac{1}{2}$ (if it is a well-balanced penny—some other fraction otherwise). By taking a sufficiently large number of throws we can get as near to $\frac{1}{2}$ as we like. For example in 10 throws, 3 might be heads and 7 tails. In 100 throws we might have 47 heads, in 1000 we might have 504, and so on. That is, one can propound the hypothesis that if the tosses of the penny are continued indefinitely, for any number ε, however small, there will be a number m of tosses such that for all $n \geqslant m$ the proportion (or "frequency") of heads after n throws is f_n such that

$$|f_n - \tfrac{1}{2}| < \varepsilon$$

Thus if ε is chosen to be 0.001 then

$$(\exists m)\ (n)\ [(n \geqslant m)\ \supset\ (|f_n - \tfrac{1}{2}| < 0.0001)]$$

and in general we have

$$(\varepsilon)\ (\exists m)\ (n)\ [(n \geqslant m)\ \supset\ (|f_n - \tfrac{1}{2}| < \varepsilon]$$

The order of the quantifiers in the above formula is important. Note also that for any choice of ε (such as 0.0001) we do not *know* any value of m such that for $n \geqslant m$ the difference between f_n and $\frac{1}{2}$ is less than ε. After ten millions tosses it is *possible*, though highly unlikely, that the next million tosses will all fall "heads", in which case of course $|f_n - \frac{1}{2}|$ is not less than 0.0001 for all $n \geqslant 10{,}000{,}000$. The hypothesis merely asserts that there *is* such a value of m.

Suppose that for any ε there is such a value of m. Then we can say that the *limiting frequency* of "heads" is $\frac{1}{2}$, i.e.,

$$\lim_{n \to \infty} f_n = \tfrac{1}{2}$$

The *frequency theory* of probability defines probability as limiting frequency. Formulae of the calculus of probability such as $P(a \bullet b, c) = P(a, c) \times P(b, a \bullet c)$ remain true when the various terms are interpreted as limiting frequencies. Thus the above formula asserts that the limiting frequency of events that are both a and b in the class of c events is equal to the limiting frequency of a events in the class of c events multiplied by the limiting frequency of b events in the class of events which are both a and c.

It will be convenient at this stage to describe another interpretation to which the probability calculus is susceptible. So far we have considered the metalinguistic (often misnamed "logical") and frequency interpretations. The next interpretation to be considered is that in which "$P(a, b)$", etc., are interpreted as *proportions of possibilities*. "$P(a, b)$" is interpreted as the numbers of possible cases in which an event is both b and a divided by the number of possible cases in which an event is an a. For example let b be the number of sides of a die (not necessarily a "fair" or "unbiased" one), and let a be the number of sides which are even numbered ones. Then

$$P(a, b) = \tfrac{3}{6}$$

Suppose that we consider the simultaneous throw of two dice. Then there are 36 different possible outcomes, namely "one" thrown with the first die and "one" with the second, "one" with the first die and "two" with the second, and so on. Let us call these 36 possible out-comes "c" events. Let an a event be a throw of "one" with the *first* die, and a b event be a throw of an even number with the *second* die. Then it is clear that

$$P(a, c) = \frac{1}{6}$$

$$P(b, a \bullet c) = \frac{3}{6}$$

$$P(a \bullet b, c) = \frac{3}{36}$$

It is easy to verify that the formula

$$P(a \bullet b, c) = P(b, a \bullet c) \times P(a, c)$$

remains true as thus interpreted as a formula about possibilities.

This simple example illustrates the way in which theorems of the calculus of probability can be inter-preted as statements about possibilities. The above formula, thus interpreted, tell us *nothing* about the *probability* of getting certain results after tossing dice, because the interpretation works just as well whether the dice are fair or loaded. This is often concealed by the fact that the different possibilities (say each of our 36 cases above) are often tacitly taken to be "equiproba-ble" (say under the frequency interpretation of proba-bility) and then of course the calculus of possibilities does yield information about probabilities (frequencies) too.

We can consider, then, an abstract calculus of prob-ability which is susceptible to at least the following three main types of interpretation: the metalinguistic, the frequency, and the possibility interpretation. Among these, the one which is of most interest to the philosophy of science is the frequency interpretation. Statements within the possibility interpretation by themselves can tell us nothing about what actually happens, and the metalinguistic interpretation is itself divisible into several subinterpretations. What sort of statement is the statement that $P(a, b) = r$ where r is some real number between 0 and 1? Perhaps it might be the statement that on the evidence b it is *rational to believe* the proposition a with a degree of belief equal to r, and there might be some way of assigning the number r by discovering how a rational person, whose only relevant evidence was b, might lay betting odds on the truth of a. In most cases, however, there will be difficulty here. Can we in this way (or in any other way) assign *any* numerical probability to the probability that the general theory of relativity is true? How could we even guess at what would be rational betting odds on its truth? Moreover to define probability in terms of rationality is open to the charge of circularity, especially if no account can be given of "rational belief" other than as "belief in what is most probable". There is, however, a restricted class of cases in which the metalinguistic interpretation works all right, because parasitically on the frequency interpretation. That is, let K be a class of things, let L be a well ordered class of things, and let the limiting frequency of things that are L (relative to the class K) be r. Then if nothing is known about something other than that it is a member of K, we can harmlessly assign r as the (metalinguistic) probability of the proposition that this thing is a member of the class L. That is, in some cases we can assign numerical metalinguistic probabilities which are parasitic on probabilities obtained on the basis of known frequencies.

In this book I shall occasionally wish to make use of metalinguistic probability statements which do not seem to be parasitic on statements about frequencies. For example I shall wish to assert that other things being equal the simpler of two hypotheses is more likely to be true. I must concede that I do not know how to justify this nevertheless rather plausible assertion, or even to say quite clearly what it means. Certainly it does not seem plausible to rest it on the dubious assertion that on **45** the whole simple theories have been shown to be true. (If it did, then this particular metalinguistic assertion would depend on a metalinguistic *frequency* assertion.)

The frequency interpretation of probability and the propensity interpretation

It is commonly held that probability assertions *within* scientific theories (as opposed to *about* them) must be analyzed as assertions about limiting frequencies. K. R. Popper[8] has recently put forward the view that they should be interpreted rather as *propensities* of physical systems. The difference between the two views can be put as follows: the frequency theorist wishes to analyze probabilities in terms of observed frequencies (as the limiting values of these), whereas, according to the propensity interpretation, probability statements can not be translated into statements about frequencies, though they are *tested by means of* observations of frequencies.

Popper's main objection to the frequency theory is as follows. Suppose that you have a loaded die, such that over a long sequence of throws the proportion of throws which turn up "six" is approximately $\frac{1}{4}$. Then one would conjecture that the limiting frequency is about $\frac{1}{4}$. Now consider another sequence, which is the same as before (namely an indefinitely long repetition of throws with the loaded die) but including, say, five throws with an unbiased die. The limiting frequency for this new sequence of throws is still $\frac{1}{4}$, since five throws with the other die make no difference to the frequency in the long run. (Still about $\frac{1}{4}$ will turn up "six".) Nevertheless surely even a frequency theorist will wish to say that for a throw with an unbiased die the probability of getting a "six" is not $\frac{1}{4}$ but $\frac{1}{6}$. The frequency theorist will give as his reason that if the unbiased die were thrown very many times the proportion of sixes in this sequence of throws would approach $\frac{1}{6}$. Popper considers that in making such a modification to his theory the frequency theorist has gone over to the propensity theory. We are not thinking of actual sequences (since clearly the few throws with the unbiased die are perfectly good members of the indefinitely long sequence consisting of the few throws with the unbiased die together with indefinitely many throws with the biased die) but of experimental arrangements. *Throwing indefinitely many times with a biased die together with five throws with the biased one* constitutes one experimental arrangement, whereas *throwing with the unbiased die* constitutes another experimental arrangement. Of course, an actual individual throw can be considered as belonging to more than one experimental arrangement.

If we accept the account of dispositional properties which will be given below in Chapter 5, we can identify propensities with actual physical states. Thus the propensity of a die to turn up "six" can be identified with (a) the symmetrical or asymmetrical distribution of matter in the cubical die *together with* (b) the neurophysiological structure of the human dice player, which explains why the angular velocity he imparts to the die is rather random and unrelated in any very accurate way to the height of his fingers above the table, and so on. Here a propensity is a further describable substructure of the physical arrangement. In quantum mechanics, however, we come across not further describable propensities (at least if present-day quantum mechanics is correct). Nevertheless, though they are not further describable, they must be thought of as objective physical states. Popper himself was led to the propensity theory by considerations of quantum mechanics, and we shall discuss some of these below in Chapter 5.

One great advantage of the propensity theory is that according to it a probability is a feature of an experimental arrangement which we hypothesize on the basis (perhaps) of observed frequencies, but the theory does not *define* probabilities in this way. The frequency theory has need of idealization or make believe. What would in fact happen if there were to be a very long sequence of throws with a die? The die would wear out and long before that the dice player would be dead. So the frequency theorist has really to talk about what would happen in an infinite sequence of throws which could not possibly exist. The propensity theorist is able to avoid this sort of difficulty. He can analyze a single case as a propensity of an experimental arrangement which it exemplifies, and this propensity can be an actual physical state.

The relation between the propensity theory and the frequency theory is rather like that between (1) a theory which identifies vanity as an actual (though perhaps unknown) neurophysiological state of the vain person which *explains* why (for example) he wears a yellow waistcoat, and (2) an account such as Ryle's, which attempts to elucidate vanity simply in terms of hypothetical statements about behavior, such as "If such and such conditions are realized he wears a bright colored waistcoat". The difficulty of giving any plausible analysis of vanity on Ryle's lines is well known. It is hard to specify the hypothetical propositions which would be needed. Consider the case of the vain man who successfully conceals his vanity (and perhaps is vain about his not appearing vain). On the other hand there is no difficulty if the vain behavior is taken not as *constituting* vanity but as being *explained by* vanity. Similarly, the element of truth in the frequency theory of probability is that hypotheses about probabilities are tested by means of observed frequencies, but an arrangement can possess a more or less probable outcome (propensity of a greater or lesser magnitude to realize the outcome) whether or not the outcome is in fact realized.

There is an important fact to be noted about the use of observed frequencies in order to test statements about probabilities. Both the advocate of the propensity theory and the frequency theorist will agree here—

that these tests are not conclusive in the way in which

tests of universal generalizations can be. That is, suppose we consider the generalization that all ravens are black. One single observation of a blue raven, provided that we could be quite certain that the object ought to be classified as a raven and that it is blue,[8] would serve to refute the hypothesis that all ravens are black. However five successive throws would not conclusively refute the hypothesis that the die was unbiased (i.e., the probability of each side falling uppermost is one sixth). We should provisionally reject the hypothesis, if these five throws constituted all our evidence about the die, but we would reject our rejection if we went on throwing and found (say) one more six, six fives, five fours, seven threes, three twos and eight ones in the next thirty throws. Of course if we are dealing with long sequences of events, probability hypotheses can be rejected with great assurance. The probability of five sixes coming up with an unbiased die is only $1/6^5$ and so if these tosses constituted all our relevant knowledge we should be wise to reject the hypothesis that the die is unbalanced. (Notice here that we have a statement of metalinguistic probability about a hypothesis, which is parasitic on a propensity or a frequency statement.) Nevertheless five successive sixes, or even five thousand successive sixes, is not *logically incompatible* with the hypothesis that the die is unbiased, in the way in which "this is a blue raven" *is* logically incompatible with "all ravens are black".

SUGGESTIONS FOR FURTHER READING

In this chapter I have largely followed the approach and terminology of W. V. Quine, and his short summary of symbolic logic in the *Encyclopedia Americana* (1957 and later editions) could well be recommended to readers in preference to the first half of the present

[8]There are difficulties about this and they will be discussed in Chapter 6. They do not affect the present issue.

chapter. It has been conveniently reprinted in Quine's *Selected Logic Papers* (New York: Random House, 1966), pp. 37–51. Quine's *Methods of Logic*, second edition, revised (New York: Holt, Rinehart and Winston, 1959), is a particularly lucid and philosophically acute textbook of modern sentential and predicate logic, with glimpses into set theory. This book uses a method of "natural deduction," which has technical advantages in facilitating proof-making, but which is harder to grasp than the usual axiomatic presentation. For the latter, see D. Hilbert and W. Ackermann, *Principles of Mathematical Logic*, translated by L. M. Hammond, G. G. Leckie, and F. Steinhardt, edited with notes by R. E. Luce (New York: Chelsea, 1950). A good textbook on logic is I. Copi, *Symbolic Logic*, second edition (New York: Macmillan, 1965). A rather advanced and detailed treatise is Alonzo Church, *Introduction to Mathematical Logic* (Princeton: Princeton University Press, 1956). On set theory, see W. V. Quine, *Set Theory and its Logic* (Cambridge: Harvard University Press, 1963). The question of fragments of predicate logic for which there are decision procedures is discussed by W. Ackermann, *Solvable Cases of the Decision Problem* (Amsterdam: North-Holland, 1954, and 2nd ed., New York: Humanities Press, 1962). On syntax, computability, and decision problems, see S. C. Kleene, *Introduction to Metamathematics* (Princeton: D. Van Nostrand, 1952); Martin Davis, *Computability and Unsolvability* (New York: McGraw-Hill, 1958); and R. Smullyan, *Theory of Formal Systems*, revised edition (Princeton: Princeton University Press, 1961). All these books require little or no previous mathematical knowledge, but they do require mathematical ability in the reader. Smullyan's book is particularly concise and makes use of very elegant and simplifying methods, but the approach of Martin Davis, *via* the theory of Turing machines, may be easier intuitively to those readers who find it easier to think of these matters in terms of what computing machines do, rather than in terms of abstract formal systems. (Though mathematically speaking, these two approaches come to much the same thing.) More popular accounts of some of these matters can be found in A. M. Turing, "Solvable and Unsolvable Problems", *Penguin Science News*, no. 31 (1954), 7–23; E. Nagel and J. R. Newman, *Gödel's Proof* (New York: New York University Press, 1958) [in conjunction with which consult Hilary Putnam's review in *Philosophy of Science*, XXVII (1960), 205–207], and W. V. Quine, "Foundations of Mathematics", *Scientific American* (September 1964), 112–127, reprinted in his *The Ways of Paradox and Other Essays* (New York: Random House, 1966), pp. 24–34. Another valuable article is Barkley Rosser, "An informal exposition of proofs of Gödel's theorems and Church's theorem", *Journal of Symbolic Logic*, IV (1939), 53–60. For arguments against intensional logics, see W. V. Quine, *Word and Object* (Cambridge: Massachusetts Institute of Technology Press, 1960), Chapter 6, especially section 41; and "Three Grades of Modal Involvement", *Proceedings of XIth International Congress of Philosophy*, XIV (Brussels, 1953), 65–81, reprinted in Quine's *The Ways of Paradox*, pp. 165–174. See also Quine's "Reply to Professor Marcus", reprinted in *The Ways of Paradox*, pp. 175–182. This, together with Professor

Marcus' paper, and an interesting discussion between Quine, Marcus, and others, appeared originally in *Synthese*, XX (1961) and in M. W. Wartofsky (ed.), *Boston Studies in the Philosophy of Science*, Vol. I (Dordrecht, Holland: D. Reidel, 1963, and New York: Humanities Press, 1963).

On probability, see E. Nagel, *Principles of the Theory of Probability, International Encyclopedia of Unified Science*, Vol. I, no. 6 (Chicago: University of Chicago Press, 1938); William Kneale, *Probability and Induction* (Oxford: Clarendon Press, 1949, and New York: Oxford University Press, 1949); and G. H. von Wright, *A Treatise on Induction and Probability* (London: Routledge & Kegan Paul, 1951). An account of the frequency theory of probability, written by one of its chief proponents and in language accessible to the nonmathematical reader, is R. von Mises, *Probability, Statistics and Truth*, second edition (London: Allen & Unwin, 1957). A frequency theory of probability is developed in K. R. Popper, *The Logic of Scientific Discovery* (London: Hutchinson, 1959, and paperback, rev. ed., New York: Harper and Row, 1965), which is a translation, with additional appendices and footnotes of Popper's *Logik der Forschung* (Vienna: Julius Springer, 1934). Since then, as was noted in the text, Popper has gone over to his "propensity interpretation" of probability, as in his article "The Propensity Interpretation of Probability", *British Journal for the Philosophy of Science*, X (1959), 25–42. C. G. Hempel, in his *Aspects of Scientific Explanation and Other Essays in the Philosophy of Science* (New York: Free Press, 1965), puts forward a dispositional account of probability which is similar to Popper's propensity theory, and he reports Rudolf Carnap, in his "Inductive Logic and Science", *Proceedings of the American Academy of Arts and Sciences*, LXXX (1951–54), 187–197, as holding in similar vein that the statistical probability of rolling an ace with a given die is a physical state ("the probability state") of the die, for which relative frequencies are symptoms. Carnap has written extensively on probability, mainly with an eye to its bearing on the philosophical problem of induction, and the treatment is therefore often rather specialized. See for example his *Logical Foundations of Probability*, second edition (Chicago: University of Chicago Press, 1962), and the summary of his position on pp. 966–979 of his "Replies and Expositions", in P. A. Schilpp (ed.), *The Philosophy of Rudolf Carnap* (La Salle, Ill.: Open Court, 1963). On a more popular level, see Carnap's article, "What is Probability?", *Scientific American* (September 1953), 128–138. Another useful paper is I. J. Good, "Kinds of Probability", *Science*, CXXIX (1959), 443–447.

3

Explanation, laws, and theories

Preliminary remarks on explanation

We are now ready to begin talking about science. It is undeniable that one of the main things which we expect to get from science is the capacity to *explain* various sorts of things. Consider a boy who gets a thrill from his high school physics because this enables him to understand pretty well how his radio works. Perhaps he has a transistorized radio. He may be in possession of a partial explanation, knowing only that the transistors perform the same functions as do the thermionic valves of an older model. Now his puzzle is no longer about the working of his radio as a whole but is about the individual transistors within it, and this leads him into modern solid state physics. Popular or semi-popular journals such as the *Scientific American* laudably cater to this sort of curiosity. What must it feel like to be a housewife (or perhaps a literary critic) who has *no* idea of how the radio works, how the refrigerator in the kitchen cools its contents, or why forcing hot gases out of the rear ends of jet engines makes an airplane accelerate forward? Or in the "natural" (as opposed to technological) sphere, consider such questions as why rainbows occur, why the tails of comets point away from the sun, how plants reproduce themselves, why pollen makes some people sneeze, and so on. These are all questions whose *asking* requires little scientific sophistication, though perhaps their *answering* may require a good deal of sophistication. A scientist is often concerned with answering easily asked questions, though of course he is also often concerned with questions which can not even be asked in commonsense terms. Consider "How does lysozyme dissolve muco-polysaccharides?"[1] A good deal of scientific education is needed before one can understand what such a question means.

Quite apart from any practical benefits we get from science (and these practical benefits all come eventually from the fact that science enables us to *predict* what will happen in various combinations of circumstances) it seems undeniable that much of the intellectual appeal of science comes from its ability to help us answer many of the "why" and "how" questions, of which a few were given in the previous paragraph. It is sometimes, of course, said that science enables us to tell "how" but never "why". Taken literally, such an assertion is clearly wrong, since many of the questions which science answers are most naturally put in the form "why ...?" Consider the question which was mentioned in the previous paragraph: "Why do the tails of comets point away from the sun?" (Answer: because of the pressure of the sun's radiation on the small particles constituting the tail.) This question is put much more naturally as a "why" question than as the "how" question "How do the tails of comets point away from the sun?"

"How do the tails of comets point away from the sun?" is not a very clear question, which might most naturally be interpreted not as a request for an explanation but as a request for a more detailed description of the manner in which the tails of comets point away

54

from the sun (e.g., whether they are many millions of miles long). Sometimes "why" and "how" are simply interchangeable: there does not seem to be any difference between asking "Why does forcing hot gases out of the rear ends of jet engines make an airplane accelerate forward?" and the question "How does forcing hot gases out of the rear ends of jet engines make an airplane accelerate forward?" Both forms of the question would be equally and naturally answered by a reference to Newton's third law of motion or to the principle of the conservation of momentum. Again, "Why does lysozyme dissolve muco-polysaccharides?" would ordinarily be taken to mean the same as "How does ...?", though I suppose it could be taken otherwise, for example as a question about the part taken by the dissolving of polysaccharides in the functioning of an organism. In some cases this teleological or functional interpretation of "Why?" is more natural: "Why do cows have two stomachs?" might be answered by "In order to digest grass" or something of the sort. A further explanation on these lines would have to be through the theory of evolution by natural selection: having two stomachs (and hence being able to digest grass) is useful (in certain circumstances) for survival. We shall have to discuss such teleological explanations in Chapter 4, but in the context of evolutionary theory they are perfectly compatible with ordinary scientific explanations: the idea that science can not deal with "why" questions presumably comes from interpreting the "why" questions as questions about the purposes of God, who created the world. We have seen, however, that "why" questions are often also "how" questions. Even when they are teleological (and so are different from the corresponding "how" questions) there need be nothing extra-scientific or theological about them because the apparent reference to purpose may vanish when the explanation is seen in the light of the theory of evolution by natural selection. **55**

What is explanation?

In the previous section we have considered some examples of requests for explanation. Can we give some general characterization of explanation? If by this is meant, "Can we give a general definition of the word 'explanation'?" we encounter the difficulty that the word is used in many widely different contexts, some of which have nothing whatever to do with the concept of scientific explanation.

Thus a mathematician may begin his book with an explanation of his notation, a scholar may explain the meaning of a text, and an air stewardess may explain the way to use life jackets and oxygen masks. Probably what is common to these uses of the word "explanation" and to the scientific use is that in all the above cases we have a suggestion of the removal of some sort of puzzlement. In some cases of course there may be in fact no puzzlement to be removed: the explanation of a text may be given by an examinee who presupposes no puzzlement in his examiners (or at least no puzzlement about the text) and the air stewardess may be carrying out regulations even though she knows that the travelers are seasoned and already know the procedures in question.

In the above non-scientific contexts the verb "explain" is a triadic predicate: i.e., *someone* explains *something* to *someone*. The word "explain" is also often used in this way in scientific contexts, as in "Newton explained to readers of the *Principia* why planets move in approximately elliptical orbits". In this way "explain" works rather like "prove": we can say that a mathematician "proves a theorem" *simpliciter* (i.e., he deduces it according to correct rules of logic from his axioms) but we also can say that he proves it to a certain person, in which case there is a suggestion that he not only derives the theorem correctly but also that he gets the other person to understand and to accept his derivation. In metamathematics we of course abstract from this pragmatic aspect of proof (i.e., from questions of the *effects* of proofs on audiences) and consider proofs only from the point of view of whether they are correct deductions from axioms. We consider neither the proof giver nor the proof receiver but merely the sentences of the proof as abstract structures. Now in discussing explanation, some writers (for example C. G. Hempel [2]) prefer to discuss the concept of explanation as far as possible in terms abstracted from pragmatic aspects: that is they concentrate on a concept of explanation which is defined in terms of its logical form (and on a concept of correct explanation which depends also on the *truth* of its premises). That is, they try to give an account of explanation which (if the explanation were expressed in a formal language) would belong to syntax and semantics. On the other hand some writers, such as Michael Scriven,[3] stress the contextual and pragmatic aspects of explanation (such as removal of puzzlement), and hold that an account which abstracts from these is not likely to be fruitful. That is, these latter philosophers would say that not much of importance is left when we abstract from the contextual and pragmatic aspects, and that a theory which abstracts from these can not be compared with such a highly successful branch of study as proof theory in metamathematics. In passing it should be observed that even proof theory in metamathematics can not wholly abstract from pragmatic considerations, insofar as there are disputes between different philosophers of mathematics as to what constitutes an *acceptable* proof: some of them ("intuitionist" or "constructivist" mathematicians) will not accept forms of proof which are acceptable to others ("classical" mathematicians). Nevertheless proof theory has such a wealth of technical achievements (such as proofs of completeness and incompleteness, decidability and undecidability) that discussions of the pragmatic aspects lurk very much in the background. It should be noticed that though, in prac- tice, proponents of the formalist and pragmatic ap- proaches to the discussion of explanation are sometimes at cross purposes with one another, there is not neces- sarily any incompatibility between the two approaches. To a large extent it may be a matter of what differ- ent philosophers think is most *interesting* about explanation.

Let us consider something of what can be said about explanation from the more formal point of view. Hem- pel[4] has distinguished two main types of scientific ex- planation, which he calls, respectively, the *deductive- nomological* and the *inductive-statistical*.

The deductive-nomological pattern of explanation

Suppose that a top is spun with an angular velocity ω about its axis, so that it precesses gently around the vertical through the point where its pointed end rests on the floor. Why does it not fall over onto its side, as it would if it were not spinning very fast? Here we have a particular fact to explain, namely the precessing of this particular top. Let us represent the sentence ex- pressing this particular fact by "E". Then there are sentences describing the exact shape of the top, its (let us suppose) homogeneous composition (at least to a high degree of approximation), its mass, and its angular velocity of rotation about its axis and its angle to the vertical when it was set spinning. Let these sentences be C_1, C_2, C_3, ... C_m. These express what are commonly called "initial conditions", though the word "initial" should not be taken as implying that the conditions temporally precede the phenomenon to be explained. They do in our example, but they need not do so in other cases. Suppose that what we had to explain, on the basis of data about the present precessional motion of the top, was why it did not fall down on its side at some slightly *earlier* time, sentences expressing its *present* state of motion would still count as "initial" conditions. "Initial" here means "initial to the problem in hand" rather than "initial in time".

Besides C_1, C_2, C_3, ... C_m we need laws L_1, L_2, ... L_n which in our example about the top will be the laws of Newtonian mechanics. Then it is possible to construct an argument

$$C_1, C_2, ... C_m$$
$$L_1, L_2, ... L_n$$

Therefore E

This is an example of the deductive nomological pattern of explanation. It would seem that whether or not possession of this form is either necessary or sufficient for explanation, it is a highly characteristic pattern of explanation. To make the account formal we have to characterize C_1, C_2, ... C_m and L_1, L_2, ... L_n formally. Now C_1, C_2, ... C_m are clearly particular propositions: they refer to particular events or states of affairs in particular regions of space and time. We can think of them as propositions containing names or definite descriptions of particular entities. The law statements, L_1, L_2, ... L_n, on the other hand, are propositions which begin with universal quantifiers and which do not contain names or definite descriptions. It is true that some propositions which make a reference to particular entities or regions of space-time are sometimes called laws: consider for example the "law" that bodies near the surface of the earth fall with an acceleration of approximately 981 cm/sec². However, we can replace the reference to the earth by "on the surface of a sphere of such-and-such mass and radius", and insert the additional statement that the earth is a body of this mass and radius. We thus split up the original proposition into an L part and a C part. Admittedly Galileo could not have done this, partly because he lacked the necessary geophysical   **59** data, but I think that nowadays any "law" which contains a reference to a particular region of space-time and which is of much interest to the philosophy of science can be split up into a genuine L part and C part.

There is, however, a more serious objection to our characterization of laws as completely general propositions. There is perhaps no other body in the universe, other than the earth, with the same mass, radius, and distance from the star of which it is a planet. In which case *any* statement mentioning the earth will be true if and only if a corresponding perfectly general statement which instead of the name "the earth" contains a clause "all bodies which have such and such a mass, radius, distance from its star" is also true. And if the predicates "having such and such a mass, etc." are not enough we could add further ones, such as "being a planet of a star with such-and-such a spectrum". In short, if there is one and only one object in the universe of which the predicates "P_1", "P_2", ... "P_k" are true we can always replace the *particular* proposition:

$$F[(\imath x)\quad (P_1 x \bullet P_2 x \quad ... \quad P_k x)]$$

by the *general* one

$$(x)\quad [(P_1 x \bullet P_2 x ... P_k x) \supset Fx]$$

so long as our discourse is in a purely extensional language. There are now two courses which a philosopher might take. He might regard the above mentioned proposition:

$$(x)\quad [(P_1 x \bullet P_2 x \quad ... \quad P_k x) \supset Fx]$$

and its like as perfectly good laws, and might therefore replace the initial conditions C_1, C_2, ... C_m in this sort of way, and similarly he might replace the particular description E of the event to be explained by a corresponding perfectly general proposition. We should then have a case of explanation of a law by other laws. Alternatively he might give up an attempt to define laws purely formally and would stigmatize such a general proposition as our:

$$(x) \quad [(P_1 x \cdot P_2 x \quad \dots \quad P_k x) \supset Fx]$$

above as a more *accidental* generalization. I shall try to make this issue clear by means of an example.

Consider a fictitious star, Delta Chaeropi (in the fictitious constellation Bandicoot). This star has six planets, and each planet has a number of satellites which happens to be a prime number. Then the proposition:

(1) (x) (x is a planet of Delta Chaeropi $\supset$
       the number of satellites of x
       is prime)

is true of everything in the universe. For either a thing is not a planet of Delta Chaeropi or it has a prime number of satellites. Nevertheless do we wish to regard (1) as a law of nature? It is presumably a mere accident that the planets of Delta Chaeropi each have a prime number of satellites. (Of course it may not be clear at this stage what, if anything, it means to say "a mere accident", but let us accept it provisionally in the hope of soon making it clearer.)

A scientist might wish to deny that our proposition (1) is a law of nature simply on the grounds that it contains the proper name "Delta Chaeropi". However there may well be a set of perfectly general predicates (i.e., not themselves containing proper names or indicator words like "here" and "now"[1]) which jointly apply only to Delta Chaeropi. Suppose that Delta Chaeropi is the only star in the universe of which a certain finite set of predicates "P_1", "P_2", "P_3", ... "P_k" is true. (Note that if the universe is an infinite one it may be rather a large assumption that such a set of predicates exists, but let us nevertheless assume that the assumption is in order.) If (1) is true then so is the proposition

[1] Therefore "... less than 100 light years away from the sun" and "... less than 100 light years from here" would not count as perfectly general predicates.

(2) (x) $[(P_1x \bullet P_2x \bullet P_3x \quad ... \quad P_kx) \supset$
x has a prime number of satellites]

We can not deny (2) the status of a law of nature on the grounds that it contains a name or uniquely referring expression, for (2) does not contain such an expression. Formally it is as general as any law of nature. And yet intuitively we may surely feel that it is not a law but merely an accidentally true generalization.

There is another reason why the attempt to distinguish laws from generalizations like (1) may break down: our distinction between perfectly general predicates and predicates containing proper names or references to particular points of space and time is by no means a clear one. Nelson Goodman has defined the predicate "grue" to mean "green prior to A.D. 2000 and blue thereafter", and "bleen" to mean "blue prior to A.D. 2000 and green thereafter". [5] If it is said that "grue" and "bleen" are not perfectly general predicates, because their definitions have a reference to A.D. 2000, it can be replied (as Goodman did) that "blue" and "green" are not perfectly general because they can be defined as "bleen prior to A.D. 2000 and grue thereafter" and "grue prior to A.D. 2000 and bleen thereafter". Intuitively we feel that "blue" and "green" are more general predicates than "grue" and "bleen" and perhaps we can justify this intuition by pointing out how much simpler it is to train a human organism to apply the predicates "blue" and "green" than it is to train it to apply the predicates "grue" and "bleen". The example does show, however, that the distinction can not be made in a purely formal way. If so, it would apparently follow that we can not distinguish laws of nature from true generalizations involving reference to a particular region of space-time in a purely formal way.

One way in which philosophers have tried to distinguish laws of nature from accidentally true generalizations is by saying that laws of nature do, whereas

accidental generalizations do not, support contrary to
fact conditionals. Thus suppose that in the space technology of the future astronomers are able to ascertain
that Delta Chaeropi has planets and that these planets
have satellites, and that the number of satellites of each
planet is discovered to be prime. (It goes without saying
that such discoveries would be quite beyond the powers
of present-day astronomers.) The astronomers would not
be inclined to say that *if* Delta Chaeropi *had* yet another
planet then the satellites of this planet would be prime in
number. That is, we might say that our proposition (1) is
not a law because it does not support a contrary to fact
conditional. Now the contrary to fact conditional is
certainly different from the ordinary conditional "⊃".
We can most plausibly give a metalinguistic analysis of
the contrary to fact conditional. To say "If Delta Chaeropi had had yet another planet, then the satellites of
this other planet would have been prime in number" is
to say that the sentence "The satellites of the $(n + 1)$th
planet of Delta Chaeropi are prime in number" is deducible from "Delta Chaeropi has $n + 1$ planets" (here I
am taking the fact that of the matter to be that Delta
Chaeropi has not $n + 1$ but n planets), together of course
with certain implicit background assumptions, such as
some accepted scientific laws. It would appear, however,
that this could not be done unless the proposition that
the satellites of the $(n + 1)$th planet are prime in number
was deduced from a law that if anything is a star answering to the description of Delta Chaeropi then it must
have planets each of which has a prime number of satellites. That is, if we attempt to elucidate the difference
between lawlike and accidental universal generalizations by referring to contrary to fact conditionals, we are
brought around in a circle, since it would now appear
that contrary to fact conditionals themselves need to be
understood by reference to the distinction between lawlike and accidental generalizations.

This circularity has been noted by A. J. Ayer, who

goes on to say that his own view is that the difference between the two kinds of universal generalizations (lawlike and accidental generalizations) is "not so much a difference in their content but in our attitude toward them". [6] This difference in attitude depends partly on the difference among the roles that the two types of generalization play in explanatory theories. We do seem to regard something as a law if it is either part of a theory or if it is something which we guess may one day be integrated into a theory. The scientist makes his guess on the basis of his general feel for his subject, and not by means of formal criteria. Thus most scientists would certainly not regard it as significant, or more than a coincidence, that all the planets of a star had satellites whose numbers were prime, just as, I imagine, most astronomers would not regard Bode's so-called "law" relating the approximate distances of the planets of the sun as a law, even neglecting the consideration that it makes reference explicitly to a particular entity, the sun.[2] That is, the astronomers would probably feel intuitively, on the basis of their knowledge of physical theory, that Bode's law is no more than an interesting coincidence and is unlikely to be integrated into any theoretical scheme.[3] Moreover I think that astronomers would still feel this way even though it were not the case that some planets diverge rather markedly from fulfilling Bode's "law".

[2]Bode's Law: Take the numbers 0, 3, 6, 12, 24, 48, 96, add 4 to each term, and divide by 10, thus getting the numbers 0.4, 0.7, 1.0, 1.6, 2.8, 5.2, 10.0, ... These approximately correspond to the average distances from the sun of the planets Mercury, Venus, Earth, Mars, Jupiter, Saturn. (The actual distances in astronomical units are 0.39, 0.72, 1.00, 1.5, 5.2, 9.54, if we allow the gap into which 2.8 fits to correspond to the minor planets, which occupy a region between Mars and Jupiter.) Uranus (discovered since the formulation of the "law") also fits fairly well (predicted distance 19.6, actual distance 19.19) but Neptune and Pluto diverge markedly, (predicted distances 38.8 and 77.2 respectively, actual distances 30.07 and 39.46).

[3]I say "integrated into" rather than "deducible from", since in any theory some laws must be ultimate and not deducible from others. Nevertheless we can still say that ultimate laws are integrated into the theory of which they form an essential part.

Statistical explanation

Hempel distinguishes two sorts of statistical explanation. The first he calls "Deductive-Statistical" explanation. This is very important in modern physics, especially since, according to quantum mechanics, the fundamental laws of nature are statistical. According to this pattern statistical laws are deduced from a set of premises which includes at least one statistical law. If we follow Popper in interpreting the probability statements of physics as statements about objective propensities, rather than as statements about limiting frequencies, then the deductive-statistical model will reduce to the deductive nomological, with at least one law in the premises being a law statement about propensities.

The deductive-nomological form differs from the form which Hempel calls the "Inductive-Statistical"[4] form of explanation in a more important way. Consider the following example: A very high proportion of human beings weigh less than 250 pounds. So we might argue as follows:

Most human beings weigh less than 250 lbs.
X is a human being.
. . . . [makes very likely that]
X weighs less than 250 lbs.

Hempel has expressed the pattern in the above form where the words "makes very likely that" (or some near equivalent) are inserted between premises and conclusion. It would seem that in reading the above we must utter the "makes very likely that" under our

---

[4] I myself regard this terminology as a little misleading, since Hempel's account can surely be accepted even by those who wish to free science from an account based on the notion of inductive argument. See Chapter 6.

breath somewhat, for if it is overheard then inverted commas will have to be understood to go round premises and conclusion, and the above "argument" will have to be understood not as an argument but as a metalinguistic *statement*. (See the remarks on pp. 37–39 of the previous chapter.) But what Hempel means is that in the above argument the relation between premises and conclusion is not one of implication but of "inductive support" or "confirmation". This makes the following important difference. If a deductive argument is a good one, it will still be a good one if further additional premises are added. This is not so with the inductive-statistical pattern. Suppose we have the additional information that X, whose weight is to be explained, is one of the wives of Rumanika, the king of Karagwe in East Africa a hundred years ago. Rumanika regarded egregious fatness as a necessity for female beauty. The queens had to suck milk through a straw practically all their waking lives, and they were beaten if they stopped sucking for too long.[7] As a result they became pretty well unable to move. Well, if we replace "X is a human being" by "X is a human being who is a queen of Karagwe a hundred years ago" in the above argument, our premises do not make it probable that X weighs less than 250 pounds. For the additional premise lends strong support to the hypothesis that X weighs at least 250 pounds.

Suppose then that we are offered an explanation of the fact that X weighs less than 250 pounds, and we are told that most human beings weigh less than 250 pounds and that X is a human being, and so it is to be expected that X weighs less than 250 pounds. Admittedly this is not much of an explanation, but according to Hempel it would count as an explanation of a sort. Now we see that in assessing its worth we have to pay attention to something outside the pattern of argument of the explanation itself, in a way in which we do not in the case of the deductive pattern of explanation. We have to make sure that an *epistemic* requirement is satisfied, namely that we have made use of all the available relevant information. We should not accept the explanation, perhaps, if we knew that X was a Queen of Karagwe (though we might if we knew that X was a Queen of Karagwe with an allergy to milk).

Modern quantum mechanics provides a field in which we can sometimes be quite sure that the epistemic requirement is satisfied. The ultimate laws of quantum mechanics are probabilistic, and hence unless quantum mechanics (as it at present exists) is false there are situations in which it is possible that there should be additional evidence which would be relevant. Consider an electron which passes through a crystal and which strikes a screen in a region R. Complete knowledge of the antecedent conditions (the state of motion of the electron prior to passing through the crystal) enables us to assert only that there is such and such a probability of the electron striking the screen in region R. *No* additional evidence, analogous to "X is a Queen of Karagwe", is here possible.

Extending the use of a phrase due to William Dray,[8] Hempel uses the term "covering law model" to cover both the deductive-nomological and inductive-statistical models of explanations of particular facts.

Incomplete explanation

Hempel has introduced two further concepts which are particularly important in the present connection. These are those of a *partial explanation* and an *explanation sketch.*[9] Suppose that we are asked to explain the fact that part of an earth satellite fell into Central Australia. We could say that the satellite was not completely clear of the rarefied regions of the earth's atmosphere, and that the friction of the satellite's passage through the atmosphere resulted in a loss of kinetic energy, and hence the satellite fell to earth. This would probably be regarded as a moderately satisfactory explanation, but notice that it is an explanation of the satellite falling to earth (at least if it is not completely vaporized during its fall through the atmosphere): it does not explain why the satellite fell into Central Australia. To explain this a great deal of further knowledge would be required of the exact orbit of the satellite, its time of getting into orbit, the position of Central Australia on the earth's surface, and probably several other relevant facts. We may say that the original explanation was (or could easily be expanded into) a complete explanation of the satellite's falling to earth, but that it was only a partial explanation of the satellite's falling into Central Australia. No doubt the concrete event of the satellite's falling to earth was as a matter of fact the same concrete event as the satellite's falling into Central Australia.[5] But according to Hempel's account, what is explained is not a concrete event but a fact. A fact is what is expressed by a true sentence and in so far as sentences can be more or less specific we can talk of facts being more or less specific.

One of the reasons why there are sometimes cross purposes between Hempel and critics of the covering law model of explanation, such as Scriven, is that the critics often want to call "an explanation" something which Hempel wishes to call "a partial explanation". It is clear that ordinary language pulls both ways. In our example of the part of the earth satellite which fell in Central Australia, it would be quite all right to say that the argument was an "explanation" of the fact of the part's *falling* in Central Australia, but equally it could be retorted that it wasn't an explanation at all because it did not explain why the part of the satellite fell in *Central Australia*. Hempel is perfectly entitled, therefore, to use the word " explanation" in a more precise way, so that the above example would constitute not an explanation

[5]Hempel, it should be noted, is not sure that the notion of "concrete event" is a very clear one.[10]

but only a partial explanation of the fact in question. Criticisms of the covering law model of explanation, in Hempel's more precise sense, are beside the point if they merely assert that explanations *in the looser sense* of the word do not always fit Hempel's model. To do this it would be necessary to show that Hempel, in attempting to make the concept of explanation more precise, was instead completely distorting it. (We shall consider some such objections later in the chapter.)

The example of the earth satellite was an example of a partial deductive-nomological explanation. It will be useful for two reasons to give now an example of a partial inductive-statistical one. In the first place partial statistical explanations are common in the more historical parts of science, such as the theory of evolution. In the second place it is important to see that we do not need to construe partial explanation in such a way that all statistical explanation should be regarded as only partial. Hempel wishes to construe "partial explanation" in such a way that statistical explanations can be partial or complete as the case may be. His reason is that modern physics makes statistical laws ultimate and hence a statistical explanation can no longer be regarded as always a "second best", perhaps to be replaced one day by a deductive-nomological one. Suppose that the laws of quantum mechanics enable us to predict that 80 percent of the electrons which pass through a crystal hit a screen in a certain region R of the screen. Then if one single electron hits the region R, the above mentioned laws will enable us to give a complete statistical explanation of the electron's hitting the screen in the region R. It will, however, give only a partial statistical explanation of a red haired man's observing the electron hit the screen in R. Thus the distinction between complete and partial explanations is applicable to inductive-statistical explanations as well as to deductive-nomological ones.

Explanation sketches

Hempel has also introduced the valuable concept of an explanation sketch. Often an explanation is stated elliptically: that is, some of the premises may not be explicitly stated, but it may be clear from the context what they are. Sometimes, however, it may not be clear what extra premises would be needed to round out the attempted argument into a properly formulated complete or partial explanation. The argument is more of a hint at an explanation, and Hempel calls such an argument an explanation sketch. Of course whether a piece of discourse should be interpreted either as an elliptically formulated complete explanation or perhaps as a partial explanation or perhaps yet again as merely an explanation sketch is a matter of judgment: the various concepts shade into one another, since we often have considerable freedom of choice as to whether to say either that a premise is tacitly understood or else that it is not a premise at all. However the following example will provide a clear case of something which could be called an explanation sketch. Suppose it is asked why a person has blue eyes, and it is said that this is because of his genes. Perhaps genes are merely thought of as "somethings-or-other" that in normal environmental circumstances lead to various phenotypic characteristics (e.g., blue eyes). It is clear that the answer to the question "why does he have blue eyes?" alludes to no genetical regularity whatever. What we have is merely an explanation sketch: a hint to look for an explanation somewhere or other in the field of genetics. It is obvious that someone who regarded "because of his genes" as an explanation would be able to find an exception here to the covering law model, but the proponent of the covering law model has a ready reply, namely by classifying the putative explanation as merely an explanation sketch.

Explanation as analogy

Writers who might concede that explanation formally fits the covering law model may nevertheless hold that there are additional requirements, such that the explanatory laws should bear some *analogy* to already accepted laws. The physicist N. R. Campbell, who wrote interestingly on the philosophy of physics a generation or so ago, stressed this point of view. [11] Consider the explanation of Boyle's law in terms of the kinetic theory of gases, in which a gas is thought of as constituted of very many perfectly elastic particles moving in accordance with the laws of Newtonian mechanics. Insofar as Boyle's law is deducible from these mechanical conceptions it fits the deductive-nomological model, but Campbell argued that unless this formal pattern of explanation were constrained by the additional requirement of analogy, various quite trivial arguments would have to be allowed to be explanations. Thus, to use his example,[12] the constancy of the ratio of the electrical resistance of a piece of metal to its absolute temperature might be "explained" by the following theory:

$$\text{Resistance } (R) = (c^2 + d^2)a$$
$$\text{Temperature } (T) = \frac{cd}{b}$$

a and b are constants and $c = d$

From the above theory we deduce that

$$\frac{R}{T} = (c^2 + d^2)a\left(\frac{b}{cd}\right) = 2ab = \text{constant}$$

The theory above is clearly trivial, yielding no real explanation of the constancy of $\frac{R}{T}$. What makes it trivial,

71

according to Campbell, is its lack of analogy with any-thing that we already know. Contrast the kinetic theory of gases, in which the postulated particles behave just *as if* they were small perfectly elastic billiard balls.

Additional constraints (over and above the ability to yield deductions of the explicanda) are doubtless needed before a theory can be explanatory and not just trivial. It was unnecessary, however, for Campbell to have settled on *analogy* for this purpose. The theories which we regard as genuinely explanatory can be used to predict facts other than those for which they were first invented, or they can be modified in a simple way so as to do so. That is, the important difference between the trivial theory of Campbell's example and the non-trivial kinetic theory of gases might be said to lie simply in the predictive fruitfulness of the latter, or at least to be closely connected with it, and not to have anything specially to do with analogy. Indeed when Campbell comes to discuss a more phenomenological type of theory, exemplified by Fourier's theory of heat conduction, he replaces the requirement of analogy by that of simplicity.[13]

It can not be denied that analogy has often been of great heuristic value for scientific theory construction. In some cases we can see why this should be so. For if gas really is a lot of particles which behave rather like minute perfectly elastic billiard balls, then it is not hard to see why a theorist who happened to think of a gas *on the analogy of* a swarm of minute perfectly elastic billiard balls should have been successful. Moreover analogy can be found in science in much less straight-forward cases. The Bohr theory of the atom had its successes, and this theory described atoms on the anal-ogy with a system of planets revolving round a sun. The theory had nevertheless to modify the analogy consid-erably, since it had to impose the quantum conditions which prevent the planetary electrons of an atom from spiraling into the nucleus, and which explain such things as discrete line spectra. These very quantum conditions are what made the theory so successful, and looking back on the matter it would appear that it is the disanalogous parts of the theory which are chiefly responsible for its success and which have stood the test of time. It is true that in the case of the more sophisticated theories which have successively replaced the Bohr theory *some* analogy with classical mechanics remains. Thus in the modern development of quantum mechanics, through the abstruse mathematical theory of Hilbert spaces, physicists have often to rely on analogy, since differential equations relating operators in Hilbert space need to be postulated, and in guessing at these physicists have been guided by analogous differential equations (relating not operators but physical quantities) in classical physics. It should be remembered, however, that this is a matter of heuristics: the correctness of a differential equation about a Hilbert space is decided not by its analogy with classical equations but by the correctness of the observational consequences which can be drawn from it. Insofar as analogy has proved a good guide this may be a lucky fact about the world, but it may also be a reflection of the fact that when investigators have little but analogy to guide them then their theories will inevitably tend to display some analogy with previous theories. Moreover, if in the history of the development of physics a theory T_0 is replaced successively by theories T_1, T_2, ... T_n, then there can easily be an analogy between T_r and T_{r+1} for various values of r, without there being any significant analogy between T_0 and T_n.

It might be held that for T_n to be a good theory there must be strong analogies between T_r and T_{r+1}, for each r for $0 \leq r < n$. There can easily be a confusion here. Even if (as is doubtful) it is a fact of human psychology that investigators are always guided by analogy, this would not show that analogy has anything to do with the goodness of a theory. Suppose that, by some fluke or by some stroke of super-genius, quantum mechanics had come into being at once in its most modern form, with Hilbert spaces and all. Then the chain T_0, T_1, ... T_n would have been replaced by the simple transition from T_0 to T_n. Surely T_n would not be any the worse for that or any the less explanatory. Probably it would not have been generally accepted by scientists since it would have been too far ahead of its time, just as was the case in the last century with Gibbs' statistical mechanics when it was first propounded. But unless one takes an extremely pragmatic view of explanation, we must say that this is a matter of the psychology and sociology of scientists, and not a matter of the goodness or badness of explanations as such.

Explanation as reduction to the familiar

The demand for analogy in theories may stem from a conception of explanation as reduction to the familiar. Thus if the solar system is more familiar to us than atoms, then the Bohr theory of the atom may appeal to us because it somehow reduces the behavior of atoms to the more familiar behavior of the solar system. Even the Bohr theory, however, introduces ideas (such as that of a quantum jump) which can not be reduced to anything in our previous experience. Scientists have moved a long way from the ideals of W. Thomson (Lord Kelvin) in the last century. Kelvin went so far as to say that he could never be satisfied that he understood anything until he could make a mechanical model of it. Thus he wished to explain the electrical properties of matter on the basis of mechanical analogies, whereas of course we now would seek to explain some of the mechanical properties of matter (such as elasticity) on the basis of the electrical properties of the particles of which matter is constituted. Certainly it is not an ideal of modern science that explanation should be a reduction to the familiar, since the basic laws of quantum mechanics and of the theory of relativity may seem very strange to commonsense intuition. However the decisive objection to thinking of explanation as reduction to the familiar is that it is often very familiar facts which may be felt to be in need of explanation. Hempel, for example,[14] mentions the case of Olbers' paradox, which suggests on the basis of certain plausible assumptions that the sky should not be dark at night, but on the contrary that it should be very bright indeed. We shall be discussing Olbers' paradox in Chapter 8 where we shall see the cosmological insights which we can get if we reflect on the familiar fact of the darkness of the night sky and possible explanations of it. There are of course all sorts of familiar facts (as well as unfamiliar ones) for which scientists seek explanations: for example, why bodies fall, why iron rusts, why salt is needed in one's diet, and why children resemble their parents. The laws and generalizations which are used to explain such facts of course eventually become familiar to the scientists who use them, but if explanation were reduction to the familiar it is hard to see why we should ever need to seek explanations of familiar facts.

Explanation as redescription

Consider the case of the rusting of iron, mentioned above. Part of the explanation of rusting consists in the identification of rusting with oxidation. Then the explanation of a case of rusting would require the fact that water vapor is present together with a law that when water vapor is present oxidation of iron occurs. We might interpret the above situation in two ways: (1) The scientist changes the meaning of "rusting" from its commonsense one of "reddening of iron when it is left out in damp" to "oxidation". Then it is the oxidation of iron which he explains. (2) It is the reddening of the iron which is explained, with the aid of an additional law "all cases of reddening of iron when it is exposed to damp are cases of oxidation".

Let us look at what differences there are, if any, between the interpretations (1) and (2) above. According to (1) the nerve of the explanation lies in the shift of meaning of the word "rust", or in other words to the *redescription* of reddening when exposed to moisture as rusting. According to (2) the nerve lies not in redescription but in the additional law which is required. But could it not nevertheless be held that to accept the *additional law* in (2) is neither more nor less than to accept the *redescription*? The account of explanation as redescription does not seem obviously different from the covering law model.

On the other hand, though there may be no formal inconsistency between a philosopher who stresses the deductive model and a philosopher who stresses redescription there may well be a very great difference in outlook. An interest in the deductive model goes naturally (though it *need not* do so) with an instrumentalist philosophy of science, a philosophy which sees the value of science primarily as a tool for predicting our experiences, whereas the account in terms of redescription may go along with a more disinterested conception of science, the conception of science as an aid to understanding what the world is like for its own sake, and quite apart from any predictive or practical values which science may have for us. [15]

Feyerabend's criticism of the deductive model

The above considerations suggest a view of explanation which holds that what is important about explanation is not so much its form (which is explicated by the deductive model) as the idea that an explanation yields understanding insofar as it provides us with a more satisfactory description of the facts. Of course if "more satisfactory" means merely "liked better" then this account of explanation would have little appeal: what is liked better by witch doctors is not what is liked better by physicists, and we must try to find an account of "more satisfactory" which is a bit more objective. It is worth looking at some interesting views about explanation which have been put forward by Paul Feyerabend. [16]

Consider the laws of phenomenological (or "classical") thermodynamics. These explain certain familiar and unfamiliar occurrences. For example the melting of ice in a glass of cordial is explained by the second law, which asserts that in a closed system entropy always increases, together with certain factual assumptions, such as that the temperature of the room in which the glass of cordial is sitting is above freezing point, and that the system consisting of the glass of cordial together with a certain volume of the surrounding air can be regarded approximately as a closed system. Now we might consider the further question, of whether the laws of phenomenological thermodynamics themselves can be explained. Physicists would tend to say that they can be explained by means of the theory of statistical thermodynamics. In fact it is often said that the theory of phenomenological thermodynamics can be "reduced" to the statistical theory, and the explanation or "reduction" here is commonly thought of in accordance with a deductive model. That is, a theory T is reduced to or explained by a theory T' if T is deducible from T' together with certain *correspondence rules*. These correspondence rules are needed because some, at least, of the concepts of T and T' will differ: thus the concept of temperature in classical thermodynamics is equated with that of average kinetic energy of molecules, which is a concept of statistical thermodynamics. Moreover it is commonly held that just as statistical thermodynamics has to be tied to classical thermodynamics by means of correspondence rules, so correspondence rules are needed to tie the terms of classical thermodynamics to those of ordinary common sense. The observations whereby we test the theories should on this view be stated in purely common sense language: not as "the temperature of this liquid is 30° C" but as "the liquid in this thin glass tube reaches up to a scratch marked '30'". We have a hierarchical picture of explanation now: (1) Commonsense observation reports are explained by deduction from classical thermodynamics plus certain correspondence rules. (2) Classical thermodynamics is explained by deduction from statistical thermodynamics together with certain correspondence rules.

The above hierarchy has three tiers, but there is no reason why there should not be hierarchies with four, five, or more tiers. Nevertheless the three-tiered picture has won an important place in modern scientific thinking, since there is an influential interpretation of quantum mechanics according to which all explanations in atomic physics must take the form: quantum mechanics → classical physics → observation reports. Physicists who accept this interpretation hold that it is impossible that quantum mechanics should be tested directly by observation reports, since they hold that part at least of the theory of the experimental apparatus must be classical. Another important example of a hierarchy of deduction is: general relativity → special relativity → Newtonian mechanics → observations of planetary motions.

Feyerabend rejects this pattern of explanation: (1) He wishes to say that when a theory T is said to be "explained" by a theory T' what really happens is that T has not been explained at all but it has been *replaced by* T'. (Far from being *explained* by the theory T', the original theory T has been shown to be *false*.) (2) He wishes to say that observational consequences can be deduced both from T and from T' *directly* (as he puts it "a theory is its own observation language"), and hence that correspondence rules are unnecessary.

Feyerabend's first criticism of the hierarchical picture is that when a theory (such as phenomenological thermodynamics), is said to be reduced to another (such as statistical thermodynamics) the two theories are often in fact inconsistent with one another. Assuming that the two theories are internally consistent we must conclude that one can not be *deduced* from the other.

Taken by itself this does not at first sight appear to be a very damaging attack on the deductive model. J. Kemeny and P. Oppenheim, who are much nearer to Hempel than to Feyerabend in their philosophy of science, have made a similar point.[17] Hempel[18] is quite in agreement that sometimes one and the same occurrence could be subsumed under mutually incompatible theories. Moreover a philosopher like Nagel[19] who gives a deductive account of the explanation of laws (or theories) could reply that it is not the laws themselves that are deduced but only their *approximate correctness*. Thus general relativity enables us to deduce the approximate correctness of Newton's law of gravitation, and the wave theory of light enables us to deduce the approximate correctness of geometrical optics. (Hilary Putnam who defends Nagel in this way, explicates "approximately true" as follows: To say that a theory is approximately true is to say that though the theory is not itself true, "a certain *logical consequence* of the theory obtained, for example, by replacing 'equals' with 'equals plus or minus delta' is true".[20])

Is it correct, however, that Newton's gravitational theory or geometrical optics is even approximately true? Newton's inverse square law is not even approximately true near a very heavy and dense body. General relativity would predict a large deviation from the inverse square law near a quasar. Again, geometrical optics gives wildly incorrect results as to what happens when light is diffracted through one or more slits. What is approximately true is not Newton's original law but *another* law which we can get from the original law by inserting the phrase "far from any very heavy and dense body". But this is tantamount to admitting that what is deduced from general relativity is not the Newtonian theory but the fact that the Newtonian theory gives approximately correct predictions in certain circumstances (why it works in practice as well as it does work). This is part of Feyerabend's own position. Nevertheless it is hard to believe that a proponent of the hierarchical account of science would not agree to these modifications of his own position.

The nub of Feyerabend's[6] objections seems rather, to lie in his contention that observation reports can not be couched in theory-neutral language, that a theory is its own observation language. There is clearly something in this. Certainly observation reports can be theory-laden, i.e., can use terminology which is explicable only within the conceptual scheme of some theory. Contrary to Eddington,[22] observation statements are *not* statements about pointer readings. A scientifically untutored peasant could certainly make a report that a black needle-like thing pointed to the figure "35" on a round clock-like thing. He could *not* report that the current through a milliammeter was thirty-five milliampères, since he would not have the concept of an electric current, and still less would he have the concept of an ampère. Nor could the statement of the peasant serve as a test of a scientific hypothesis.[7] The milliammeter might not be correctly calibrated, or it might have a resistance in parallel with it, or it might even be empty and have a gremlin inside it operating the dial. The peasant's statement is compatible with all these possibilities. A perusal

---

[6]And of Wilfrid Sellars' position, which is intermediate between those of Nagel and Feyerabend.[21]

[7]Nevertheless, as Feyerabend points out, [23] we, if we knew about electricity and ampères, could use *the fact that* the peasant had made his statement as a test of an electrical hypothesis.

of a selection of scientists' experimental reports would show how theory-laden even the simplest observation reports in science must commonly be.

We get the apparently paradoxical situation, now, that if an observation sentence O is to express a crucial test between two conceptually different theories T_1 and T_2, then O must really express two different propositions O_1 and O_2. That is, in expressing O_1 it is laden with the concepts of the theory T_1 and in expressing O_2 it is laden with the concepts of the theory T_2.

Now the usual picture of a crucial experiment is as follows (where T_1, T_2 are the rival theories, A is a conjunction of propositions expressing boundary conditions, and O is an observation sentence):

$$(A \bullet T_1) \supset O$$
$$(A \bullet T_2) \supset \sim O$$
$$O \bullet A$$
$$\therefore \sim T_2$$

On Feyerabend's view this has to be replaced by the pattern:

$$(A \bullet T_1) \supset O_1$$
$$(A \bullet T_2) \supset \sim O_2$$
$$O_2 \bullet A$$
$$\therefore \sim T_2$$

Note that O_1 and O_2 will be morphologically the same sentence, but we regard O as it functions in the context of T_1 as a sentence O_1 and O as it functions in the context of T_2 as a different sentence O_2.

(Perhaps A should be split into two sentences namely A_1 and A_2, just as O splits into O_1 and O_2, but we can neglect this refinement.)

Now to refute the theory T_2 the adherent of T_1 must assert O_2. (We may assume that the truth of A is not in question.) But what the adherent of T_1 will be asserting will not be O_2 but O_1. Feyerabend points out, however, that O_1 and O_2 are pragmatically equivalent[8] in the sense that the very same objective situation which causes an adherent of T_1 to assert O_1 will cause an adherent of T_2 to assert O_2.

In this way Feyerabend is able to give an account of crucial experiments between incompatible and conceptually different theories which is consistent with his view that an observation sentence has different meanings in the contexts of the two theories. What the adherent of T_1 does is to consider tentatively what the adherent of T_2 would have to say were he to deny the proposition O_2 which is the pragmatic equivalent of O_1.

Sometimes a theory T_1 may survive after a test which is not even possible within the context of a less satisfactory theory T_2. A good example used by Feyerabend is that of the Brownian movement.[25] An example of Brownian movement is the erratic movement which can be observed in microscopic pollen grains which are suspended in a liquid. The erratic movement is due to the irregular bombardment of the pollen grains by the molecules of the liquid.[9] This phenomenon is a violation of classical thermodynamics, since the pollen grains, together with the surrounding fluid, constitute a heat engine of a type inadmissible according to the second law of classical thermodynamics. However no direct *experimental* confrontation of phenomenological thermodynamics with the phenomenon of Brownian movement is possible: it would be quite impossible to devise thermometers which would be sensitive enough to measure the heat exchanges between pollen and fluid or which would not themselves produce heat exchanges which would swamp the quantities to be measured. Nevertheless from the standpoint of statistical thermo-

[8]This pragmatic account of observation statements is similar to one put forward originally by Carnap[24] but which seems later to have been abandoned by him.

[9]The quantitative phenomena of Brownian motion were predicted correctly by Einstein on the basis of theoretical calculations of statistical mechanics and the kinetic theory of matter, which are the main pillars of statistical thermodynamics.[26]

dynamics Brownian movement can be shown to imply violations of the second law of thermodynamics (fluctuations involving temporary *decreases* of the entropy of a system).

This example of Feyerabend's shows that the test of a theory is not just that it predicts approximately the observational results of some earlier and accepted theory. It is that the new theory should be made to confront the observational facts *directly,* and even that the earlier theory can be rejected on the basis of an observational test which would be quite impossible so long as we thought within the conceptual scheme of the old theory. Of course the fact that we can deduce from the new theory that the old theory would be successful within the observational domain within which it in fact *has* been successful, enables us to regard these successful observational tests of the old theory as *ipso facto* successful observational tests of the new theory.

For example, as Feyerabend himself concedes, it would *in practice* be impossible to use general relativity in celestial mechanics (i.e., the theory of the detailed motions of the planets and their satellites around the sun). Newtonian mechanics has to be used, and general relativity comes in only with those special cases (such as that of the advance of the perihelion of Mercury) for which it appears that the Newtonian theory gives incorrect predictions. But insofar as it can be deduced from general relativity that Newtonian mechanics gives approximately accurate predictions in those circumstances in which Newtonian mechanics *has* been successful, the successes of Newtonian mechanics can be written down as successes for the general theory of relativity.

Criticisms of Feyerabend's use of the concept of "meaning"

Many modern philosophers and semanticists are very suspicious of the word "meaning"; exactly what we ought to mean by it is rather unclear, and Quine even advocates that we should avoid talk of "meanings" and of "same meaning" and "different meaning" altogether.

Consider the concept of temperature. According to statistical thermodynamics this is a certain statistical property. For example the temperature of a gas is the average kinetic energy of its molecules. In classical thermodynamics temperature is defined quite differently: in terms of heat exchanges in the operation of a perfect heat engine. Before classical thermodynamics temperature was simply whatever it is that thermometers measure. There does therefore seem to be some justification (despite the obscurity of the concept of meaning) for Feyerabend's claim that observation reports made in the contexts of different theories (say, reports of temperature as made respectively by Galileo and by proponents of classical and statistical thermodynamics respectively) have different meanings. Hilary Putnam has indeed called attention to a bad reason which Feyerabend has given for saying that Galileo meant something different by "temperature" from what we mean now: namely that the thermometer measures not temperature but a function both of temperature and effects of atmospheric pressure, differences in the behavior of fluids of various chemical compositions which might be used in the thermometer, and so on.[27] According to Putnam, Galileo meant by "temperature" simply some intrinsic property of a substance that the thermometer measures, not necessarily accurately, and that Galileo could understand as well as we could the statement that measured temperature does not correspond exactly to true temperature.[28] Then presumably according to Putnam, the proponent of classical thermodynamics and the proponent of statistical thermodynamics would both mean by "temperature" the same thing that Galileo did, namely the intrinsic property of bodies that thermometers measure, not necessarily accurately, and a "definition" of temperature given by theoretical physicists is really a factual statement asserting that the property given in the definition is in fact the property alluded to by the Galilean definition. (This is much like the factual assertion that the property of redness is the property which is common to exactly three cars in the street outside.[29]) I cannot see, however, that this contention could be substantiated by examination of the accounts of temperature which are given in scientific treatises.[10]

Theory-neutral concepts and common sense

In the previous section Putnam was reported as giving an account of the concept of temperature which was neutral between various theories. If this was a correct account then the concept of temperature could be called theory-neutral. That certain concepts have this characteristic is a view which Feyerabend has called "the hole theory of meaning".[31] I think that this is a misnomer, since it is not a theory of meaning but an account of the meanings of certain concepts. Feyerabend objects to it on methodological grounds. The richer we make our concepts the more testable we make our assertions. This is certainly a good reason why in science we should make many of our observation sentences *not* theory-neutral, but it does not show that it is *never* advantageous to have *some* of them theory-neutral. Suppose that the test between general relativity and Newtonian mechanics to be by means of the prediction that if the former theory is correct then our telescope, when we make a certain observation, will point over that chimney pot and not over that palm tree. (This is hardly a very realistic supposition, considering the refinements and the delicacy of observation which would in fact be required, but let me assume it so as to

[10]It is instructive to look at the definition of *temperature* in the Penguin *Dictionary of Science*[30] which is in terms of the rate of change of heat, which leads us to the definition of *heat*, which is in terms of *energy*. We are plunged at once into theory.

make my point clearly.) Does this mean that "chimney pot" means something different in the contexts of the two theories? Perhaps it does, if on the Einsteinian account a chimney pot is a four-dimensional invariant in space-time, whereas on the Newtonian account it is a three-dimensional spatial solid which endures through time.[11] But why should not "chimney pot" be taken simply to mean something neutral between these theories, defined solely in terms of the architectural function which chimney pots subserve? And "palm tree" similarly, might be given a botanical definition which was neutral between the physical theories.[32]

Moreover we need not follow Feyerabend in saying that commonsense language implies falsehoods. Sometimes it does, to be sure, as when we say "cricket is in his blood: his father was quite a good cricketer and his maternal grandfather captained Australia". We now really ought to say "in his genes", not "in his blood". (Am I being pedantic here? Not so long as white South Africans refuse to be given Negro blood in blood transfusions!) Nevertheless it is wrong to say that commonsense or any other language is infected with falsehood, since presumably the contradictory of any sentence must be in the language, and either the sentence or its contradictory must be true.[33] We can even use the *language* of the phlogiston theory to assert truths, for example "phlogiston does not exist"!

If much of commonsense language is theory-neutral, then it is possible that observation reports could be formulated in a theory-neutral way. Moreover, even when observation sentences are not theory-neutral, the pattern of the test of a theory will simply split into *two* deductive patterns. (As on p. 81.) Also, the formal pattern of explanation will still follow the Hempelian deductive pattern. There is indeed no real contradiction between Hempel's account of explanation in terms of its

[11]It is, however, doubtful whether this is a real difference, since there is nothing to prevent the Newtonian himself from thinking in terms of space-time.

deductive pattern and Feyerabend's emphasis on explanation as redescription. We come to redescribe rust as oxidation, say, and then deduce a particular case of oxidation from chemical theory together with certain initial conditions. Hempel might wish to complicate the account by keeping to some commonsense or theory-neutral meaning of "rust", and augmenting the explanation by introducing the proposition "All (or most?) cases of rust (in the commonsense meaning) are cases of rust in the sense of oxidation". But this will not alter the fact that the explanation comes about when the scientist sees a piece of rust as a case of oxidation.

Indeed, far from considering the view of explanation as redescription to be at variance with the Hempelian account, we may say that scientific redescription is essentially connected with deduction from laws (which is what Hempel stresses). The ideal of science is not a description of the world in the sense of a huge inventory, but is that of a *simple* description, which means that all sorts of phenomena should be deducible from a few laws.

I do not, therefore, think that there are formal inconsistencies between Hempel's and Feyerabend's theories of explanation. Feyerabend is, however, especially concerned not so much with routine explanations within well tested theories, as with those cases of *progress* in explanation, when we give up some theory in favor of a better one.[12]

Sir George Thomson has questioned whether it is the primary aim of science to give explanations.[34] It is, he thinks, at least as much the discovery of *new effects*. Similarly, I would say that the most interesting thing

[12]I have been concerned to consider Feyerabend's theory of explanation where it appears to impinge on Hempel's, and I have tried to reconcile the two. Nevertheless the writings of such philosophers as Hempel and Nagel, on the one hand, and Feyerabend, on the other hand, have a very different flavor: the former suggest a rather conservative attitude to scientific theories, whereas the latter are passionately nonconformist in outlook. Nor have I done justice to the richness of the insights and the exciting conjectures which can be found in Feyerabend's papers.

about science is that it tells us what the world is like by means of simple and unitary theories. Hence if new effects, or old ones for that matter, can be described scientifically, this can be done only by producing some theory of them which will be deductive in pattern, and which will therefore yield explanations of the Hempelian pattern. So to say that the main aim of science is to yield explanations and to say that it is to describe the world is not really to say something very different.

SUGGESTIONS FOR FURTHER READING

For C. G. Hempel's theory of explanation, the best and most recent presentation is Chapter 12, "Aspects of Scientific Explanation", of his *Aspects of Scientific Explanation and Other Essays in the Philosophy of Science* (New York: Free Press, 1964), but Chapters 9–11 are also concerned with this topic. For Ernest Nagel's view see his *Structure of Science* (New York: Harcourt, Brace, and World, 1961), especially Chapters 2, 3, and 11. I compared Nagel's view with those of Paul Feyerabend and Wilfrid Sellars, and there were comments on my paper by Hilary Putnam and by Sellars, and then Feyerabend's comments on these papers: see J. J. C. Smart, "Conflicting Views about Explanation", in R. S. Cohen and M. W. Wartofsky (eds.), *Boston Studies in the Philosophy of Science*, Vol. II (New York: Humanities Press, 1965), pp. 157–169; Wilfrid Sellars, "Scientific Realism or Irenic Instrumentalism", *ibid.*, pp. 171–204; Hilary Putnam, "How not to talk about Meaning", *ibid.* pp. 205–222; and Paul Feyerabend, "Reply to Criticism", *ibid.*, pp. 223–261. For Sellars again, see Wilfrid Sellars, *Science, Perception and Reality* (London: Routledge & Kegan Paul, 1963, and New York: Humanities Press, 1963), Chapters 1 and 4 [Chapter 4 originally appeared in H. Feigl and G. Maxwell (eds.), *Current Issues in the Philosophy of Science* (New York: Holt, Rinehart and Winston, 1961), in which there is also a comment by Feyerabend]. For Feyerabend see especially his papers: "Explanation, Reduction, and Empiricism", in H. Feigl and G. Maxwell (eds.), *Scientific Explanation, Space and Time, Minnesota Studies in the Philosophy of Science*, Vol. III (Minneapolis: University of Minnesota Press, 1962), pp. 22–97; "How to be a Good Empiricist—A Plea for Tolerance in Matters Epistemological", in B. Baumrin (ed.), *Philosophy of Science, The Delaware Seminar*, Vol. 2 (New York: Interscience Publishers, 1963) pp. 3–39; and "Problems of Empiricism", in R. G. Colodny (ed.), *Beyond the Edge of Certainty* (Pittsburgh: University of Pittsburgh Press, 1965) pp. 145–260. Feyerabend's views on explanation are criticized in

Dudley Shapere, "Meaning and Scientific Change", in R. G. Colodny (ed.), *Mind and Cosmos* (Pittsburgh: University of Pittsburgh Press, 1966), pp. 41–85. Other relevant articles are: P. Achinstein, "On the Meaning of Scientific Terms", *Journal of Philosophy*, LXI (1964), 497–509, P. K. Feyerabend, "On the Meaning of Scientific Terms", *ibid.*, LXII (1965) 266–274, and Robert E. Butts, "Feyerabend and the Pragmatic Theory of Observation", *Philosophy of Science*, XXXIII (1966), 383–394. Shorter articles on explanation are: John Hospers, "What is Explanation?", in Antony Flew (ed.), *Essays in Conceptual Analysis* (London: Macmillan, 1956, and New York: St. Martin's Press, 1956), pp. 94–119, which stresses the deductive model; and G. Schlesinger, "What is Science For?", *Australian Journal of Science*, XXVI (1963), 163–167, which argues for explanation as redescription. A rather unusual approach is that in Sylvain Bromberger's interesting paper, "A Theory about the Theory of Theory and about the Theory of Theories", in B. Baumrin (ed.), *The Delaware Seminar*, Vol. 2, *op. cit.*, pp. 79–106, and in his article "Why-Questions" in R. G. Colodny (ed.), *Mind and Cosmos*, *op. cit.*, pp. 86–111. Michael Scriven is a leading proponent of the contextualist account of explanation. See his paper "Explanations, Predictions and Laws", in H. Feigl and G. Maxwell (eds.), *Minnesota Studies in the Philosophy of Science*, Vol. III, *op. cit.*, pp. 170–230. May Brodbeck in the same volume, pp. 231–272, defends the deductive model of explanation against earlier objections by Scriven. Another paper by Scriven is "The Limits of Physical Explanation", in B. Baumrin (ed.), *The Delaware Seminar*, Vol. 2, *op. cit.*, pp. 107–135. On the question of distinguishing laws of nature from accidental regularities, see Ernest Nagel, *The Structure of Science, op. cit.*, Chapter 4; and A. J. Ayer's review of Nagel in *Scientific American* (June 1961), 197–203. See also H. Reichenbach, *Nomological Statements and Admissible Operations* (Amsterdam: North Holland, 1954, and New York: Humanities Press, 1954). For a quite different view of laws of nature (that they are "principles of natural necessity"), see W. Kneale, *Probability and Induction* (Oxford: Oxford University Press, 1949), sections 16–19.

4

Explanation in biological sciences

Historical sciences

Much of biology is historical in nature: it is *natural history* in the sense that it is concerned with particular facts about the terrestrial world around us. Part of biology even involves a *historical narrative*: I am here thinking of the story of the evolution of species. Outside biology we also find sciences which are essentially historical. For example geology concerns itself with the detailed study of the earth's crust, and hence with a set of particular facts. Geology of course uses general laws of physics and chemistry within its explanations of these particular facts, but this is a feature which does not detract from its status as history, since its main concern is with the particular facts themselves and not with the particular facts *qua* tests of physical and chemical laws. Much of astronomy, again, must be classified as history: consider for example the detailed description of the solar system. Some of astronomy, however, must be regarded as physics, i.e., as concerned with laws of physics rather than with particular astronomical facts.

This is when the stars and other astronomical bodies are regarded as a sort of natural laboratory which produces phenomena which can be used as *tests* of physical theories. When the primary interest of astronomy is that of *cosmology* we meet an intermediate situation which is hard to classify. Consider the explanation of the generation of energy within stars: this proceeds by the application of nuclear physics. Is this "history", i.e., is it explanation of facts about particular stars, or perhaps a piece of natural history about certain observed types of stars, or is it explanation of a genuine law of nature about stars of a certain sort? Or is the recession of the galaxies from one another to be regarded as a piece of natural history about the universe, or is it to be regarded as a law of nature about galaxies? In cosmology, it seems, the distinction between natural history and scientific theory becomes blurred. However I hope to make the distinction clear enough when we talk about biology.

Natural history and taxonomy in biology

When a student begins learning botany or zoology, he is introduced to some natural history, i.e., some generalizations about organisms which are to be found on the earth's surface. For example he is told about the characteristic differences between animals, plants, bacteria and viruses, how they reproduce (whether sexually or asexually), how they are single cells or consist of a multitude of cells, what can be seen to happen when cells divide, and so on. The things the student learns in this way are generalizations about terrestrial organisms, and they are not expected — at this stage anyway — to be applicable everywhere and everywhen in the universe. For example, in learning that the cells of animals and plants contain chromosomes the student does not have to consider the speculative question as to whether all animals and plants which may exist on planets of distant stars consist of cells or whether the cells of such distant animals and plants contain structures which are identifiable as chromosomes. The student is simply learning some terrestrial natural history. It is more sophisticated than the natural history which we associate with game keepers and boy scouts, since in order to see chromosomes, for example, certain laboratory instruments and techniques are needed (which may indirectly involve some knowledge of physical and chemical theory, as in the design of microscopes and the use of stains) but it is natural history all the same, in being concerned with terrestrially applicable generalizations rather than with universal laws of nature. Moreover, since plants, animals and living cells are complex and diverse things, there is no reason why some of these generalizations should not have even terrestrial exceptions to them. Compare the generalization that motor cars have radiators.[1] This is quite a useful one, even though we may come to learn that there are exceptions in the case of air cooled cars. Such exceptions are quite innocuous: in learning how a radiator functions we do not need to worry about the fact that in cars without radiators this function is performed differently. An exception to a generalization of natural history is scientifically harmless: it merely leads us to change "all" to "nearly all". Thus the generalization that all animals which suckle their young do not lay eggs has had to be changed simply to the generalization that all animals which suckle their young, except for the platypus and the echidna, do not lay eggs. This may of course lead to an interesting investigation of the internal economy of the platypus and the echidna, just as someone who has been brought up in the belief that all cars have radiators will want to have a good look at the inside of an air-cooled car. Nevertheless, an exception to a generalization of natural history is even to be expected, in a way in which an

[1] I am here using "radiator" to mean "radiator which makes use of a circulating liquid".

exception to a putative law of nature comes as a surprise and is a serious matter.

Consider the generalization that cows have four legs. This does not mean that all cows have four legs. There is no reason why a freak calf should not be born with three or five legs. So the generalization that cows have four legs is not meant seriously to exclude the suggestion that some cows do not have four legs. Similarly the generalization that cars have radiators is not affected by the existence of air-cooled cars. Nor is the physical explanation of how a radiator functions in a radiator cooled car made one whit less effective by the fact that some cars do not have radiators. In the same sort of way the biochemical and biophysical explanations of the workings of organisms are not in the least invalidated by the fact that there may be no laws about organisms but only exception-ridden generalizations.[2]

Suppose that there were a pair of three-legged cows which surprisingly were able to produce nothing but three-legged calves, and that we thus got a breed of three-legged cows. In this case the statement that cows do not always have four legs would have a taxonomic importance which the existence of three-legged cows as mere three-legged freaks could not give it. Perhaps we might consider the three-legged cows to be a distinct newly evolved sub-species. Indeed if the new strain of three-legged cows could not interbreed with the four-legged ones we should probably recognize this strain as constituting a distinct species.

The classification of living things into species (and

[2]We must not jump from the above considerations to the unwarranted conclusion that these generalizations are not expressible within the notation of predicate logic, supplemented by a suitable set of biological and other predicates. They do show, however, that the formalization of "cows have four legs" must be considerably more complicated than "(x) x is a cow $\supset x$ has four legs". We need to be able to formalize the idea of a thing being a member of a species most members of which have four legs, and all this could become quite complicated, since the notion of a species involves that of family interrelationships and of being able to inter-breed. The notion of a species also involves reference to a particular, e.g., the planet Earth. See pp. 60–61 above and pp. 95–96 below.

more widely, into genera, families, orders, classes,[3] phyla, and kingdoms), was originally begun before the theory of evolution. However even in pre-evolutionary days the characteristics of organisms which seemed important to the taxonomist were often not those which strike the layman as important: indeed they are often characteristics of which the layman is unaware. We should now say that a taxonomic classification is adequate if and only if it properly reflects the family relationships of species on the evolutionary family tree.[4] When we see that the classification into species, genera, etc., must be done in ways which conform with evolutionary hypotheses, then it no longer seems essential that we should possess universal truths of a law-like nature about the objects which are classified in these ways, and we need not be put off by the possibility of three-legged cows (to revert to our rather homely and biologically rather naive example). Cows are defined by their hereditary relationships to other (mostly four-legged) cows and not by the possession of characteristics like four-leggedness. There are indeed some characteristics which all cows possess. For example they all have hearts and they all have bones, since without hearts and without bones they would not be viable. Nevertheless if there could be odd heartless or boneless cows then the biologist would simply study them, and he would not be in the

[3]In the taxonomic, not the set theoretic, sense, of course.
[4]Of course, these relationships are not always known, especially in the case of prehistoric organisms, but it is to be hoped that the taxonomic classification could be seen to fit the family tree if this were known in detail. The remark in the text in fact needs qualification in the light of statistical taxonomists like Robert R. Sokal,[1] who stress the impossibility of making detailed classifications, which fit the evolutionary pattern since too little of the details of evolutionary history can be known for this to be feasible. They therefore eschew evolutionary considerations. As far as I can make out, their work is mainly useful in order to produce classificatory system which would be most useful for purposes of information retrieval in the biological sciences. This does not seem to conflict with the claims of an evolutionary taxonomy to possess greater theoretical interest, even though it might be less practicable to carry it out in detail. It must be added, however, that Sokal has also claimed that sometimes the classifications which we get by statistical methods do turn out to be of evolutionary significance.

95

position of a physicist who had found exceptions to a previously successful law of nature.

In fact, any generalization of descriptive biology is part of the natural history of the earth, and in most cases it will not be true unless it is qualified by some explicit or implicit reference to our planet. Otherwise it is quite probably falsified by some phenomenon of extra-terrestrial natural history. Of course the situation would be different if we had far greater knowledge than we possess at present. Suppose that we had complete biochemical knowledge of the genotype of a species. We might (at least if we were incomparably more clever than in fact we are) be able to deduce that organisms which had such and such a genotype (the genotype being expressed accurately by means of a number of complex chemical formulas, one for each gene), developing in such and such a physical and chemical environment, would grow up to have such and such phenotypic characteristics. In this case the proposition that organisms with genotypic characteristics G developing in an environment E would have phenotypic characteristics P would be a theorem of physics and chemistry. It would now possess the cosmic universality which generalizations of natural history have been seen to lack. It would be asserted as applying everywhere and everywhen in the universe, and could indeed be deduced as a hypothetical proposition whether or not there were organisms of the sort in question, and it would have no reference, explicit or implicit, to the planet Earth.

In the previous paragraph we were considering a fantasy, since it is doubtful whether such detailed knowledge would be possible even in the remote future. Are there any propositions in biology as it exists today which are clearly biological (and not just propositions of physics or chemistry used in biological explanations), which nevertheless are not propositions of natural history and which possess cosmic applicability?[5] We shall return to this question later in this chapter.

Explanation in biology

In the most advanced state of a biological science, its explanations are seen to be biochemical or even biophysical. Consider, as a simple example, the question of how living cells get energy from the combination of glucose ($C_6H_{12}O_6$) and oxygen O_2. If glucose is burnt in a flame the reaction is simply

$$C_6H_{12}O_6 + 6O_2 \rightarrow 6CO_2 + 6H_2O$$

In the conversion of glucose and oxygen to carbon dioxide and water, energy is emitted rather violently in the form of heat and light. A cell needs to get energy at a low temperature and at a gentle rate. In order to make the above mentioned reaction go at low temperature and gradually, the reaction needs to be broken down into a chain of intermediate reactions, each of which is catalyzed by certain enzymes (protein molecules which act as catalysts for certain specific reactions). The detailed description and explanation of this chain of reactions is clearly a piece of organic chemistry. The *biology* simply comes in by means of the such assertions as that the cells in question contain adenosine triphosphate (ATP) and adenosine diphosphate (ADP), two of the most important enzymes involved in the process. This is clearly a piece of natural history, since we do not need at this stage to worry about whether cells in distant planets contain ATP and ADP or how exactly they metabolize. (Of course the piece of natural history can perhaps be further explained by another piece of natu-

[5]I am using "cosmic applicability" in a rather loose sense, indicating that the proposition would be of interest to scientists anywhere and anywhen. In the *logical* sense of "applicable" it is predicates or open sentences which are applicable, not propositions. In fact, the open sentence "x is a terrestrial tiger $\supset$ x has stripes" is true of anything everywhere and anywhen, since anything outside the earth is not a terrestrial tiger.

ral history—that the cells contain nucleic acids of various sorts—plus more chemistry.)

It is useful to compare a biological explanation, such as the one discussed in the previous paragraph, with an engineer's explanation of the behavior of a radio. First of all, he has the wiring diagram, which states that the apparatus in question has various components: battery, coils, condensers, resistances, valves, transformers, loudspeaker, etc. A lot of this is fairly gross common-sense stuff: to say that a wire joins this component to that one is very like saying that a cell contains certain organelles which are visible under the microscope. Some of the engineer's descriptions are of a more refined sort, making use of some theoretical concepts: e.g., a thermionic valve is something with a filament which emits electrons and an anode something which attracts these electrons—descriptions only a person with some background of theory can understand. Nevertheless that this particular piece of hardware which I see before me in this piece of apparatus is a valve, is a particular statement. We can regard this as comparable to a scientifically refined piece of natural history like "cells contain ATP" or "chromosomes contain DNA", as opposed to the crude "tigers have stripes" or even "this cell contains chromosomes".

I wish to suggest, therefore, that just as explanations in electronics involve the use of laws of physics in conjunction with propositions about hardware (often stated in the form of wiring diagrams), much of biology consists in the use of propositions of physics and chemistry in conjunction with propositions of natural history (both of the more refined and the cruder sorts). Of course there is a difference between electronics and biology in that the former is an applied science, whereas although biology has its practical applications it is largely pursued simply in order to satisfy intellectual curiosity. The electronics engineer is primarily concerned with designing apparatus, and only secondarily with explanations of it. However this does not in the least invalidate our comparison between explanations in biology and in electronics.

We may also note a type of explanation which is not yet biochemical or physiological but which is on the way to being biochemical or biophysical. For example, a disease may be explained as due to the lack of some vitamin. It is obvious that such explanations had some value even before much was known about the chemistry of vitamins. The vitamin was described as a substance which was typically found in certain foods and which was necessary to the functioning of the body in a manner which was not yet understood. Pre-biochemical explanations in terms of vitamins, hormones and the like could be compared with an engineer's schematic diagram which does not go into detail, but whose detail could be filled in with more knowledge. For example, the schematic diagram (or "block" diagram, as it is sometimes called) for a superheterodyne radio receiver may show that the signal from the aerial is fed into a radio-frequency amplifier, from there into a frequency changer, and from there into two intermediate frequency amplifiers in series, and from there into a detector, and from there into an audiofrequency amplifier, and finally into the loudspeaker. It will not specify the detailed circuits of each stage, but the stages will be specified by reference to their functions in the whole assembly. The difference between "intermediate-frequency amplifier" and the detailed circuit of this part of the receiver is rather like the difference between the expression "vitamin C" and the detailed chemical formula for ascorbic acid.[6] Similarly, someone without a

----

[6]Not *quite*. That ascorbic acid prevents scurvy can not be seen from the chemical formula for ascorbic acid alone: knowledge of the biochemistry of scurvy is also needed. On the other hand, that a part of a circuit is an intermediate frequency amplifier could be seen from looking at this part of the circuit alone. A better analogy might be a circuit in a television receiver pre-tuned to receive a certain transmitting station. The functional description is "circuit tuned to receive such and such a station". The full electronic explanation of this requires knowledge of *both* the electrical characteristics of the circuit *and* of the transmitter.

knowledge of solid state physics might simply think of transistors as things which perform the functions previously carried out by thermionic valves: he has only a dim conception of the *working* of a transistor, just as someone who did not know the biochemistry of vitamin C would have a dim conception of its working in the body, and would know only that it is something needed by the body in very small amounts, that it is not synthesized by the body but has to be obtained from outside, and that without it the body gets diseased in certain ways.

Teleological and evolutionary explanation in biology

In the previous section it will be noticed that certain teleological expressions have been used. For example "needed by the organism" or "necessary for the prevention of disease". Similarly teleological words were used in the electronic context: to say that a part of a radio is a "frequency changer" is to specify the part by means of the function it performs. Even an individual component can be so specified: to someone who does not know the manner in which the working of a transistor can be explained the word "transistor" will mean perhaps no more than "crystal with impurities in it and electrodes attached in such and such ways". Indeed a man may not know even this much of the natural history of transistors, and for him a transistor will be defined functionally as something which rectifies or amplifies signals.

Suppose that we ask why a given radio receiver possesses a frequency changer. (Not all do.) We might say that the designer of the receiver wanted to make it sensitive to weak signals. Amplification at radio and intermediate frequencies, before the detector stage (at which the signal is converted to audio-frequency) gives more sensitivity than does amplification at the audio-frequency stage. Amplification at radio-frequency is difficult, since instabilities easily occur. Hence it is usual to have no more than one stage of amplification at radio-frequency, and to carry out most amplification in intermediate frequency stages. The answer, then, to the question of why radio receivers frequently contain frequency changers lies in the answer that this method is one which enables amplification to be combined with sensitivity. It presupposes, of course, that the designer of the radio *wants* amplification to be combined with sensitivity. Suppose now that we had a generalization of natural history to the effect that most designers of radio sets want both much amplification and good sensitivity. It would then be easy to construct a statistical explanation or partial explanation on the Hempelian pattern (*Cf.* Chapter 3) of the fact that a given radio set contains a frequency changer. It would contain propositions of electronics (themselves explicable by means of wiring diagrams and laws of nature) and also a proposition about what most designers of radio sets want from them. (The explanation will turn out to be only a partial one if there are more ways than the frequency-changer, or superheterodyne, method of achieving considerable sensitivity together with much amplification.)

Now compare a teleological explanation in biology. Suppose that we ask why animals of certain kinds have kidneys. It may be said in answer to this question that the purpose of kidneys is to remove waste chemicals and to regulate the amount of water in the tissues. Without kidneys these animals would not live. Until the time of Charles Darwin, a putative explanation of the existence of kidneys would have referred back to the purposes of God: it would have been assumed that God wished these animals to be viable, and indeed vigorous, just as the designer of the radio set wished it to combine considerable sensitivity and considerable amplification. Such a reference to the purposes of God would not yield a scientific explanation in as much as the theological propositions required would not (presumably) form part of an observationally testable system. Since Darwin a reference to the purposes of God has become unnecessary, because to a great extent the theory of evolution explains why organisms are to a great extent *as if* they had been designed. Evolution also explains, by the way, as theology could not very easily do, why many organisms are as if they were in some respects *badly* designed. For example human sinuses do not drain well (as some of us have discovered to our cost), since we have evolved from animals which went about on all fours and head down instead of head up. The design of sinus which conferred a selective advantage on these animals is not advantageous to us, and the process of evolution by mutation and natural selection has not been able to correct the matter, and probably it never will be able to do so. (Some evolutionary changes are irreversible, for well understood reasons.)

The theory of evolution gives us explanations or partial explanations of cases of *apparent* design, i.e., cases which would on a pre-evolutionary theological view (and perhaps on a Lamarckian type of evolutionary theory) be ascribed to actual design and actual purpose, much in the way in which the features of a radio set are, partially at least, explained by the purposes of its designer. The theory also gives us explanations or partial explanations of cases of apparent *mis*-design (as in the case of the sinuses mentioned in the last paragraph). Sometimes an explanation (or partial explanation) of apparent *mis*-design can be quite subtle. For example it may postulate genetical linkage, due to two genes being situated on the same chromosome. (The linkage is greater if they are *near* one another on the chromosome and so less likely to be separated by *crossing over* of chromosomes.) A disadvantageous phenotypic characteristic can be selected because it may be genetically linked to a selectively *advantageous* characteristic.

It should be noted that though we talk of the "theory" of evolution, what we find in books on this subject is mostly *history*, in the sense that it is concerned with tracing the evolution of terrestrial species: a particular historical process, though a very long continued and grand one. Paleontology is quite obviously historical. We do not usually find explanations of paleontological facts but only partial explanations or explanation sketches. For example if paleontology produces fossil evidence for certain phenotypic characteristics it may be conjectured that these characteristics occurred because they conferred some selective advantage or because in some earlier stage of evolution they had done so, or because they were genetically linked to some character which is or once was selectively advantageous. This may be most naturally taken merely as an explanation sketch, a hint to look at possible ways of explaining the occurrence of the characteristics in question. An explanation sketch can indeed even be cast in the form of a Hempelian statistical explanation:

Most phenotypic characteristics arise as a result of natural selection.
This characteristic is a phenotypic one.
. . . .
So probably this characteristic arose as a result of natural selection.

However such an "explanation" is not of much value and would be better treated merely as an explanation sketch. It is very vague. For example the notion of "arising as a result of natural selection" is very broad, if it is allowed to take in the very round about way in which natural selection often works. (*Cf.* the remarks made earlier about linkage.)

The historical character of the theory of evolution shows itself very clearly from the fact that the occurrence of the phenomena to be explained is discoverable only from *historical records*. For this reason, even though we can give explanations, partial explanations, or perhaps only explanation sketches of the past course of evolution, we can not usually predict the evolutionary future. (*Sometimes* we can predict the evolutionary future. When a new drug is invented to combat one kind of bacteria you can usually bet heavily that a strain of these bacteria which is resistant to the drug will soon evolve.)

Consider a simple case of evolutionary explanation, that of the melanism of moths. This has occurred in the industrial areas of England during the last century and a half. Smoke from chimneys has blackened the foliage of trees, and pale colored moths have more easily been seen, and so eaten by birds. Now it is pretty certain that there is a gene for darkness of hue in the population, since some darker moths always appear among moths of various species, and in most non-industrial surroundings they of course usually are seen and eaten before their paler relations are. Hence the gene for darkness of hue normally gets *eliminated*. However in industrial areas the advantage may be very strongly in favor of the dark moths, and it may be the gene for whiteness which gets eliminated from the population. It is clear that if the conjectures of the last few sentences were spelt out in detail the whole explanation could be cast in a Hempelian deductive form. What is interesting, however, is that our only evidence for some evolutionary conjectures may be that the event to be explained has occurred. It will be instructive to compare the case of failure of a bridge, which is explained on the hypothesis of metal fatigue which was intense enough to cause the failure.[2] A deductive explanation on the Hempelian model is possible,[3] but this is so only because the general premise "all metals with the same amount of fatigue as that of the metal of this bridge collapse under such and such a strain" is arrived at on the independent evidence (from memory, newspaper reports, etc.) that the bridge did in fact collapse. Similarly, deductive explanations of an evolutionary sort may be formulated on the Hempelian model: they are based on the generalizations (which according to me are not laws of nature) that certain genes carry a selective advantage in a certain locality at a certain time, together with certain other generalizations, such as that the rate at which genes mutate is compatible with selection in fact occurring.[7]

Since the hypotheses needed in an evolutionary explanation are often conjectures for which the fact to be explained provides the main evidence, our ability to explain the past far outruns our ability (which is almost negligible) to predict the evolutionary future. We have *records* of the past (mostly fossil records) but no records of the future. (This last asymmetry has a deep physical explanation which will be discussed in Chapter 8.)

The historical nature of evolutionary explanations or partial explanations can be seen very clearly if we consider the evolution of the horse from a four-toed creature to a one-toed animal. This went in two spurts: from four-toed to three-toed, and much later from three-toed to one-toed. [5] Each spurt was followed by periods of slower mechanical adjustments in the animals' bodies, so as to fit in best with the new sort of foot. Now let us suppose that by some sort of miracle, a biologist with all our modern knowledge of genetics, biochemistry, etc., and also with the general idea of evolution by natural selection, lived in the prehistoric age in which the horse's foot was about to evolve from the four-toed to the three-toed type. It is quite clear that he would have been totally unable to predict the change from the four-toed to the three-toed form, still less the manner in which (or even that) the three-toed state would be followed by the one-toed state. We can give some sort of explanation simply because from the fossil record we know what happened and therefore can make well founded conjectures about the biological

[7]Both the rate of mutation to genes which confer the selective advantage and the rate of mutation *back* to the original allelomorphs has to be considered, and the sort of statistical analysis which was pioneered by R. A. Fisher[4] may be necessary.

facts which are needed to provide an explanation, for example, that there were certain mutations of genes. Furthermore, from the geological record, we are in possession of non-biological data, e.g., about climatic changes, which are needed in the explanation, but which would be unavailable to our imaginary prehistoric biologist.

These considerations by no means go to show that evolutionary explanations can not be fitted into the Hempelian deductive or statistical model, as Scriven seems to have thought. However, when so called evolutionary explanations are spelt out to fit the Hempelian model, they will often stand revealed as mere partial explanations. For example, from certain conjectures we may be able to deduce that a species will have one of a class of phenotypic characteristics, though not that it will have the particular one that it has. If so, this will constitute merely a partial explanation of the possession of the characteristic in question.

Explanations in evolutionary theory make use of generalizations, but these are generalizations of natural history, rather than laws of nature. For example that all (or a certain proportion of) moths in a certain locality and at a certain period of history carry a recessive gene for melanism is surely to be classified as a piece of natural history, not as a law of nature. (For the reasons given on pp. 95–96.) Similarly, the political or social historian makes use of (often rather truistic) generalizations about certain types of human being. From a logical point of view the so called "theory" of evolution is not theory, in the sense of a well articulated body of laws of nature, but is history. Darwin was not engaged in the same sort of activity as Newton, and he should not be judged by the same criteria. Michael Scriven has suggested that the recognition of the *historical* character of the theory of evolution might be of value to social scientists: their sciences do not await a second Newton, since the paradigm of Darwin shows how a scientist may be able to furnish explanations even though the nature of his subject matter may prevent him from being able to offer predictions in the way in which Newton could.[6]

Mathematics in ecology and evolutionary theory

The historical character of the theory of evolution is not incompatible with the fact that the theory of evolution may make use of subtle mathematical analysis, as in the work of Sir Ronald Fisher. Conjectures about the frequencies of genes in populations, of their mutation rates, and so on, are, by our criteria conjectures of natural history, rather than of laws of nature, but there is no mystery in the fact that to discover their implications requires sophisticated mathematical analysis. The same remark applies to ecology, which is the study of the relation of plant and animal communities to their environments, and in particular the variations in their populations. Suppose that the birth rate of a certain sort of animal is such and such, the number of them which can live on a certain area of country is such and such, and suppose we have similar statistics for other kinds of animals (including any predators) which have to live off the same country, then mathematical analysis will enable us to calculate the population changes in the various kinds of animal. Sometimes the situation will be such that a kind of animal becomes extinct, and sometimes there may be oscillations: more prey leads to more predators which leads to fewer prey which leads to fewer predators which leads to more prey, and so on. Sometimes again, the analysis may lead to even more complicated predictions. The essential point, however, from our point of view is that from certain propositions of natural history, (for example about the birth rate of a species of kangaroo in a certain place and at a certain time), other propositions of natural history are deduced, (for example that there will not be any such kangaroos at this place and time ten years hence). The mathematics which is used is all pure mathematics, and the non-mathematical propositions which are used are typically statements of natural history and not laws of nature.

Cosmic biology

Even though the details of the evolutionary process on earth are a matter for study as a piece of terrestrial history, we may ask whether there are nevertheless some general propositions about evolution which are scientifically theoretical in nature, i.e., comparable with theoretical laws in physics in being universal and applicable anywhere and anywhen in the universe.[8]

It seems pretty certain that anywhere in the universe where there is life, living organisms will have to have a genetic code, made up out of discrete units much as the alphabet contains a number of discrete units (the letters), and that whatever medium this code consists of it will have to be such that coded information can be reproduced exactly or almost exactly. If it is reproduced exactly it may not remain quite stable in the period between the time at which it is reproduced and the time at which it in turn reproduces itself. It is as if a document were to be copied over and over again with great accuracy, except for occasional isolated errors now and then. In terrestrial organisms the code consists of molecules of deoxyribonucleic acid (DNA). Each DNA molecule consists of a chain of amino-acids, of which there are 20 sorts, and the "alphabet" of the code consists of triplets of these amino-acids. The errors which occur either during or between reproduction of the code are identified with the mutations which were postulated in genetics. It should not be regarded as remarkable that such mutations occur: perhaps what should be regarded as more remarkable is the great *stability* of DNA molecules, and that changes in them occur as rarely as they do. (A book without misprints is

[8]Taking the term "applicable" with due caution: *cf*. the footnote to p. 97.

a much greater wonder than is a book with misprints!)

Is it true of living creatures anywhere and anywhen in the universe that their genetic code must consist of DNA? Whether this is so or not, it seems plausible that anywhere and anywhen living creatures must have some genetic code or other, and that this code will not be completely stable. In which case it seems plausible that the following proposition is true everywhere and everywhen: "Wherever in the universe there is life and there is a changing environment, evolution will occur".[9] This certainly seems to be something like a biological law of nature, though it is a bit vague in its formulation. It rests on the fact that from what we know of the ways in which living creatures could possibly have originated from nonliving matter, they must work on physical (or chemical) principles and must incorporate a self-replicating genetic code. So perhaps the above mentioned proposition is one of the few biological assertions which can be regarded as a true law of nature, quite universal in scope and containing no element of natural history. However it is not *important* to biologists in the way in which a physical law can be important to physicists: a biologist could decline to accept it and still could carry on perfectly well with his ordinary work, which is that of explaining the behavior of *terrestrial* organisms. After all, the proposition would be doubted by a biologist who doubted whether everywhere in the universe life possessed the characteristic of mortality.

Are there any other possible laws which apply everywhere and everywhen about living things? A suggested candidate might be: "All living matter contains DNA". What does "living matter" mean? What about self-reproducing machines,[7] which perhaps were con-

[9]The requirement of a changing environment is necessary, because though evolution often will occur in a static environment, it need not, since organisms might already be adapted in the best possible way to this environment (i.e., any mutations whatever would lead to less adaptedness). Even though the physical environment is static, there of course can be evolution if there are two species of organism which interact, since any change in one will constitute a change in the environment of the other.

structed by living beings? Perhaps they might even enslave the beings who constructed them, and might themselves evolve by natural selection. (Their code might be on a tape, instead of in DNA, but occasional misprints might constitute mutations.) What reason would there be to deny the epithet "living" to such beings? If it is objected that living beings are never *constructed*, then this seems arbitrary. It used to be thought that Adam was constructed by God, but this did not seem to be taken as a reason for denying the term "living" to Adam or his descendants. However let us suppose that in some way a definition of "living" could be produced which would deny the term "living" to self-reproducing machines. Perhaps one way to do this would be to stipulate that the genetic code must be realized in the structure of *molecules*. Would it then be true that all living beings contain DNA? This question clearly depends partly on another question: are all living systems based on carbon compounds? Perhaps there are systems based on silicon compounds instead of carbon ones, and clearly these would not contain DNA, which is a carbon compound. Supposing that there are grounds for thinking that silicon compounds could not have the required variety and complexity necessary to form living systems, then the question still arises as to whether there could be carbon compounds other than DNA which would have the required self-replicating properties. Do we know this or do we even have reason to suppose it?

Let us have a brief look at the question of whether all living systems in the universe are based on carbon. Reasons can be given for supposing an affirmative answer to this question. Because of its four valency bonds, carbon is able, especially in combination with hydrogen, to form chains and rings, and hence it can lead to the formation of very complex molecules. Silicon has four valency bonds too, and so speculations have been made about possible silicon based living systems. However though silicon may have promising chemical properties it probably does not have the right physical[10] properties. At ordinary temperatures its compounds are hard solids: for example the hard rock quartz, which is silicon dioxide. Living cells have to consist largely of liquid, in order that the complex chemical reactions can take place. It would seem that living systems based on silicon would have to exist in an environment in which quartz would be liquid, or possibly even gaseous. On our planet, for example, the possibility of life depends on the fact that carbon dioxide exists in a gaseous form at a temperature at which it is soluble in water, the water being in liquid form. Would there be analogous gases and liquids associated with silicon at the temperature at which quartz is liquid? Again, it has been suggested that a nitrogen-phosphorus-chlorine chain, swimming in melted salts, might form the basis of living systems.[8] But as W. T. Williams has pointed out[9] the trouble about these speculations is that you find that you have to make an awful lot at the same time, all dovetailing suitably into one another. For this reason, Williams remarks, "chemically alien worlds, though conceivable, tend to be implausible". For example, it would not do to postulate a living system dependent on liquid ammonia, which could exist only on a cold planet like Jupiter, and also on liquid silicon oxides, which could exist only in an extremely hot environment. It may well be that the only system and environment for which everything fits together in the right way is a carbon system in a chemical and physical environment like that which is provided on our planet Earth.

Though it was published more than fifty years ago, L. J. Henderson's book *The Fitness of the Environment*,[10] which deals in detail with the particular combination of happy accidents which are furnished by our terrestrial environment, is an excellent source for considerations relevant to the questions we have

[10]*Physical*, in the sense of being opposed to *chemical*.

been discussing in the last paragraph. I am of course not competent to discuss these questions myself, but the above remarks have been made in order to suggest the sorts of way in which scientists might be able to argue for and against the supposition that the universe contains living systems based on a very different chemical basis from our own. At any rate this should indicate the difficulty of formulating laws of biology which would be applicable everywhere and everywhen in the universe.

Psychology

It is worth considering how far the point of view of this chapter is applicable to psychology. After all, psychology is concerned with the explanation of human and animal behavior, and so must surely be regarded as a branch of biology. A complete understanding of human or animal behavior, from a scientific point of view, would seem to depend upon a complete understanding of the neurophysiological structure of the human or animal brain. This is a vast task, especially as there seems to be reason to suppose that the detailed circuitry of any two brains is different in the two cases, just as any two human fingerprints are not quite alike. Human beings do not come in such similar models as radio receivers of a certain make, though even in the case of radio apparatus we find that models which appear to be exactly similar may behave disconcertingly differently, on account of minute and not easily detectable differences.

By analogy with electronics, it would appear at first sight, therefore, that detailed explanations of human and animal behavior would have to await exact knowledge of the neurophysiological circuitry (as well as on other things, of course, such as knowledge about the production of hormones by various glands). Consequently it would perhaps appear that as we are very far from knowledge of the detailed circuitry of individual humans and animals we must be very far from achieving psychological explanations, at least of a scientifically respectable sort. However if we look once more at the electronics analogy we can see reason for more hope. It will be recollected that an electronic explanation does not always go into detail but remains at the more abstract level of the block diagram. Thus it will say, for example, that the output from a radio-frequency amplifier is fed into a frequency changer stage, and from there into an intermediate frequency amplifier, and so on. It leaves open just what the detailed circuitry of these stages is, for example, whether the amplification is by thermionic valves or by transistors, and whether the frequency changer consists of two separate valves or of one valve with many electrodes. Perhaps, then, some of the "intervening variables" or "hypothetical constructs" postulated by psychologists are best thought of either as elements in a "block diagram" explanation of the working of the organism (especially of its neural circuitry) or as properties, states, or activities of such elements. That is, the psychologist's concepts, such as "drive", "inhibition", "need", "belief", etc., are to be compared with the electronic concepts of "intermediate frequency amplifier", "oscillation", "feed back", etc., and not with "transistor", "1000 ohm resistance", etc.[11]

The block diagram of a radio receiver provides an explanation of its working, though not so deep an explanation as the complete wiring diagram. That is, it explains how it is that sounds come out of the loudspeaker corresponding to the frequency which is impressed by modulation on to the carrier wave to which the radio-frequency stage is tuned. It gives only a *partial* explanation, it should be noted, of the fact that *loud* sounds,[12] for example, come out of the loudspeaker. To

---

[11]Compare the similarity to an electronics engineer's block diagram of the diagrams in J. A. Deutsch's *The Structural Basis of Behavior*.[11]
[12]And still less that the particular sounds of "Waltzing Matilda" come out.

do more we should have to know not only the strength of the incoming signal and the setting of the audio-volume control, but detailed circuit characteristics, which the block diagram does not give. Similarly a psychological explanation, even if it explains a piece of *behavior* (such as showing anger), will very likely give only a *partial* explanation of a particular *movement* (such as a person's fist moving rapidly and striking someone's nose). The concept of *behavior* is in a way more abstract than that of a movement and in a way is less abstract. That is, many different sorts of movement may count as one sort of behavior. To use an example given by J. A. Fodor,[12] running to the right and swimming to the right in a *T* maze may count as the same piece of behavior (turning right) within the context of a psychological explanation. The explanation, that is, may be that of the organism's turning right, and may not be concerned with whether it is a matter of running or swimming. On the other hand, instances of the very same movement may count as different pieces of behavior if their causation in the central nervous system (or elsewhere) is different. For example if someone punches an acquaintance on the nose because of a reflex jerk, this does not count as the same sort of behavior (attacking, say) as would a punch on the nose which originates because of anger and a desire to injure the acquaintance. The distinction between movement and behavior is therefore by no means incompatible with a mechanistic view of human and animal psychology.

This point may be made clear, perhaps, if we consider a pilotless aircraft which is designed to home on to a distant target by means of a purposive mechanism.[13] It is blown off course, let us suppose, but the purposive mechanism within the rocket ensures that it is brought back on course. That is, the aircraft contains receptors and a computer which enable the amount and direction of the aircraft's aberration from its correct course to be

[13]For a discussion of purposive mechanisms, see Chapter 9 below.

represented by physical quantities which are fed into another mechanism in the aircraft which steers it back on course again. Let us contrast the aircraft's coming back on course because of its purposive mechanism on the one hand, and its being blown back onto its course by a stray gust of wind on the other. The former corresponds to behavior (punching a person on the nose) whereas the latter corresponds to a "mere movement" (accidentally knocking one's fist against someone's nose).

The explanation of behavior is in some ways more difficult and in some ways easier than is that of mere physical movements. Thus the movements involved in reflex jerks can be explained by means of generalizations of natural history such as "A blow on a certain part of the knee of most humans causes that foot to jerk up slightly", and a further explanation in terms of neurophysiology is not too difficult. On the other hand the particular movements involved in a piece of behavior may be harder to explain than the behavior itself: there may be a psychological explanation of the block diagram sort of my turning left down a side street to where I know I may get a pint of beer, but not of my turning left with a stride of exactly $30\frac{1}{2}$ inches and a simultaneous click of my fingers.

B. A. Farrell, in an interesting article "On the Limits of Experimental Psychology"[13] argues persuasively that one can not hope to go far in experimental psychology merely by seeking laws (or generalizations, as I would rather say) of the stimulus-response type. Internal states of and processes in the animal's nervous system are clearly important and for this reason there may not be any simple generalization relating stimulus to response. Each new stimulus changes the internal state of the animal and internal states themselves may cause changes in internal states. Farrell suggests that we should follow the lead of the physicist, and try to explain facts about the large in terms of facts about the very small. In the case of the explanation of behavior this means getting down to the neuronal level or even below it. And, of course, there are experimental psychologists whose work is carried out very much from a physiological point of view. Other psychologists, who, like Farrell, reject the purely "stimulus-response" or behavioristic approach to psychology, are nevertheless more skeptical of the value of physiological considerations. A leading exponent of this point of view, J. A. Deutsch, holds that in the present state of physiological knowledge at any rate, it is most valuable to proceed by postulating elements having a certain abstract structure, or which perform certain abstractly defined functions. Consider, he says, the insightful learning machine which he describes in his book.[14] When the machine learns something it changes its state in a certain way, but exactly how this happens does not matter, so long as it is the change of some suitable device from one suitable state to another. In an electronic embodiment of the machine the element might be a dekatron selector, and in an electro-mechanical one it might be done by a self-holding relay. Alternatively, it might be done mechanically by a uniselector arm coming to rest. Now clearly we can talk of such a switching device without bothering about its physical embodiment. It can be described abstractly, or in terms of its function, even though we do not know the details of its physical realization. Now it may happen that we may have good empirical evidence for an abstract structural explanation of the working of an animal or man, treating him as a "black box" whose internal structural states we conjecture from overt behavior, and yet we may have rather weak grounds for speculations about the neurophysiological realization of the abstract structure. Also, many different neurophysiological structures may possibly function similarly, and hence the black box approach leads to a very useful simplification, insofar as animals can be treated as if they were more similar internally than they perhaps are.

Deutsch objects to physiological speculations in psychology on methodological grounds.[15] He points out that if a structural hypothesis for which there is good evidence is given a physiological embodiment which is rather speculative, rejection of the physiology at some subsequent stage of investigation may lead psychologists wrongly to reject the abstract structure of the hypothesis. He also objects that a false air of precision is often lent to a psychological explanation by the identification of elements of the explanatory mechanism with physiological entities, and so weaknesses in the structural part of the explanation can be overlooked.

The above considerations are clearly tactical. Deutsch by no means rejects physiological considerations out of hand. He agrees that from physiological observations we can get some evidence or at least hints about the structure of psychological mechanisms. Nor is there anything in what Deutsch says which precludes the possibility of detailed physiological explanations in psychology (though the very complexity of the nervous system might make this unlikely). The point of view of the provider of block diagrams in electronics is by no means incompatible with the hope of providing detailed circuits at some other stage of inquiry. Sometimes, moreover, even in electronics a physical explanation need not await knowledge of the detailed circuitry. Consider: "the radio has failed because its batteries have run down". Similarly it may be possible to give an explanation of someone's lack of intelligence by pointing to a thyroid deficiency.

Farrell, on his side, while suggesting that it might be good strategy to try to get down to the neuronal level or even below it, also explicitly advocates investigations in the manner of Deutsch (whom he mentions), i.e., conjecturing about and testing large scale structural elements of the nervous system. (It is important to remember, by the way, that one piece of apparatus can function as two elements of the structural explanation: compare a telephone line carrying speech on several channel frequencies. In a communication diagram it might be shown as several different lines.)

In a valuable article in which he advocates a view of psychological explanation which is rather similar to Deutsch's, J. A. Fodor[16] points out clearly enough that a function is not a piece of hardware or software. This is true enough, but the elements of the psychological explanation can be structural elements abstractly defined by their function or (if one wishes to avoid the appearance of unwanted teleology) *what they do*. Fodor gives a mechanical analogy. Take the functional expression "valve lifter" and the mechanical expression "camshaft". In a functional explanation it can be left open whether or not valve lifting is done by means of a camshaft or by some other method. "'A drive is not a neurological state'", says Fodor, "has the same logical status as the remark 'A valve lifter is not a camshaft'".[17] Here I think that Fodor's language may be a little misleading. Some camshafts (when connected appropriately to valves) are in fact valve lifters, and similarly it is surely legitimate to conjecture that some neurophysiological states are in fact the things which are described as drives in the psychologist's more abstract description. The phrases "A drive is not a neurological state" and "A valve lifter is not a camshaft" seem to be misleading: they may suggest that all or some drives are something other than neurological states and that all or some valve lifters are not camshafts, whereas what Fodor really means is rather that the *concept* of a drive is not the same as the *concept* of a neurological state and that the *concept* of a valve lifter is not the same as the *concept* of a camshaft. And this is clearly true and important.

118   Explanations in psychology, whether behavioristic,

structural, or neurophysiological, all rest on what, from the point of view of the present book, are not laws strictly speaking, but generalizations of natural history. The generalization that a certain stimulus applied to a certain type of animal in certain situations leads to a certain type of response is clearly one about that type of terrestrial animal (and even so it will have exceptions in the case of abnormal individuals of the species). Similarly, hypotheses about structural elements or about detailed physiological circuitry constitute generalizations of inferred natural history, rather than laws. Nevertheless "black boxes" often are made so that they behave in very regular ways, and so, in some respects organisms can be very regular in their behavior. Natural selection has seen to this. If we consider how many times we have crossed a busy street or have avoided being hit on the head by a rapidly moving hard ball, we can see how almost lawlike some of the aspects of our behavior must be. This explains why some psychologists have been led to think of psychology as more like physics than it really is, but its relation to biology and the analogy with electronics should go some way to correct this impression.

SUGGESTIONS FOR FURTHER READING

On the difference between laws of nature and generalizations of natural history, see Stephen Toulmin, *The Philosophy of Science* (London: Hutchinson, 1953, and paperback, New York: Harper and Row, 1960), especially pp. 44–56. On the historical character of evolutionary theory, Michael Scriven's article "Explanation and Prediction in Evolutionary Theory", *Science*, CXXX (1959), 477–482, is very stimulating and full of good insights. On methodology in psychology see J. A. Deutsch, *The Structural Basis of Behaviour* (London: Cambridge University Press, 1960, and Chicago: Chicago University Press, 1960), Chapter 1; Jerry A. Fodor, "Explanation in Psychology", in Max Black (eds.), *Philosophy in America* (London: Allen and Unwin, 1965, and Ithaca, N.Y.: Cornell University Press, 1965), pp. 161–179; and B. A. Farrell, "On the Limits of Experimental Psychology", *British Jour-*

nal of Psychology, LVI (1955), 165–177. Contrast the skeptical remarks in L. Wittgenstein, *Philosophical Investigations* (New York: Macmillan, 1953), p. 232, and also the very behaviorist approach advocated by B. F. Skinner. See for example Skinner's *Science and Human Behaviour* (New York: Macmillan, 1953, and paperback, New York: Free Press, 1965). An acute criticism of the behavioristic point of view is given by N. Chomsky in his review of Skinner's *Verbal Behaviour* in *Language*, XXXV (1959), 26–58. A leading advocate of the physiological point of view is D. O. Hebb. See his *Organization of Behaviour* (New York: Wiley, 1961), and for some qualifications, his paper "Alice in Wonderland, or Psychology among the Biological Sciences" in H. F. Harlow and C. N. Woolsey (eds.), *Biological and Biochemical Bases of Behaviour* (Madison: University of Wisconsin Press, 1958).

General works on the philosophy of biology include J. H. Woodger, *Biological Principles* (London: Kegan Paul, 1929, and New York: Humanities Press, 1966) and Felix Mainx, "Foundations of Biology", *International Encyclopedia of Unified Science* (Chicago: University of Chicago Press, 1955). F. A. Hayek has written an interesting article, "The Theory of Complex Phenomena", in Mario Bunge (ed.), *The Critical Approach to Science and Philosophy, In Honor of Karl Popper* (New York: Free Press, 1964). On teleological explanation in biology see Ernest Nagel, *The Structure of Science* (New York: Harcourt, Brace and World, 1961), Chapter 12, and R. B. Braithwaite, *Scientific Explanation* (London: Cambridge University Press, 1953, and paperback, New York: Harper and Row, 1960), Chapter 10. On questions relating to life on other worlds see the article by W. T. Williams, "Problems of Alien Biology", *Humanist*, LXXIX (November 1964), 329–332; L. J. Henderson, *The Fitness of the Environment* (New York: Macmillan, 1913, and paperback, Boston: Beacon Press, 1958); A. I. Oparin, *The Origin of Life*, translated by Sergius Morgulis, second edition with a new introduction by the translator (New York: Dover, 1953); and George Wald, "The Origin of Life" in *The Physics and Chemistry of Life* [A Scientific American Book] (New York: Simon and Schuster, 1955). Merle B. Turner, *Philosophy and the Science of Behavior* (New York: Appleton-Century-Crofts, 1965), is a fairly comprehensive survey of the philosophy and methodology of experimental and theoretical psychology, and contains a wealth of references to the literature.

5

Laws
and theories
in physics

Experimental laws, measurement, and approximation

Some laws in science are accepted on the basis of
experimental observations even before they (or some
close analogue of them) can be deduced from any well-
knit body of theory. Consider Ohm's Law. This can
now be explained on the basis of solid state physics, but
the derivation is by no means easy, and it could be done
only in recent years. For the most part Ohm's Law has
been, and is still, accepted as a generalization from
experimental observations. Suppose that readings of
potential difference across a resistance E and of current
through the resistance I are taken, and the results are
plotted on a graph. It will be discovered that the points
thus plotted lie approximately on a straight line. Because of experimental error the points will not lie *exactly* on a straight line, but a straight line will provide a
good fit, such that none of the plotted points lie farther
from it than can be explained by experimental error. Of
course we could get an exact curve by drawing a zigzag
or wavy curve through all the plotted points, but there

would be no advantage in this for two reasons. To do so would be to assume that there is always a zero experimental error, which is unlikely. Of course the exact set of experimental errors implied by the straight line is antecedently equally unlikely, except that we have a prejudice in favor of simplicity, and therefore take the straight line as more probable than the zigzag or wavy line. Another reason for taking the straight line as illustrating the law, rather than the zigzag or wavy one, is that if we make more observations our new plotted points will not in general lie on our original zigzag or wavy line. We might as well draw the smoothest possible curve consistent with the known (or conjectured) experimental margin of error.

Purely experimental laws are often stated in the form of a polynomial because any continuous mathematical function of a single variable whose first, second, third, etc., derivatives exist, can be approximately represented by a polynomial with a finite number of terms. (Consider for example the law of dependence of electrical resistance on temperature.) Further accuracy can always be achieved by increasing the number of terms. Thus suppose that at first the experimental observations suggest the law "$y = a_0 + a_1 x$". In the light of more accurate experiments it may be found that a law "$y = a_0 + a_1 x + a_2 x^2$" provides a better fit. Later on, even more accurate experiments may lead to the law "$y = a_0 x + a_1 x + a_2 x^2 + a_3 x^3$", and so on, though this process does not usually go on very far.

Sometimes, however, the reading will be seen to fit some well known mathematical function (within the limits of experimental error) and so a law such as "$y = \sin x$" or "$y = \log x$" or "$y = e^x$" may be proposed. It may even be that some quite complicated looking functions may be conjectured as experimental laws: for example Snell's Law in geometrical optics is of the form:

$$y = \sin^{-1} (\text{constant} \times \sin x)$$

Nevertheless the law is in fact prettier than it looks here, as can be seen from the usual way of writing it:

$$\frac{\sin y}{\sin x} = \text{constant}$$

It is obvious, however, that in the absence of a theoretical derivation, that is, if the law at a given stage of scientific progress is a purely experimental one, there may be no particular reason for writing it in the form of a complex function instead of as a suitable polynomial. It is convenient to follow scientific practice by sometimes referring to purely experimental laws, i.e., laws which are known solely as a result of generalization from observations, and which as yet, at any rate, have not been deduced from some well tested theory, as "empirical" laws. This is a narrower usage of the term "empirical" than the one which is followed by many philosophers, who would class even theoretical laws as "empirical" simply because they are not deducible from propositions of logic and pure mathematics. When a scientist criticizes a law by calling it "merely empirical" he means much more than that it is not deducible from logic and pure mathematics — indeed if he meant this the adverb "merely" would be quite inappropriate.

Sometimes, even though we are not in possession of a theory which suggests a certain combination of certain mathematical functions (such as sine, logarithmic, and exponential functions) as giving a law, there are often good reasons for seeing if we can fit our experimental results to a law compounded out of such functions. This is because we know from experience that such functions often do crop up in physics and elsewhere. The sine function is of course associated with wave phenomena. Exponential laws will clearly come up when the rate of increase or decrease of a certain quantity is proportional to the value of that quantity. For example, the rate of decay of radium in a rock is proportional to the amount of radium in the rock, and the rate of increase of a population of rabbits will be in proportion to the size of the population, so long as there are no limiting factors, such as starvation or too many predators. So we may often have *quasi*-theoretical reasons for conjecturing an exponential law, for example, when a certain polynomial would fit our data within the limits of experimental or observational error. In the case of laws relating to three or more variables, it is not easy to produce a suitable polynomial, and one will usually have to guess at more complicated mathematical functions anyway.

One characteristic of experimental laws is their limited accuracy. For example Boyle's law "PV = constant" is true only of an ideal gas: that is, it is not quite true of any actual gas. A better approximation to the truth is Van der Waals' equation: "$\left(P + \dfrac{a}{V^2}\right)(V - b)$ = constant".

But even this is not quite true of actual gases. In fact Boyle's law is deducible from a model which supposes that the molecules of a gas are point masses. Van der Waals' law is nearer the truth and is deducible from a law which assumes that molecules are not point masses but elastic spheres of not negligible volumes. Neither of these models quite corresponds to our best theoretical knowledge about gases (and that is why we regard them as models only, and not as theories).

Boyle's law and Van der Waals' law describe the variation of pressure with volume in a gas which is at constant temperature. When we take temperature t into consideration, they become "$PV = (t + c)$" and "$\left(P + \dfrac{a}{V^2}\right)(V - b) = R(t + c)$" respectively, where R and c are constant. Let $T = t + c$, and we get the well known expression "RT" for the right hand side of the equation. T is the absolute temperature. (If t is centigrade temperature, then $c = 273$, approximately.) A conceptual move which is of considerable philosophical interest can now be made. At the time Boyle's law was discovered P, the pressure, and V, the volume, were defined as in mechanics and geometry respectively, but temperature was defined in terms of equal graduations of a mercury thermometer. Why *equal* graduations? At this time there would have been only the rather empirical reason that if we make thermometers using other liquids instead of mercury we find that temperatures as defined by equal graduations of these thermometers agree with those defined by taking equal graduations in a mercury thermometer, and so it looked as though temperature defined in this kind of way does correspond, approximately at least, to something fairly simple in nature. The discovery of Boyle's law, of course, would have strongly heightened this suspicion, which was later justified by the kinetic theory, which showed that the temperature of a gas, as crudely defined by mercury thermometers, does in fact correspond fairly closely to something in nature (in fact the average kinetic energy of the molecules of a gas). However the conceptual move, which was alluded to at the beginning of this paragraph, did not need to await the kinetic theory. The move consists in *defining* temperature by means of the behavior of an ideal gas (i.e., one which obeys Boyle's law exactly). The behavior of an ideal gas can not be discovered by examining such gases, since there aren't any, but we get it by extrapolating from the behavior of actual gases, which approximate in various degrees to exact conformity with Boyle's law. From now on "$PV = RT$" is used to define temperature, and the mercury thermometer comes to be merely an indicator of temperature, rather as the speedometer of a car indicates velocity. The thermometer no longer defines temperature any more than the speedometer defines velocity.

Since temperature as defined by "$PV = RT$" clearly depends on relationships of the form "$PV = $ constant" it can not be defined before we have been able to define

125

pressure and volume. These last are in themselves quite sophisticated concepts: pressure is defined in terms of force and area, where force is a theoretical concept of mechanics and area (and volume) a geometrical concept dependent on geometrical theory. It is true that it is possible to give a crude operational definition of volume (not dependent on theory). This could be done as follows. Two containers are said to have the same volume if an amount of liquid which exactly fills one will, when poured into the other, exactly fill it too. A container A has a volume equal to the sum of the volumes of containers B and C, if, when B and C are both filled with liquid and this liquid is poured into A, the liquid fills A. A solid A has the same volume as a container B if the amount of liquid needed to fill a container C, into which A has been put, is the same as is needed to fill C if instead of A the liquid which exactly fills B is put into C. It is easy to see how on this basis it is possible to define the concept of something having $\frac{m}{n}$ times the volume of another, where m and n are integers. It is clear, however, that such an operationally defined concept of volume is very limited in application. It could be applied only in situations relating to easily handled medium sized objects: it could not be applied to minute crystals or to vast astronomical objects, or even in such contexts as meteorology. In fact further analysis suggests very few fields in which such an operationally defined concept of volume could be used to state even empirical laws.

Nevertheless, if volume *were* defined in the operational manner which has just been sketched, it would constitute what N. R. Campbell has called a *fundamental* magnitude.[1] For a property[1] to constitute a fundamental magnitude it must be the case that the following conditions hold:

---

[1] Or possibly a relation. Thus on a relational theory of length (rest length, let us say, so as not to involve complications from the theory of relativity) the magnitude *length* would be a relation, not a property.

(1) The property can be possessed in different degrees which possess an *order*. Thus suppose that it were the case that the relation of *scratching* is asymmetrical and transitive, i.e., "(x) (y) x scratches $y \supset \sim y$ scratches x" and "(x) (y) (z) $[(x$ scratches $y \cdot y$ scratches $z) \supset x$ scratches $z]$" are both true. (This is almost but not quite the case in fact, since there are some exceptional cases in which a sample of one substance will scratch a sample of another which will scratch a sample of a third, and yet the sample of the third will scratch the sample of the first.) Then the relation of *scratching* could be used to define hardness as a property, degrees of which would possess an order.[2]

(2) There is a suitable operation with the formal properties of *addition*. Thus in the case of volume, pouring the liquid which exactly fills container A together with the liquid which exactly fills container B into some larger container C which is then exactly filled, is an operation which corresponds formally to the arithmetical operation of addition, as stated by the equation "$a + b = c$".

Hardness fulfills or almost fulfills (1) but not (2). Volume as operationally defined in the manner mentioned above fulfills both (1) and (2).[3]

Campbell went on to define a *derived* magnitude as follows. Suppose that X and Y are fundamental magnitudes, and that in certain conditions the values of X and Y fulfill the empirical law "$f(x, y) = c$" where c is a constant. Now let the conditions be varied by altering a certain property of the experimental arrangement (e.g., temperature). The law "$f(x, y) = c$" allows us to define the magnitude c of the varied property. Thus if (as is in fact not the case) pressure and volume were fundamen-

[2]As in Mohs' scale of hardness, which was at one time used by mineralogists. This was based on the assumption of the asymmetry and transitivity of the relation *scratches*.[2]

[3]As to (1): we can say that a volume of container A is greater than that of container B if liquid can be poured from A so as completely to fill B, but liquid can not be poured from B so as completely to fill A.

127

tal magnitudes, then the gas law "$PV = RT$" would define temperature T as a derived magnitude. (Here R is of course just a constant of proportion, so as to allow suitable units for T, i.e., to let the difference in temperature between melting ice and boiling water be 100, as on the centigrade scale.) And indeed this is what has happened with $PV = RT$, with the following qualifications. (a) "$PV = RT$" is an idealization of the empirical laws about actual gases. (b) Pressure and volume are not fundamental magnitudes in Campbell's sense, since they are defined in terms of the primitive concepts of mechanics and geometry, and these primitive concepts can not be operationally defined but need to be implicitly defined by the part they play in the theories.

In fact it is doubtful whether in the present state of physics there are any important fundamental magnitudes in Campbell's sense, and so our account of empirical laws needs to take account of the fact that the concepts used in them are theory laden, even though the laws themselves do not have any explanations within the theories which define their concepts. Let us consider the concept of length as it would be if it were operationally defined as a fundamental magnitude in Campbell's sense and contrast it with the concept of length as it actually occurs in physics.

Consider a number of straight pieces of wood. Let us define straightness operationally without bringing in the concept of length. In Figure 1, which is meant to show pieces of wood, A and B fit one another, A does not fit C, and C fits B. We say that the edges of A, B, C are not straight. In the case of the pieces of wood D, E, F, D fits E, E fits F and F fits D. We say that the pieces of wood *are* straight. We must also assume that we have ascertained that the pieces of wood are *rigid*, where rigidity is operationally defined as follows: two objects are rigid (or approximately rigid) if they fit one another (end to end, say) and it is not easy to distort them so that they no longer fit one another. If two straight rigid pieces of

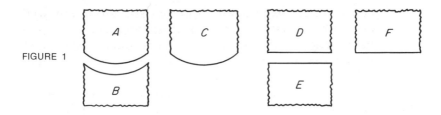

wood fit one another end to end we say that they have the same length. If two straight pieces of wood are set end to end so that they fit a third straight piece of wood, we say that the sum of the lengths of the first two is equal to the length of the third one. (Setting end to end here provides a physical operation corresponding to addition.) Taking one bit of wood as standard (like the meter bar in Paris) we can build up a scale of length, and construct and calibrate rulers. Length as thus operationally defined is a fundamental magnitude in Campbell's sense. Moreover, the related concept of distance between two objects can be defined as the length of a straight piece of wood which would fit end to end between the two objects.

We must notice, however, that such a concept of length or distance is by no means the concept of length which we find in physics. For one thing, the present standard of length is the wavelength of cesium light, which can be understood only by means of theory. Again, when the physicist talks about the distance of an electron from its nucleus or of the diameter of a galaxy he is obviously not talking about what happens if we put medium-sized macroscopic objects end to end. There might even have been no rigid macroscopic objects in the world at all, and yet stars would still have had radii, photons would still have possessed wavelengths, and the distances between galaxies would doubtless still be increasing. No doubt there would have been no human beings to find out these lengths and distances, and it might even be impossible for purely gaseous intelli- **129** gences to get experimental physics started. It may well be the case that, as a matter of *history*, men could not have reached the scientific, theory-laden, concept of length except *via* a cruder concept to which Campbell's account of fundamental measurement does justice. Consider the first time that the wavelength of cesium (or any other) light was used as a standard of length. We still needed calibrated scales on our spectrometer, and we needed a ruled grating, with a knowledge of the number of lines which were spaced equidistantly on the grating, and this means that we needed to use a cruder concept of length before we could use the more refined one. That is, we need a fundamental measurement, or something like it, before we can use our more refined methods. This procedure can be justified theoretically, since there are theoretical reasons for believing that graduations which are equidistant by our conventions of fundamental measurement are approximately equidistant in terms of our more refined theoretical concept.

It is worth while to note the difference between a system of measurement proper and the mere use of calibrated instruments. The speedometer of a motor car tells us the velocity of the car but it does not enable us to *measure* the velocity. It is an *indicator* rather than a *meter*. What I mean by this is that the speedometer (or its prototype) is presumably calibrated by means of a series of measurements of velocity, which are done directly by measuring distance travelled and time taken to travel. The assimilation of measurement to the reading of calibrated instruments presumably led Sir Arthur Eddington to the very misleading statement that scientific laws are about *pointer readings*.[3] N. R. Campbell has suggested that Eddington's idea that science is about pointer readings may be one of the things that led him to his idealistic philosophy of science.[4]

Since modern theoretical ideas have come to pervade the whole conceptual apparatus of physics, it is hard to find any properties which are fundamental magnitudes in Campbell's sense. The magnitudes in even quite empirical laws can be stated in terms of theoretical magnitudes. Consider Ohm's law, $\frac{E}{I}$ = constant, where E is the potential difference between the ends of a conductor and I is the current through the conductor. It is true that an operational definition of amount of current could be given (for example electrochemically, in terms of the amount of metal deposited per second on an electrode in a solution of a certain salt) but it is more natural to think of current in theoretical terms, as the rate at which electrons pass a point in the conductor. The latter definition, we feel, tells us what electric current really is, whereas the electrochemical one gives merely a *test* for there being a current of a certain magnitude. Nevertheless, though the concepts by means of which the law is stated may be theoretical, the law itself can still be a purely experimental one in the sense that it can not be derived from the axioms of the theory. This may be for two reasons: (a) The theory may not be powerful enough. (b) The theory may be powerful enough but sufficient mathematical ingenuity may not have been applied to the problem of discovering the derivation. In case (a) the presence of merely empirical laws is a sign of an unsatisfactory state of scientific knowledge. In case (b) this is not so, at least in the same way. If a reliance on empirical laws is due simply to an inability to deal mathematically with a very complex situation or to specify in sufficient detail all of a complex set of boundary conditions, it is not then due to a lack of the right theoretical conceptions in physics. For example, in the case of the successive attempts to get even a remote approximation to the law of conductivity of electrolytes (which has been cited by Michael Scriven in an article[5] in which he supports the view that a key property of physical laws is *inaccuracy*), I would suppose that the difficulties are due to mathematical and physical complexities and not to a lack of appropriate theoretical laws or to any inaccuracy in the *basic* laws of physics. In such a case the failure to explain the empirical laws does not have very much theoretical interest: it does not show a weakness in our conception of the fundamental laws of nature in the way that the experiments demonstrating the nonconservation of parity brought about a change in basic physical theory.

Whereas it does seem correct that empirical laws can be asserted only as approximations, Michael Scriven's contention[6] that inaccuracy is a key property of physical laws in general is more doubtful. Besides empirical laws he adduces such cases as (1) Newton's laws of motion and of gravitation and (2) the first and second laws of thermodynamics. These are theoretical laws, not empirical ones, since they are not direct generalizations from observations but are postulates of a theory, and are tested indirectly by comparing the consequences of the theory as a whole with experimental or observational facts.[4] We can agree that theoretical laws can be considered as approximations in those cases where they give approximately correct predictions even though the theories to which they belong have been shown to be false. But, contrary to Scriven, these cases do *not* show that most laws of nature are inaccurate, and that most of the laws which have been thought to be laws of nature are not really laws of nature at all because the theories in question have been shown to be incorrect. There is nothing to prevent us from saying that the progress of science has not merely shown Newtonian mechanics and classical thermodynamics to be approx-

[4]There is, nevertheless, a sense in which an individual law can be tested. Suppose we find that a theory T does not quite fit the observational facts, but a theory T', which differs from T only in that one particular law of T has been replaced by another, does fit the facts. Then we may say that most of T is all right and the trouble lies in only one of its laws. This situation is merely a special case of that in which all or some of the laws of T have to be replaced, as in the replacement of Newtonian mechanics by special or general relativity.

imations but has *falsified* them.[5] In his reply to comments by Henryk Mehlberg[7] who cites the law that every electric charge is a multiple of a single unit, and suggests that, in general, propositions about discrete quantities will be contrary to Scriven's thesis, Scriven admits that some laws are propositions "to which no exception is now known".[8] But is not this talk about exceptions misleading? The trouble with Newton's law of gravitation is not that it has a few exceptions: it gives false predictions everywhere, even though the discrepancies, which we know must exist by deducing them from Einstein's theory, are in most cases too small to be detected by observation. In the face of examples of exceptionless laws, Scriven modified his thesis to the following: it is not very *important* that laws of nature are without exceptions.[9] Changing "without exceptions" to "not quite accurate", I would agree that this is so in the case of empirical laws: since the laws are empirical, we have no theoretical reasons for being worried about the fact of their slight inaccuracy. However, in the case of a theoretical law, inaccuracies and exceptions are very important indeed: even the smallest discrepancy shows that there is something wrong with the theory (unless, of course, we can explain the discrepancy away—through an inadequate experimental arrangement, for example). This may lead to a modification of the theory or even to the replacement of the theory by a radically different one (for example a wave theory replaced by a particle theory).

Theories as pictures of reality

If, in accordance with the point of view taken at the end of the previous paragraph, we consider an inaccu-

[5]Statistical mechanics show the incorrectness of the second law of thermodynamics. The first law still stands as far as statistical mechanics itself is concerned, but I suppose that it could be said to be falsified by the conversion of mass into energy and vice-versa. Scriven himself does not contend that the *third* law of thermodynamics is either false or inaccurate.

racy in a theory to be a serious criticism of it, so that it follows that a correct theory is *not* inaccurate, *not* a mere approximation in the way that an empirical law is, the problem arises as to whether we have any reason to believe that *any* of our theories are correct. This is partly a matter of the philosophical problem of induction, with which we shall be concerned in the next chapter, but it arises naturally, apart from any subtle philosophical considerations, from the reflection that in the past all fundamental physical theories have been overthrown in favor of better ones, and we surely have no reason for believing that our present theories will be retained in the future. Now if we say that all theories in the last analysis are false, what reason have we for taking a realistic view of them, instead of regarding them, like empirical laws, as simply devices for giving practically useful predictions? We surely wish to retain the idea that, even if the general theory of relativity gets overthrown, it perhaps might still prove to be "nearer the truth" than the Newtonian gravitational theory. Unless science advances by some sort of successive approximation to the truth, what is the *theoretical* advantage (as opposed to the *practical* advantage) of replacing one theory by another? Admittedly if we make observations that falsify a theory T, so that we replace T by T', we can say that T has been falsified whereas T' is still in the running. Nevertheless, if we look at the history of science, it seems to be a very good bet that T' is going to be falsified too. In what sense, then, can we say that when T is replaced by T' we are nearer to a correct picture of the world? Suppose that T is a particle theory which comes to be replaced by a field theory T' which in the future is going to be replaced by a particle theory T'' which in turn is going to be replaced by a field theory T''' . . . Now consider the following two metaphysical hypotheses: (a) the world consists of particles, and talk about fields is just a way of talking about the interactions of particles, and (b) the world really consists of a space-time field and talk about particles is really only talk about singularities in the field. So far as the ontology of the theories T, T', T'', T''' is concerned we would appear to be oscillating wildly between truth and falsehood in the sequence of theories, should either (a) be true or (b) be true. I do not here wish to suggest that (a) and (b) need to exhaust all the possible alternatives, any more than I wish to suggest that "Have you stopped beating your wife, yes or no?" is a fair question. Let us just suppose that either (a) or (b) is in fact true and the other false.

In some cases, of course, it is clear what could be meant by saying that one theory is a better picture of the world than is another. Suppose that space were Euclidean. Then it would be clear that there is a sense in which a non-Euclidean geometry of constant curvature $2R$ would provide a better picture of the world than a similar non-Euclidean geometry of constant curvature R. Here the two theories do not differ in ontology but quantitatively, as is reflected by the relative accuracy of their predictions. But how would we compare, let us say, a theory which was broadly correct in its ontology but whose predictions were rather inaccurate as against a theory which was incorrect in its ontology but which made fairly accurate predictions? It seems to me that there is here an unsolved problem for those philosophers who wish, as I do, to give a realistic account of scientific theories. The problem does not arise for those philosophers of science who regard physical theories as mere devices for prediction of our experiences, in other words those philosophers of science who can be classified as phenomenalists, operationists, or instrumentalists. I shall try, however, to show that there are serious objections to such non-realist philosophies of science.

Someone who adopts an instrumentalist philosophy of science may be asked what theories are instruments *for*. The answer usually given is that they are instruments for making predictions, which, if the instrumen- **135** talist view of theories is seriously held, must be made in some nontheoretical or theory-neutral observation language. The considerations on pp. 75–82 suggest that such a theory-neutral observation language is hard to find. Ordinarily, observation sentences are theory-laden: e.g., "the current in that wire is 5 milliamperes". If the observation sentence were made theory-neutral, e.g., "the needle of that instrument is opposite the numeral '5'", it would need to be supplemented with suitable correspondence rules, e.g., "when a needle of an instrument [followed by a suitably detailed description of the instrument] points to the numeral '5' then the current through it is 5 milliamperes". Such correspondence rules are easier to sketch than to state; in the above example I have, for example, omitted to state it in a suitably probabilistic form, since surely no milliammeter is always faultless, and the needle of a milliammeter could be opposite the numeral "5" and yet the current through the milliammeter be very different from 5 milliamperes.

If we keep to a realist philosophy of science there is no difficulty about saying that when looking at a milliammeter we may directly observe that the current through it is 5 milliamperes. The milliammeter functions as an extension of our ordinary senses. We do of course have to learn some theory so that we can make such observations: perception is not merely a passive reception of sensations but involves active cerebral processes. Many of these are perhaps innate to us and in any case we are not conscious of them. Consider for example the way in which signals from the eyes enable computations based on the convergence of the eyes to be made by the brain, thus giving us an ability to (unthinkingly) judge the distances of nearby objects. In the case of the milliammeter the information process depends also on consciously learned skills. If we look at the matter in this light, the possibility of error in milliammeters is epistemologically not different from the possibility of error in human senses. The possibility of such error is not a disastrous one, since just as ordinary sense illusions can be discovered by making more (also possibly fallible) sense perceptions, so can errors in scientific instruments be discovered by making more (also possibly fallible) scientific observations.

Since observation reports are themselves indirectly testable (e.g., by making other observations), there is no need to suppose that science has to rest on any absolutely infallible bedrock. There is no harm in admitting that we *may* well be mistaken *anywhere* so long as we do not have to admit that we are *probably* mistaken *everywhere*. Failure to appreciate this point is perhaps one of the causes of the philosophical doctrine of *phenomenalism*, according to which all statements about material objects are held to be statements about actual and possible sense data (i.e., about what sense data are had *if* other sense data are had). Sense datum statements merely say what it looks, sounds, feels, smells, or tastes to be the case, and "I have a pink-rat-ish sense datum", clearly can be true whether or not the rat before us is pink, and indeed whether or not there is a rat before us at all. According to phenomenalism, theoretical science reduces to a system of rules wherewith to correlate and predict our sense experiences. A pioneer of this sort of philosophy of science (though the purity of his phenomenalism was impaired by the possibly inessential theological ramifications of his version, and so this version differed in some respects from modern phenomenalism) was Bishop Berkeley.[10] Around the beginning of this century a phenomenalist philosophy was powerfully put forward by the Austrian philosopher of science Ernst Mach,[11] and such a view has become attractive to a good many physicists, who perhaps have not subjected it to very careful philosophical criticism.

Instrumentalism and operationism

Since this is a book on the philosophy of science, not on general metaphysics, I shall not here engage in a discussion of phenomenalism in general philosophy, but will merely remark that it has been subjected to some very damaging criticism. In particular I would refer the interested reader to the chapter "Phenomenalism" in Wilfrid Sellars, *Science, Perception and Reality*.[12] There are, however, certain philosophies of science, such as instrumentalism and operationism, which are very like phenomenalism. Just as the phenomenalist holds that all statements about physical objects (whether commonsense objects like tables or scientific objects like electrons) are really about sense data, so these doctrines reduce theoretical science to a way of talking about macroscopic objects. Thus on the instrumentalist view scientific theories do not consist of meaningful statements about the world but are computational devices which enable us to predict what we shall see when we look at laboratory instruments and other medium sized objects. Operationism differs from instrumentalism in that it holds that scientific theories consist of meaningful statements, but it shares the tendency of instrumentalism to deny the realistic interpretation of theoretical statements, i.e., the tendency to deny that they are about independently existing theoretical entities (e.g., electrons, mesons, photons). According to operationism all the concepts of theoretical physics have to be defined in terms of operations with medium sized objects, such as laboratory instruments. In this view the relation between statements about electrons and statements about photographic plates, for example, is the same as the relation between statements about photographic plates and statements about sense data in the phenomenalist view.

The doctrine of operationism was advocated by the physicist P. W. Bridgman, though he had a distaste for the grandiloquent word "operationism" itself. [13] His idea was that all the concepts in science must be defined in terms of the operations which must be performed in order to ascertain whether the concept can be applied. In the case of quantitative concepts, they must be defined in terms of measuring operations. Thus "electron" might be defined by reference to operations with Wilson cloud chambers or with photo-electric cells. "Length" might be defined by means of operations with rulers. (However, recall the objections to this on p. 129 above.) All this is a bit vague, and the theory gets vaguer still when Bridgman concedes that theoretical concepts are introduced partly at least by means of "paper and pencil" operations. (Consider such a recondite concept as isotopic spin in quantum mechanics, for example. It is obvious that such a concept can not be related directly to experimental operations. If it can be related to experiments, this can be only after a considerable amount of theoretical work.) To admit paper and pencil operations is surely to trivialize the doctrine of operationism: any sort of definition would seem to do, even some sort of implicit definition in terms of the postulates of a theory. The claims of operationism seem to fade out into a vague stress on the need for scientific theories to be experimentally or observationally testable in some way. If so, the point can surely be made in more precise language and without the misleading talk about "operations". This sort of talk is especially misleading insofar as it suggests quite gratuitously that when we talk about electrons, neutrons, etc., we are really talking about laboratory instruments and pencil jottings on pieces of paper.

Bridgman has supported his advocacy of operationism by the contention that it was an operational approach which led Einstein to the *special* theory of relativity. [14] In the same paper Bridgman objects to the *general* theory of relativity because it seems to him to lack an operational approach. On the contrary, I would suggest that the operationist-looking presentation which we find in Einstein's original paper on the special theory of relativity[15] was not essential to the paper and detracted from its clarity. Einstein's definition of simultaneity in terms of observers with measuring rods and clocks is obviously quite artificial. We can discuss whether or not two events here and on Arcturus are simultaneous with reference to a set of axes without any mythology about an observer on Arcturus equipped with a clock and able to flash light signals back to us. If a theory did need such talk, it would be a weakness in the theory, since we know of no such observer on Arcturus. The essentials of Einstein's definition of simultaneity can in fact be given without the operationist mythology, and this is what is often done in modern treatises on the subject.[16] I would conjecture that the operationist form in which Einstein put forward special relativity was perhaps due to a philosophical positivism which sat rather lightly on him and which he came later to reject.[6] Of course it might be argued that even though operationism is not essential to the special theory of relativity it might have been of heuristic value in enabling Einstein to arrive at the theory. Such an argument is of course irrelevant to the *truth* of operationism: even a fairy story might happen to put the right idea into a scientist's mind. It also invites the objection that *non*-operationist thinking has also been of value, as in Einstein's development of the *general* theory of relativity. It is true that Bridgman finds the general theory unsatisfactory because of the difficulty of providing an operationist account of it, but his objection here must, on pain of circularity, be based on such philosophical reasons as might be brought in favor of operationism independ-

[6]That Einstein was at one time sympathetic to positivism comes out in his reference to Hume and Mach in his intellectual autobiography, in which he also clearly shows that in later life at least he came quite explicitly to reject any such positivist tendency.[17]

ently of support from the actual practice of Einstein and other scientists.

If operationism, when broadened by including "paper and pencil operations", is to be anything more exciting than a mere insistence on the testability of theories, it must, I think, be interpreted as a form of instrumentalism. Instrumentalism does allow a free play of theoretical construction, but according to it theories are mere uninterpreted formalisms[7] whereby we can predict the behavior of macroscopic objects, for example laboratory instruments. Instrumentalism may be criticised in two ways: (a) from a metaphysical point of view; (b) from a methodological point of view. I shall take the metaphysical criticism first.

Metaphysical critique of instrumentalism and operationism

The appeal of instrumentalism lies partly in the fact that we know about the sub-microscopic entities of physics only by making observations on macroscopic ones: we look at photographic plates, ammeters, pieces of litmus paper, and so on. An interpretation of scientific theories which suggests that they are really only aids to talking about the behavior of macroscopic objects is one which would seem to effect an economy, in that it absolves us from the necessity of postulating entities whose existence is perhaps dubious. This point of view is often reinforced by positivistic theories of meaning. Since we can not point to or directly observe the sub-microscopic entities of physics, and if it is thought that

---

[7]Such formalisms are sometimes referred to as "algorithms".[18] This can be misleading, because in logic and mathematics "algorithm" usually means "decision procedure", and it is easy to deduce from Church's theorem that there is no algorithm or decision procedure for a calculus rich enough to express a physical theory. That is, in the philosophy of science "algorithm" is sometimes used differently from the way in which it is used in mathematical logic, which seems a pity. For the same reason it can be misleading to say that the mathematical parts of physics are "computational devices", since this might suggest falsely that there are decision procedures and that there is no need for ingenuity to prove theorems in mathematical physics.

meaning can be given to words only by pointing to perceptible objects or to experimental operations, then it would seem that it is very questionable whether physical theories have any meaning and whether they should not rather be treated as mere formalisms which are uninterpreted except insofar as they connect up with observations on macroscopic objects. If the doctrine is that what can meaningfully be said to exist must be *in principle* perceptible, it comes up against difficulties. How could we decide whether or not it is *logically* possible to perceive an electron or a neutrino? If it is said that it is *physically* impossible to see or touch an electron or a neutrino, then of course this is true enough, but the realist will want to say that this is simply because of laws of nature about electrons and neutrinos.

Even on a very empiricist theory of meaning, the contention that sentences ostensibly about things too small to be perceived are meaningless is incoherent. Suppose that it is agreed (as I should not in fact agree) that scientific terms have meanings if and only if their meaning can be given ostensively (or in part ostensively) in the way in which perhaps words like "table", "square", and "red" might be introduced. We may suppose also that the word "perceive" is introduced in this sort of way too, for how else could the "in principle perceptible" thesis about meaning even be stated? Then the description "particles smaller than any which were, are, or will be perceived", or (if the modal word "can" is allowed by the empiricist theory of meaning) "particles smaller than any which can be perceived" must be meaningful by the empiricist criterion of meaning.

The instrumentalist position is sometimes put in the form that physical theories are not assertions about the world but "inference tickets" (see Gilbert Ryle[19]), or "techniques of explanation" (see Stephen Toulmin[8]).

[8]In his chapter "Theories and Maps" in *The Philosophy of Science*.[20] The comparison with maps suggests at first a realistic view of theories, but as the

Whether this is so or not, scientific theories are certainly not presented so that they look like rules of inference. They are presented as a system of propositions which can be deduced from a set of postulates, the fundamental laws of the theory. There is no effective rule for deciding what is a theorem of a theory, except possibly in the case of very weak theories. Any moderately powerful theory would need to be formalized within the full predicate calculus, and it is a consequence of Church's theorem that there is no effective method (decision procedure) for picking out theorems of this calculus. We can know that something is a theorem only if we hit on a way of deducing it from the postulates. However, perhaps the instrumentalist might still be able to claim that the postulates of a theory are rules, and that the rules of inference are *second order* rules for deducing derivative rules. It is interesting to note that in trying to bring out the rule-like, rather than propositional, character of a theory, Toulmin makes use of the example of geometrical optics, which need not be asserted propositionally but could be regarded as a technique for drawing diagrams.

The instrumentalist need not say, as an operationist might have to, that theoretical sentences are equivalent to, or translatable into, certain classes of sentences about macroscopic observable objects. Instrumentalism does allow theoretical concepts to be quite free constructions of the theorist. The instrumentalist, however, would agree with the operationist in holding that in science no statements are made about entities other than macroscopic observables. The operationist would hold this on the ground that the theoretical statements are translatable into statements about observables, whereas the instrumentalist would deny translatability.

---

analogy is worked out by Toulmin his idea seems to be mainly that theories enable us to find our way about *the phenomena* just as maps enable us to find our way about the countryside. It is not absolutely clear that Toulmin's view really is instrumentalist, but the most natural interpretation of what he says seems to me to be an instrumentalist one. **143**

According to the instrumentalist, theoretical sentences do not really express statements about entities because they do not really express statements at all: they express rules for making predictions about observables. Since both the operationist and the instrumentalist agree on the main issue, that scientific theories are really concerned with macroscopic observables, the difference between them is not important metaphysically. For this reason I propose to lump the two theories together as varieties of what might be called "macro-phenomenalism", in order to distinguish it from the ordinary metaphysical phenomenalism which reduces everything to sense data[9].

Obviously the most effective way of defending macro-phenomenalism would be by giving a proof that theoretical terms can always be eliminated from science. Before such a proof, or attempted proof, can get under way, it is clearly necessary to divide the scientific vocabulary into two classes: the observational terms and the theoretical terms. We have already seen cause to doubt whether this can be done. The specification of observation *sentences* by their vocabulary (observational terms only) is at variance with the pragmatic account of observation sentences, according to which a sentence can count as an observation sentence provided that in a particular perceptual context a scientist can quickly decide on its truth or falsity without explicit thought or calculation.[10] According to the pragmatic account of observation sentences there is no reason why these sentences should not contain theoretical terms, i.e., terms which would not be intelligible to unscientific common sense. Thus "This photographic plate shows a curved beta particle track" or even "The current in that wire is ten milliamperes" can be observation sentences, if the pragmatic account of observation sen-

---

[9]A phenomenalist will also be a macro-phenomenalist, but a macro-phenomenalist need not be a phenomenalist: that is, he can be a realist about medium sized observables, such as his laboratory instruments.

[10]See pp. 80–82 above and references to Feyerabend and Carnap.

tences is correct. If this is so, the characterization of observation sentences by reference to vocabulary is hardly a promising one. However let us go along with the macro-phenomenalist temporarily and let us concede to him, for the sake of argument, that there is a workable difference between observational and theoretical terms in a theory. Let us also allow logical terms, such as "some", "not", "and", as well as terms of pure mathematics (including syntax), to count as part of the observational vocabulary. This seems reasonable, since logic and pure mathematics can be understood by a person who knows no physics. We can then divide the vocabulary V of a scientific theory into two parts V_O and V_T respectively, where V_O contains the observational, logical, and mathematical terms, and V_T contains the remaining ones. We shall now consider two devices which have been proposed in order to show that V_T is dispensable.

The first of these is the *Ramsey sentence*.[21] Let A be a set of postulates for a scientific theory. Suppose that the conjunct of A is the sentence

"$F(\Phi_1, \Phi_2, \ldots \Phi_n)$", where "$\Phi_1$", "$\Phi_2$", $\ldots$ "Φ_n"

are the predicates which occur in A and which belong to V_T. We can write "$F(\Phi_1, \Phi_2, \ldots \Phi_n)$" in set theoretical notation as "$F'(K_1, K_2, \ldots K_n)$", where each K_i is a class of m-tuples of which the m-ary predicate Φ_i is true. Now replace "$F'(K_1, K_2, \ldots K_n)$" by the sentence "$(\exists X_1)\ (\exists X_2) \ldots (\exists X_n)\ F'(X_1, X_2, \ldots X_n)$" in which the constants "K_1", "K_2", $\ldots$ "K_n" have disappeared in favor of bound variables. This is the Ramsey sentence of the theory. For example if "Φ_k" is the predicate "is an electron", then "K_k" will be the expression "class of electrons", and in the Ramsey sentence we just have "there is a X_k such that $\ldots$ ".[11]

[11]It is more usual to write the Ramsey sentence simply in the form
$$(\exists \phi_1)\ (\exists \phi_2) \ldots (\exists \phi_n)\ F(\phi_1, \phi_2, \ldots \phi_n)$$
quantifying over predicates, instead of classes. However I follow Quine in feel-

The Ramsey sentence does indeed enable us to dispense with the *vocabulary* V_T, but the defender of a realistic philosophy of science can still deny any ontological implications to this maneuver. The possibility of replacing the axioms of a theory of electrons containing the predicate " . . . is an electron" by a suitable "$(\exists K_k)$ (. . . ϵK_k . . .)" does not prevent the latter statement from making an existential assertion equivalent to that of the existence of electrons. The assumption of the truth of the Ramsey sentence sets limits on the membership of the classes K_i precisely similar to that set by the original theory to the extensions of the predicates "is an electron", etc. The assertion, "there are electrons", for example, is then replaced by the part of the Ramsey sentence " . . . $(\exists K_k)$ . . . $(\exists x)$ (. . . $x \epsilon K_k$ . . .)" which asserts that there is a nonempty class K_k. Again, let us assume that " . . . is too small to be perceived" and " . . . is able to cause tracks in cloud chambers" are part of the observation vocabulary.[12] Then if the original theory implies

"(x) (x is an electron $\supset$ x is too small to be perceived and x is able to cause tracks in cloud chambers)"

then so also the Ramsey sentence implies

" . . . $(\exists K_k)$ . . . $(\exists x)$ . . . ($x \epsilon K_k \supset x$ is too small to be perceived and x is able to cause tracks in cloud chambers)"

---

ing strong doubts about the propriety of quantifying over predicates,[22] and so I have preferred to express the Ramsey sentence as a quantification over classes.

[12]I do not much like including the modal expressions "to be perceived" and "able to cause" as part of the observational or other vocabulary of a theory, but I find it hard to invent a suitable example without them. I would myself take this as a severe criticism of the idea of defining observation sentences by reference to a vocabulary, an idea which I have conceded to the proponents of the Ramsey sentence approach only for the sake of argument.

What in fact the Ramsey sentence technique does is to replace a theory about electrons and protons (say) by a theory about certain classes of things which are abstractly specified so that the relations among these things are isomorphic to those relations which the original theory asserted to hold between electrons and protons. If the original theory asserts the existence of electrons, the Ramsey sentence will contain a part of the form " . . . $(\exists K_k)$ . . . $(\exists x)$ x ϵK_k" and so will in fact carry the same ontological implication.

It is, of course, true that *both* the original theory and its Ramsey sentence equivalent *might* (so far as the foregoing argument is concerned) *both* be interpreted instrumentally and without ontological implications. But equally *both* the original theory and its Ramsey sentence equivalent could be interpreted realistically. The device of the Ramsey sentence cuts no metaphysical ice one way or the other.

Another method for eliminating the V_T part of a theory comes from Craig's Theorem. [23] To understand what this is, a few preliminary explanations may be in order. When one thinks of an axiom system perhaps one thinks of a *finite* set of axioms. However in logic and mathematics one sometimes finds it useful to construct systems with infinite sets of axioms. Thus in a finite axiomatization of sentential logic we may specify "$p \supset (q \supset p)$" as an axiom, and there may be a *rule of substitution*, a rule of inference, which authorizes replacement of sentence letters by well formed formulae. Clearly the same can be achieved by having no rule of substitution but by specifying an infinite set of axioms as follows: any formulae of the form "$A \supset (B \supset A)$" is a theorem. It is understood that the places of "A" and "B" in the above formula have to be taken by well formed formulae of sentential logic, and, since there is an effective (or recursive) procedure for deciding whether or not a formula of sentential logic is well formed or not, there is no difficulty in deciding whether or not any given sentence belongs to the infinite set of axioms in question.[13] (Infinite axiom systems may indeed be particularly convenient in logic in that they enable us to dispense with the rule of substitution.)

In general, an infinite set of axioms is permissible if there is an effective way of deciding whether or not a given sentence belongs to the set. That is, there must be a *decision procedure* or algorithm which enables us to show that (a) the sentence is in the set, if it is in it, and (b) the sentence is not in the set, if it is not in it. For example, it would not do to specify as an infinite set of axioms: all the valid formulae of the predicate calculus. This is because, by Church's theorem, there would be no effective method of deciding whether a formula was an axiom. There is indeed a method of showing (eventually) that a formula is a valid formula of predicate logic if it is one, but we can never tell, by a routine method, that a formula is *not* a valid formula of predicate logic. Hence, however long we have been applying our routine of churning out valid formulae, if the formula under consideration has not turned up we can never know whether this is because we have not gone on churning out valid formulae long enough to turn it up or whether it is that it would *never* turn up however long we churned out valid formulae. Again, it would do even worse to specify as an axiom set all truths of elementary number theory. As a corollary of Gödel's incompleteness theorem there is no routine for churning out all truths of elementary number theory, let alone any routine for churning out all non-truths. But an infinite set of axioms is all right so long as there is an effective procedure for deciding whether or not a sentence belongs to the set. Roughly we can say that an infinite

---

[13]Indeed it is obvious that the restriction to well formed formulae of *sentential logic* is unnecessary, and that an infinite set of axioms "$A \supset (B \supset A)$" can be used as part of the axiomatization of predicate logic, elementary number theory or set theory, or any other theory for which an effective specification of what is a well formed sentence can be proposed.

set of axioms is all right so long as it is possible[14] to build a computer which will give us a "yes" or "no" answer to a question of the form "Is sentence S in the set or not?"

Now let T be a given physical theory whose vocabulary is V, containing the parts V_O and V_T. Craig's theorem shows how we can replace T by a theory T' which contains none of the terms in V_T, and in which all the theorems of T which contain only expressions of V_O are also provable. That is, despite the lack of the conceptual apparatus of V_T the theory T' is as powerful, as far as proving theorems in V_O is concerned, as was the original theory T. Nevertheless the vocabulary of T' is wider than V_O in that we supplement V_O with a metalinguistic apparatus which enables us to talk about expressions in the original theory T and to express the syntax of T. Thus "A is provable in T" will be expressible in T'. This is done through the technique of Gödel numbering whereby a unique natural number is associated with any sequence of expressions or sequence of sequences of expressions in the vocabulary of T. "A is provable in T" is thus mapped onto a sentence of elementary number theory and "provable in T" corresponds to a recursive arithmetical function, i.e., one which enables us in routine fashion to tell whether or not a certain arithmetical property holds of a number. In particular we can tell whether it holds of the Gödel number associated with some sentence A.

Now let A be a theorem of T which contains only the terms V_O. (Of course a *proof* of A within T will very likely contain terms from V_T.) We now stipulate that the sentence A • A • A • . . . A (a conjunction of n A's) will be an axiom of T' if and only if n is the Gödel num-

[14]"Possible" here *at least* means "mathematically possible". But in practice a stronger sense of "possible" is needed. Obviously it would not be any good if there was an algorithm for deciding the question whether a sentence was in a set of axioms but the algorithm was such a slow working one that even with sentences of moderate complexity a fast electronic computer would take years to produce the answer! An infinite set of axioms as envisaged by Craig's theorem would indeed fall short of this practical requirement.

ber of a proof of A in T. It is easy to see that it is all right to specify an infinite set of axioms in this way, i.e., that there is an effective way of telling whether or not a given sentence of T' is in the set or not. For if we count up the number of A's in A • A • A • . . . A (there will be an awful lot of them[15]) we can then find out whether this number is the Gödel number of a sequence of sequences of expressions in T, and furthermore whether this Gödel number is that of a sequence of sequences of expressions which constitutes a proof of A within T.

It is clear that the dodge is to replace T with a theory T' which contains none of the vocabulary of T but which does give us means to talk about the theoretical *expressions* of T. If T contains the word "electron" then T' will contain the word "'electron'". It might be thought, then, that the possibility of replacing T by T' suggests an instrumentalist interpretation of T. If we can get along by talking about the *language* of T, for example about the word "electron", instead of about electrons, does this not suggest that when we appear to be talking about electrons we are really only using an elaborate inference device for getting us from certain V_0 sentences to certain other V_0 sentences? On the contrary, however, I would suggest that the realist could reply, with far more justice, that the mentioned considerations show nothing of the sort. He could point out that Craig's method can be applied only after we have first constructed the theory T, and that the success of T' is explained by the fact that the original theory T is true of the things that it is ostensibly about: in other words by the fact that there really are electrons or whatever is postulated by the theory T. If there were no such things, and if T were not true in a realist way, would not the success of T' be quite inexplicable? One would have to suppose that there were innumerable lucky accidents about the behavior of things mentioned in the observa-

[15]This consideration militates against the *practical* (as opposed to the mathematical) possibility of using a theory like T'. See footnote 14 above.

tional vocabulary, so that they behaved miraculously *as if* they were brought about by the nonexistent things ostensibly talked about in the theoretical vocabulary.

This brings us to a general point about instrumentalism. An instrumentalist is of course instrumentalist about all theories, whereas a realist can be realist about some theories (those which he believes to be true) and instrumentalist about others (which he believes to be useful, though not true). The distinction between the two sorts of theories is marked in scientific language by calling the ostensible subject matter of the latter sort of theory a "model": indeed it is one of the serious criticisms of instrumentalism that it blurs this important distinction.[24] The chief realist objection to instrumentalism is, as I have suggested, that on the instrumentalist view it is a surprising and inexplicable fact that the world is such that V_O facts can be related to V_O facts by means of V_T sentences, whereas on the realist view there is nothing mysterious at all: if the V_T sentences really are about the hidden mechanisms of the universe after all, then *of course* they can be expected to help us to relate V_O sentences to other V_O sentences. Consider a man (in the sixteenth century) who is realist about the Copernican hypothesis but instrumentalist about the Ptolemaic one. He can explain the instrumental usefulness of the Ptolemaic system of epicycles because he can prove that the Ptolemaic system can produce almost the same predictions about the apparent motions of the planets as does the Copernican hypothesis. Hence the assumption of the realist truth of the Copernican hypothesis explains the instrumental usefulness of the Ptolemaic one. Such an explanation of the instrumental usefulness of certain theories would not be possible if *all* theories were regarded as merely instrumental. Similarly, it is hard to believe that the regularities which appear on the macroscopic level should be just *as if* they were due to things on the sub-microscopic level. (Just as in ordinary phenomenalism there is a puzzle as to why sense data such as that of a cat's tail on the left of a sofa should be followed by sense data of a cat's head and whiskers on the right of a sofa. On the realist assumption that our sense experiences are caused by an independently existing cat which walks behind the sofa, whether or not we have any sense data, this sequence of sense data is of course readily explained.) If we have nothing but instrumental laws, they may explain in the sense of enabling us to predict, but they do not explain in the sense of reducing the brutishness of brute facts.

It should be added that someone who accepted the instrumentalist use of Craig's theorem would, *qua* scientific discoverer, have at least to pretend to himself to be a realist in the context of discovery. It is only to finished theories that Craig's method could be applied. Without at least something of a realist attitude it is unlikely that he would ever guess at the theory in the first place. Hempel has pointed out[25] that since Craig's method requires a purely deductive systematization it would not enable us to reason inductively as in the following example. Because of observational data $O_1, O_2, \ldots O_n$ a certain substance is probably of the theoretical sort S_i (that is, "S_i" is part of V_T) and so it probably has the effect S_k (here "S_k" is also part of V_T), since our theory asserts that if something is of the sort S_i it leads to something of the sort S_k. Anything of the sort S_k leads to the observational result O_m. So *probably* O_m. A further difficulty for the macro-phenomenalist is the following one. He holds that sentences ostensibly about electrons are really mere calculation devices, and so electrons can be said to be theoretical fictions. But if electrons are theoretical fictions and fountain pens are real objects, where do we draw the line between the real and the fictional? Are bacteria fictions? (They can be seen but only through microscopes.) Are viruses? These can not be seen through ordinary microscopes, but they can be seen with electron microscopes. Are protein molecules (which are not much smaller than viruses)? Is everything which can not be seen by the naked eye a theoretical fiction? If so, then things which can be seen only through a magnifying glass are a fiction, and yet they look very like things which can be seen by the naked eye.

It should be noticed that the objection of "Where do we draw the line?" is an objection to the macro-phenomenalist who is a realist about medium sized physical objects, but is not an objection to the ordinary philosophical phenomenalist, who holds that the stuff of the world consists in sense data. For him electrons and tables are in the same boat: both are theoretical fictions. But I am taking it for granted that orthodox phenomenalism is not a tenable philosophical position. A particularly intriguing question for the macro-phenomenalist is this. Suppose that he says that a molecule is a theoretical fiction whereas a visible grain of dust is not. What will he say of a small, yet visible crystal? Grover Maxwell has pointed out that according to modern valency theory a crystal can be regarded as a single macro-molecule, in which case some molecules are presumably not theoretical entities but observable ones.[26]

In any case the notion of "observable thing" is far from clear. Are we to say that we do not observe tables but only colored areas of light and shade? Is it not an interpretation of the data of visual experience that what we see is something that we could write on and not a cunning piece of stage property made of canvas? If we discount those interpretations which the commonsensical brain makes on the information which is carried to it in electrochemical pulses through the optic nerves, we shall have to say that even tables are not observables and we shall be back into the theory of orthodox phenomenalism.[16] If ordinary perception is inevitably de-

---

[16]It could well be argued that the "sense data" of orthodox phenomenalism are more dubious theoretical entities than are electrons. Unless, that is "I have a table-ish sense datum" is just an odd way of saying "it looks to me that there is a

pendent on our ordinary conceptual scheme, why can not the scientist's perception be formed partly by his theoretical knowledge? For example, if he sees a scintillation on a screen can he not say "I saw an electron hit the screen"? It is true that the scintillation may mislead him in this way, and he may be wrong in interpreting his visual experience as being that of an electron hitting the screen, but, equally, commonsense perception is open to illusion, which is well exploited by magicians. Similarly, when looking at an ammeter, why should a scientist not say that he observes a current of ten amperes, rather than the coincidence of a pointer with a numeral? All this suggests the pragmatic theory of observation sentences, to which we alluded on p. 82 above. As we have noted, this has been forcibly advocated by P. K. Feyerabend,[27] and it was at one time advocated by Rudolf Carnap.[28]

Feyerabend illuminatingly thinks of the human perceptual system (eye and brain) as a scientific instrument. Scientific instruments, such as thermometers and galvanometers, simply constitute an extension of the human body, and, given suitable scientific sophistication, we can use them so as to assert *immediately* the existence of such things as temperatures and electric currents, just as, granted merely commonsense sophistication and as a result of photons striking his retinas, a man can assert *immediately* that there is a three-dimensional, hard, wooden object in front of him. When we look at observation in this way, we see no reason for drawing a sharp line between "commonsense observation language" and the language of scientific theory. (When I say that the sugar in my teacup has *dissolved*, am I talking common sense or science?) It becomes impossible to use the distinction between a theoretical language and an observation language to demarcate a

---

table", but such emasculated sense datum talk is not strong enough to carry the theoretical weight of phenomenalism.

line between "real things" and "theoretical fictions". We can of course treat the things ostensibly mentioned in false but still practically useful theories as fictions. But in the case of theories which have stood up to test and which (at present at least) are believed true, we have no good reason to refuse to treat the entities mentioned therein as objects of veridical observation.

Methodological critique of instrumentalism

Popper has argued that an instrumentalist theory of physics is unable to account for the scientist's interest in testing remote implications of his theory.[29] If a theory were merely a practical computation device, then failure of a test would not be a refutation of the theory but would merely constitute a limitation of its applicability. This *methodological* criticism of instrumentalism has been powerfully developed by Feyerabend. In contrast to Popper, Feyerabend holds that *present-day* quantum mechanics does demand an instrumentalist interpretation.[30] However Feyerabend holds that scientists should not let the matter rest there, and should actively search for a theory which would be capable of a realistic interpretation. Since an instrumentalist theory is so much less refutable than is a realist theory, instrumentalism leads to complacency about tests of a theory. Feyerabend considers the clash in the sixteenth century between the Ptolemaic and Copernican hypotheses about planetary motions. If Copernicus, Galileo, and others had all accepted an instrumentalist position, as perhaps did Cardinal Bellarmine, Galileo's opponent, then the Copernican theory would not have become accepted. At the stage in which science then was, the Ptolemaic hypothesis was more convenient as an instrument of prediction, partly because it was the accepted technique of the day and so could be applied more easily. Within the limits of observation which were then available it could easily be

155

made (with the postulation of sufficient epicycles) to give predictions about the positions of the planets at least as accurate as could the Copernican hypothesis. It could also be easily adapted to even more accurate observations simply by adding on more epicycles. According to Feyerabend this last fact was the chief trouble with it: by accommodating itself to ever more accurate observations by means of the technique of constructing extra epicycles it protected itself against possible refutation, and made itself untestable. In this way it became a barrier to scientific progress, which can occur only through theories which are open to refutation.

Let us say that a theory is weakly testable if contrary observations would lead only to a fairly obvious modification of it, but that it is strongly testable only if the theory can not always be saved by such a fairly obvious *ad hoc* modification. Thus if it were a fact that the Ptolemaic hypothesis could always have been saved by the addition of suitable epicycles, then the theory would have been weakly testable but not strongly testable. It is characteristic of instrumentalist theories to be weakly testable only. For this reason Feyerabend holds that it would be a good thing if scientific discovery and innovation should result in the replacement of the contemporary quantum mechanics by a strongly testable theory. For according to him, modern quantum mechanics is *not* susceptible of a realist interpretation but requires the instrumentalist interpretation associated with the Copenhagen school which makes it weakly testable only. It is true that the Copenhagen interpretation has frequently been defended by its advocates in a way which makes use of bad philosophical arguments. Some of these arguments are similar to those for ordinary philosophical phenomenalism and would be arguments against any realist theory whatever. Others depend on the inference from "We can't find out whether or not there is a so-and-so" to "There aren't any so-and-so's at all", which is a *non-sequitur*. For example, it

156

is often said that the interaction between a measuring instrument and an electron prevents us from being able to discover both the position and the momentum of an electron below the limits of accuracy set by Heisenberg's indeterminacy principle. It is then concluded that the electron has no definite position and momentum. This is either a *non-sequitur* or else depends on very debatable positivistic assumptions as suppressed premises. Nevertheless, Feyerabend holds, the Copenhagen interpretation can be defended by good *physical* arguments which remain to be reckoned with even though we have rejected the bad *philosophical* arguments.

Quantum mechanics and instrumentalism

Let us discuss one of the physical considerations which bring out the difficulty in thinking of an electron as a real particle, and which consequently suggest an instrumentalist philosophy of quantum mechanics. This is the well known "two slit" experiment. See Figure 2. Consider a point source S which emits electrons. These pass through two slits A and B in a screen X. The elec-

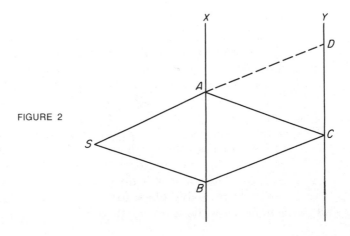

FIGURE 2

trons then hit a further screen Y where their impact is observed as a blackening of a photographic surface or as scintillations on a fluorescent surface. (In an actual experiment the "slits" are gaps in a crystal lattice, and the situation is slightly more complicated, but the present idealized account is sufficient for our purpose.)

If both slits are open the stream of electrons will cause a series of interference bands (dark regions on a photographic plate) on the surface Y, with the greatest intensity at the central point C and with gradually falling intensities as we move to bands above or below C. The phenomenon is exactly what we would expect if the stream of electrons in fact consisted of waves: similar interference phenomena are predictable in the classical theory of physical optics. So far the experiment suggests that we should think of the electrons not as particles but as waves.

Now suppose that the intensity of the electron beam from S is reduced. When it gets very weak, what is observed is not that the interference bands on Y simply become very faint. What is observed is that individual electrons strike the screen Y in various places. If Y is a fluorescent surface the impacts can be observed as minute scintillations. It will be seen that the scintillations occur in the regions where the interference bands occurred before, and hence these bands represent regions of high probability for the impact of electrons. These facts suggest that we should give up the wave picture of the electron in favor of a particle picture.

The particle picture will not do, however, because it is the existence of both slits which is needed for the interference pattern. This is inexplicable on the particle picture, since a particle presumably has to pass through one slit or the other. If it passes through A it is hard to see how it could matter whether the slit B is open or closed. Nevertheless it does matter. If B is closed then the most probable place for an electron to hit Y is not C but D. Now how on earth does the electron, when it passes through A, know whether B is open or closed? Or, to put it less anthropomorphically, what physical influence could an open or closed slit at B have on a particle at A?

These difficulties do not trouble an adherent of the Copenhagen interpretation, since he regards the theory as merely a convenient instrument with which to make predictions. He is therefore perfectly happy to use a wave picture on Mondays, Wednesdays, and Fridays (when predicting interference patterns) and a particle picture on Tuesdays, Thursdays, and Saturdays (when predicting individual scintillations). Even though the two pictures are incompatible with one another, the use of both of them (at different times) enables the correct predictions to be made.[31]

It should be noticed that according to the Copenhagen interpretation the electron does not have simultaneously both a definite position and a definite momentum. When it strikes Y its position becomes definite but its momentum is quite indefinite. When passing the screen X both its momentum and its position are indefinite, and so one must not say that it has passed either through the slit A or through the slit B. Let us now consider some of the difficulties which arise if we try to propose an alternative to the Copenhagen interpretation and to think instead of the electron purely as a particle with a definite trajectory, as Popper has attempted to do.[32] It must be remembered that the usual interpretation of the wave-function in quantum mechanics is that it represents probabilities. Thus the interference bands on the screen represent regions where the probability waves from A and B reinforce one another. These probabilities are usually interpreted as frequencies. To say that the probability of an electron hitting a screen at one place is greater than it is at another is to say that on the average a greater proportion of electrons hit the screen at the one place than at the other one. The first part of Popper's account is to

159

replace the frequency conception of probability by the propensity interpretation. We discussed this in Chapter 2 above (see pp. 46–48). Propensities are for Popper hypothetical posits of science, just as much as electrons or forces are. There is no difficulty in thinking of propensities as real states of real entities. Then, according to Popper, an electron in the situation of the two slit experiment, with both slits open, has a real propensity to go to certain places, such as C, on the screen Y, rather than to others. If we alter the experimental situation so that only the slit A is open, then the propensity changes, so that most electrons go to D and hardly any go to C. According to Popper the electron really does go through one slit or the other, but the propensity in the case where B is open is different from the propensity when slit B is shut. One must recall that according to Popper a propensity belongs not just to one element in an experimental arrangement, such as an electron, but to the arrangement as a whole. If we talk of the propensity of an electron to do something, this must be understood as an ellipsis for talk of the propensity of the electron *in a certain arrangement* to do something.

Nevertheless there still seems to be something of a mystery. The influence of slit B in altering the propensity seems to smack of action at a distance, and it is hard to see on what physical principles it could be explained. On Popper's account, the electron has both a definite position and a definite momentum at all times (even though Heisenberg's principle prevents us from ascertaining both of these), and so it has a well defined trajectory. It follows that if one electron with a certain momentum at the slit A goes to C while another goes to C', then the second electron must have acquired momentum in the direction CC' which the first one did not possess. See Figure 3. It is clear, therefore, that if we work with well defined trajectories the principle of conservation of momentum has to be given up.

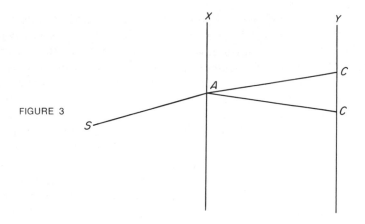

FIGURE 3

Feyerabend reports[33] that in a private communication Popper has stated that in his view the conservation laws apply statistically to large numbers of particles but that they are not valid in individual cases. Feyerabend concedes that it is *possible* that microphysics could be developed in such a way that the conservation laws (for individual cases) were rejected. However no one knows how to do this as yet, and until such a theory is developed which is equal or superior in predictive power to present quantum mechanics, Popper's solution of the problem of giving a realistic interpretation to quantum mechanics must be speculative only. The conservation laws are well entrenched in contemporary physics, and have very much experimental support. Feyerabend of course agrees that the fact that they have much experimental support is not decisive, since experiments have to be interpreted in the light of theories, and the support which they give to a theory may be due to the limited range in which we have tried to apply and test our theory. (Aristotle's theory of motion which requires a force to keep a body at constant velocity had a good deal of support from everyday experience.) Nevertheless there is at least considerable doubt as to whether a successful theory can be developed which rejects the conservation laws. Feyerabend's position therefore is that for *physical* reasons it is hard not to accept an instrumentalist attitude to quantum mechanics, but nevertheless, for methodological reasons, this is a bad thing, and we should search hopefully for a realist, and hence more radically testable theory of quantum mechanics.

While conceding to Feyerabend that there are quite good *physical* reasons for accepting an instrumentalist attitude to quantum mechanics (even though the *philosophical* arguments in favor of instrumentalism are bad ones), I would wish to suggest that the physical arguments in favor of instrumentalism are not *compelling* ones. Even in the absence of a better and *more obviously* realistic theory of quantum mechanics, can we not be realistic about existing quantum mechanics? The two slit experiment (and other similar considerations) surely show only that electrons and the like are rather queer entities, for example that they are not precisely located in space and that their characteristics are rather different from the sort with which we are familiar in classical physics. Thus they are very different from familiar objects in that they do not have sharp trajectories and momenta. Moreover some of the laws which they obey are of an unusual type. Margenau has pointed out[34] that Pauli's exclusion principle prevents two free electrons from having *exactly* the same velocity even though they may be billions of miles apart. (However the difference between their permitted velocities becomes so small as to make no matter except at approximately subatomic distances.) Such a law seems to imply action at a distance. In this way, as well as in not having sharp trajectories or momenta electrons are queer things. But need we refuse to admit that they, as well as other even queerer particles, are real? Electrons may be characterizable as neither waves nor particles, even though theory may find it convenient to treat them as one or the other, depending on the occasion.[17] Alternatively, we might hold that modern physics is instrumentalist, but may nevertheless constitute an approximation to, or a hint at, a realist theory. That is, a realist theory, even though it is unknown to us as yet, is "in the offing". For if this were not so, how could the success of an instrumentalist theory be explained? Otherwise the success of the instrumentalist theory would have to depend on too many mere coincidences on the macroscopic level.

Laws, theories, and logic

Any axiomatizable mathematical theory can be expressed in the terminology of predicate logic by adding to the vocabulary of predicate logic certain constant predicates,[18] and by introducing certain axioms involving these constant predicates. I shall take it that this is so with any theory in physics, even though actually to axiomatize a theory in this way is no easy task even in relatively tractable cases, as an inspection of the axiomatization of the relatively simple case of classical particle mechanics by McKinsey, Sugar, and Suppes[36] would clearly show. (And even so, these writers do not formalize the underlying logic but make use of an intuitive set theory.) With a live physical theory, such as quantum mechanics, which is continually shifting, and some of whose parts may even not be strictly compatible with others, axiomatization is hardly practicable. Nevertheless it is useful to think of some future axiomatization of any particular historical stage of physics as a theoretical ideal. A deduction of a law L

---

[17]Margenau, in his book *Open Vistas*[35] cites A. N. Whitehead, who held that things can exist without simple location.

[18]For example set theory introduces the constant binary predicate "ϵ". See pp. 33–36 above.

from more fundamental ones $B_1, B_2, \ldots B_n$ may be thought of as valid if the law $(B_1 \bullet B_2 \bullet \ldots B_n) \supset L$ is deducible in the fictitious axiomatization. What in practice happens in physics is that the proposition $(B_1, B_2 \ldots B_n) \supset L$ is deduced by means which the logician and pure mathematician would not regard as completely rigorous.

I have been assuming here that the laws of nature can be formulated within an extensional logic.[19] Thus if we confine our attention, for the sake of simplicity, to a simple form of law "All A's are B's" this can be expressed simply as "$(x) \, Ax \supset Bx$". As against this, some philosophers hold that the above law needs to be expressed by means of the so-called strong conditional, which may be symbolized by "$\rightarrow$". Thus the sentence "$(x) \, Ax \supset Bx$" just says that nothing is an A without being a B, and is vacuously true when nothing in fact is an A. On the other hand the proposition "$(x) \, Ax \rightarrow Bx$" is held to assert that a thing's being an A *necessitates* its being a B, and in particular the nonexistence of A's does not ensure the truth of "$(x) \, Ax \rightarrow Bx$". For example, let "A" be the predicate "is not acted on by a force" and "B" be the predicate "moves with uniform velocity in a straight line". Then if Newton's first law of motion is expressed by the formula "$(x) \, Ax \supset Bx$" it becomes vacuously true if there are no bodies in the universe that are not acted on by a force, whereas "$(x) \, Ax \rightarrow Bx$" would not be vacuous in this way.

Nevertheless other philosophers, of whom I am one, would still wish to argue that an extensional logic, using the weak conditional "$\supset$", is perfectly adequate for scientific purposes. Now if these arguments can be sustained, then on grounds of simplicity alone we ought to eschew the strong conditional. It should also be remembered that impressive arguments have been put forward by Quine[37] against quantificational modal logic, which is what would be needed to formalize a

[19]See pp. 39–40.

scientific theory using the strong conditional. But even if a form of quantificational modal logic can be produced which would hedge itself against Quine's objections, as is claimed by Rudolf Carnap[38] and others, it would still be rather complicated and messy compared with the simplicity and elegance of ordinary predicate logic, and so we should look rather carefully at the credentials of any argument which purports to show the indispensability of strong conditionals for science.

Let us first of all consider the objection that an extensional logic makes some laws to be vacuously true. Thus perhaps Newton's first law of motion is vacuously true because nowhere in the universe are there any bodies not acted on by a force. One reply to this would be "So what?" That is, even if the law should be vacuously true, does it matter? Even if *vacuously* true it would still be *true*. In any case the example of Newton's first law of motion is a rather peculiar one, since it does not seem to be needed in Newtonian mechanics because it is a special case of the *second* law, which states that force is proportional to acceleration. Hence, obviously, if there is no force then there is zero acceleration.

The first law is sometimes invoked in order to define an inertial system, but in fact this is not necessary. Consider how an inertial system can be defined in celestial mechanics (the mechanics of the solar system). We have a number of bodies $M_1, M_2, \ldots M_n$. It is found that axes can be chosen such that the mutual accelerations of the bodies at any given instant can be decomposed into components $f_{12}, f_{21}, f_{13}, f_{31}$, etc., such that f_{kl} and f_{lk} belong to the kth and lth bodies respectively and are in opposite directions, in the straight line joining these bodies, and positive real numbers $m_1, m_2, \ldots m_n$ can be assigned to these bodies so that $m_k f_{kl} = m_l f_{lk}$. Such a system of axes is called an inertial system. It can be shown that such a system of axes must exist. (Note, however, that this does *not* constitute an analytic solution of the n-body problem. The actual values of m_1,

$m_2, \ldots m_n$ are determined by a method of successive approximation.) This is how inertial systems of axes are defined in astronomy, and there is no better way. The fiction of a body which is not acted on by a force does not help in practice at all.[20]

I would suggest, then, that if a scientific theory is correctly formulated none of its axioms need be such as to be vacuously true. Nevertheless, *if* it should be necessary to include vacuously true laws in the axiomatic development of a theory, such laws can never do any harm. Consider a law "$(x)\ Ax \supset Bx$" which happens to be vacuously true because there are no A's. We can never use it in order to argue for (let us suppose) a false conclusion "Ba". Our argument would be of the form

(1) $(x)\ Ax \supset Bx$

(2) Aa

(3) $\therefore Ba$

We are precluded from arguing in this manner simply because if (1) is vacuously true then (2) must be false, and so we can not be entitled to use it as a premise. In short, to admit vacuous truths to a system can not enable us to deduce any falsehoods. (This indeed is obvious if we reflect that *vacuous* truths are still vacuous *truths*!)

Suppose that it had never been decided anywhere in the universe to make an atomic bomb. In this case, the proposition

---

[20]In conversation my friend Richard Routley has raised the interesting question of whether in *special relativity* Newton's first law may be needed in order to define an inertial system. Certainly in special relativity the simple relationships of Newton's third law of motion ($m_k f_{kl} = m_l f_{lk}$) do not hold except for collisions, and the analysis is considerably more complicated. Nevertheless it is not clear to me that it is impossible even in special relativity to produce a definition of "inertial system" without making use of the fiction of bodies which are not acted on by a force. In practice, in special relativity we take a Newtonian inertial system as approximating to an inertial system of axes. Appealing to a *fictitious* entity, a body not acted on by a force, gets nowhere, not even as an approximation. In *theory* in special relativity we could appeal to a set of axes for which the third law was obeyed in collision phenomena, but the method would of course be of little use in practice, since collisions are fortunately rare in the subject matter of celestial mechanics.

(4) (x) (y) [x is a lump of uranium 235 (of more than a certain critical size) and y is a lump of uranium 235 (of the same size) and x is impelled against y $\supset$ there is a colossal explosion]

would have been vacuously true. Moreover scientists would still have wished to assert the *subjunctive* conditional

(5) (x) (y) [if x *were* a lump of uranium 235 (of more than a certain critical size) and y were a lump of uranium 235 (of the same size) and x were impelled against y then there *would be* a colossal explosion]

and would wish to deny

(6) (x) (y) [if x *were* a lump of uranium 235 (of more than a certain critical size) and y were a lump of uranium 235 (of the same size) and x were impelled against y then the sun *would* turn bright purple].

That is, it might be said, scientists would wish to assert the subjunctive conditional (5) and to deny the subjunctive conditional (6). Neither could be vacuously true, and both, it might be said, need to be analyzed in terms of the strong conditional. However even if this is so, we can reply that a scientist would not be seriously impeded if we denied him the use of strong or subjunctive conditionals. Instead of asserting (5) he can express what he has in mind by asserting the *metalinguistic* proposition

(7) The sentence (4) follows from a well tested theory.

Similarly, instead of denying (6) he can get his point across by means of the metalinguistic proposition

(8) The sentence (9) does not follow from a well tested theory, where (9) is the sentence

(9) (x) (y) [x is a lump of uranium 235 (of more than a   **167**

certain critical size) and y is a lump of uranium 235 (of the same size) and x is impelled against $y \supset$ the sun turns bright purple].

In this discussion I myself not only have mentioned but also have used modalities and perhaps also strong conditionals. These should be regarded as serving for suitable metalinguistic statements (indeed meta-metalinguistic ones), which it would be difficult and rather inelegant to set down in full. The reader, if he cares, might try to produce suitable statements in the metalanguage of my present discourse.

The present suggestion is, then, that subjunctive and strong conditionals can be replaced by assertions about what follows from what is in a well tested theory. These metalinguistic statements can all be expressed in an extensional language, using the weak conditional "$\supset$". Now since the concept of "well tested theory" is not a formal one, and its application has to be left to the tact and judgment of scientists, our metalinguistic idiom which does the job of these conditionals is in a sense not completely formalizable. On the other hand it should be noted that once we decide what well tested theory we have in mind, and if this theory is formalized, then our metalinguistic assertions can be formalized, since the notion "follows from" can be rigorously defined using the methods of metamathematics (syntax).

It is sometimes said that even if strong conditionals are not needed in scientific theories, they are still needed in the laboratory. Suppose that a scientist says to himself: "If I connect up the wires in my apparatus in this way I will burn it out and if I connect them in this other way I will give myself a violent electric shock". Having said this to himself he decides to connect up the wires in *neither* of these ways, and so what he says, if interpreted extensionally, is vacuously true. It is of course not the vacuous truth of this sentence which interests him. Once more, however, we can say that what he is wondering about is whether certain conditionals follow from his background of theoretical knowledge, and that he is using this metalinguistic information as an aid to practical decision making. Thus if the scientist knows that from a proposition A there follows the proposition "I shall get a violent electric shock" he does his best to ensure the falsity of A. Even in the laboratory, therefore, it would seem that a scientist can get by with the weak conditional "$\supset$" together with certain metalinguistic concepts expressible within an extensional logic.

Similar considerations help to shed light on the topic of dispositional properties. It has often been pointed out that if (for example) "salt (sodium chloride) is soluble in water" is analyzed as

(10) (x) (x is sodium chloride and x is immersed in water $\supset$ x dissolves)

then it is vacuously true if no piece of sodium chloride ever has or ever will be immersed in water. Of course the sea is full of sodium chloride, and obviously sodium chloride has in fact been immersed in water, but some philosophers would still wish to leave themselves room to say that even in a universe in which sodium chloride never had been and never would be immersed in water we could still discuss the question, as a nontrivial one, of whether sodium chloride was soluble in water. We can give some part of what these philosophers want by saying that (10) follows from the laws of nature together with certain sentences describing the structure of sodium chloride. Indeed (10) is a theorem of the quantum theory of the chemical bond. Moreover even before modern valency theory had been thought of (10) could be construed as anticipating for some theory of solubility still to be developed.

Would not the quantum theory of the chemical bond itself need to postulate dispositional properties of more fundamental things, such as electrons? Yet some philosophers might express a wish to be able to say that in a universe in which there were no protons, it would still be true that *if* there *were* both protons and electrons they *would* attract one another. There are two ways in which this move might be countered. It could be said that

(11) (x) (y) (x is a proton and y is an electron $\supset x$ and
        y attract one another)

is an axiom of the theory, and its position as an axiom is enough to give it a nontrivial status, quite apart from any question of the existence of protons. Secondly, it might be remarked that we simply should *not* wish to say what electrons would be like if there were no protons. At this very fundamental level physics and cosmology are probably too intimately related for us to make any suppositions about what would be the laws of nature if the facts of the case (initial or boundary conditions) were different. For example, if J. A. Wheeler's theory of electrons and protons as opposite ends of "worm holes" belonging to a multiply-connected space-time were to be accepted,[21] what sense would it make to ask whether electrons would have a charge if there were no protons? What sense would it make even to envisage electrons without protons?

In any case, if we replace statements about dispositions by extensional statements in terms of universal quantifiers and "$\supset$", this will never lead us into falsehood when talking about the actual world. Trivial truths, such as of the form "$(x) Fx \supset Gx$" when "$\sim(\exists x)$ Fx" is true, can never be harmful when we keep within an extensional point of view and do not try to discuss non-actual but possible worlds. (We can leave it to certain metaphysicians to worry about whether there is any sense in such talk of non-actual worlds.) If we do wish to talk ostensibly about possible worlds, we can

[21]See pp. 240–241 below.

say what we need to say if we use a meta-theoretic (metalinguistic) idiom, for example by discussing the deducibility of certain sentences in a theory from others. If we can not say what we wish to say by means of a meta-theoretic idiom, then it may be suggested that we do not really know what we are talking about.

SUGGESTIONS FOR FURTHER READING

On fundamental and derived measurement, and related concepts, besides N. R. Campbell, *An Account of the Principles of Measurement and Calculation* (London: Longmans, Green, 1928) and *Foundations of Science* (New York: Dover, 1957), Part II, see Brian Ellis, *Basic Concepts of Measurement* (New York: Cambridge University Press, 1966); C. W. Churchman and P. Ratoosh (eds.), *Measurement: Definitions and Theories* (New York: Wiley, 1959); and S. S. Stevens, "On the Theory of Scales of Measurement", *Science*, CIII (1946), 677–680. On the inaccuracy of physical laws see Michael Scriven, "The Key Property of Physical Laws – Inaccuracy", in Herbert Feigl and Grover Maxwell (eds.), *Current Issues in the Philosophy of Science* (New York: Holt, Rinehart and Winston, 1961), pp. 91–101, with rejoinder by H. Mehlberg, *ibid.*, pp. 102–103, and reply by Scriven, *ibid.*, pp. 103–104. See also D. H. Mellor, "Experimental Error and Deducibility", *Philosophy of Science*, XXXII (1965), 105–122, which bears also on Feyerabend's and Sellars' criticisms of the orthodox hierarchical account of scientific explanation, which was discussed in Chapter 3 above.

On the issue of realism versus instrumentalism in physics, a thoroughgoing discussion from a metaphysically rather neutral position will be found in C. G. Hempel, "The Theoretician's Dilemma", in H. Feigl, M. Scriven and G. Maxwell (eds.), *Minnesota Studies in the Philosophy of Science*, Vol. II (Minneapolis: University of Minnesota Press, 1958), pp. 37–98, and also in Ernest Nagel, *The Structure of Science* (New York: Harcourt, Brace and World, 1961), Chapter 6. A view which is not easily classifiable either as unambiguously realist or as unambiguously instrumentalist is that of Stephen Toulmin, in his *Philosophy of Science* (London: Hutchinson, 1953, and paperback, New York: Harper and Row, 1960). This leans partly on Ryle's concept of laws of nature as "inference tickets" or "inference licences". See G. Ryle, *Concept of Mind* (London: Hutchinson, 1949, and paperback, New York: Barnes and Noble, 1950). This conception of laws of nature has been criticised by H. Gavin Alexander, "General Statements as Rules of Inference?", *Minnesota Studies in the Philosophy of Science*, Vol. II, *op. cit.*, pp. 309–329. For operationism, see P. W. Bridgman, *The Logic of Modern Physics* (New York: Macmillan, 1927, and paperback, 1960). A philosophical defense of the Copenhagen interpretation of quantum mechanics is given by N. R. Hanson, "The Copenhagen Interpretation of Quantum Theory", *American Journal of Physics*, XXVII (1959), 1–15, and in an abridged form has been reprinted in A. Danto and S. Morgenbesser (eds.), *Philosophy of Science* (New York: Meridian Books, 1960). See also Hanson's "Five Cautions for the Copenhagen Interpretation's Critics", *Philosophy of Science*, XXVI (1959), 325–337. Attempts by K. R. Popper at a realistic interpretation of quantum theory are to be found in Chapter 9 of his *The Logic of Scientific Discovery* (London: Routledge and Kegan Paul, 1963, and paperback, rev. ed., New York: Harper and Row, 1965), and his paper "The Propensity Interpretation of Probability and the Quantum Theory", and the ensuing discussion of S. Körner (ed.), *Observation and Interpretation in the Philosophy of Physics* (New York: Dover, 1957), pp. 65–70 and 78–89. On the quantum mechanical theory of measurement, as it bears on questions of realism and instrumentalism in physics, see H. Margenau, "Measurements and Quantum States", *Philosophy of Science*, XXX (1963), 1–16 and 138–157, and Hilary Putnam, "A Philosopher Looks at Quantum Mechanics" in R. G. Colodny (ed.), *Beyond the Edge of Certainty* (Englewood Cliffs, N. J.: Prentice-Hall, 1965), pp. 75–101. On Berkeley as a precursor of Mach as a scientific phenomenalist, see Chapter 6 of Popper's *Conjectures and Refutations* (New York: Basic Books, 1963).

Very many of P. K. Feyerabend's papers deal with matters relevant to the issue of realism and instrumentalism in physics, but in particular should be mentioned his "Problems of Microphysics" in R. G. Colodny (ed.), *Frontiers of Science and Philosophy* (Pittsburgh: University of Pittsburgh Press, 1962), pp. 189–283, and "Realism and Instrumentalism" in Mario Bunge (ed.), *The Critical Approach to Science and Philosophy* (New York: Free Press, 1964), pp. 280–308. See also J. J. C. Smart, *Philosophy and Scientific Realism* (London: Routledge and Kegan Paul, 1963), Chapter 2; Wilfrid Sellars, *Science, Perception and Reality* (London: Routledge and Kegan Paul, 1963), Chapters 3 and 4; Grover Maxwell, "The Ontological Status of Theoretical Entities", in Herbert Feigl and Grover Maxwell (eds.), *Minnesota Studies in the Philosophy of Science*, Vol. III (Minneapolis: University of Minnesota Press, 1962), pp. 3–27; Marshall Spector, "Models and Theories", *British Journal for the Philosophy of Science*, XVI (1965), 121–142; Marshall Spector, "Theory and Observation", *British Journal for the Philosophy of Science*, XVII (1966), 1–20 and 89–104; R. Harré, *Theories and Things* (New York: Sheed and Ward, 1961); Max Born, "Physical Reality", *Philosophical Quarterly*, III (1953), 139–150; C. F. Presley, "Laws and Theories in the Physical Sciences", *Australasian Journal of Philosophy*, XXXII (1954), 79–103 [reprinted with references omitted in A. Danto and S. Morgenbesser (eds.), *Philosophy of Science* (New York: Meridian Books, 1960), pp. 205–225]; J. B. Thornton, "Scientific Entities", *Australasian Journal of Philosophy*, XXXI (1953), 1–21 and 73–100; and Joseph Agassi, "Sensationalism", *Mind*, LXXV (1966), 1–24. On the historical question of whether Einstein was an operationist or positivist, see Robert

Neidorf, "Is Einstein a Positivist?", *Philosophy of Science*, XXX (1963), 173–188.
An exposition of Craig's theorem, with a discussion of its philosophical relevance, is to be found in Hilary Putnam's paper "Craig's Theorem", *Journal of Philosophy*, LXII (1965), 251–260. A rejoinder to this paper by E. Nagel is on pp. 429–432 of the same volume of the journal, in which Nagel takes issue with Putnam's account of the treatment of Craig's theorem in Nagel's book *The Structure of Science* (New York: Harcourt, Brace and World, 1961), pp. 134–137. Another discussion of Craig's theorem will be found in J. J. C. Smart, *Philosophy and Scientific Realism, op. cit.*, pp. 29–32. On laws of nature in extensional logics and the question of dispositional properties, see H. Reichenbach, *Nomological Statements and Admissible Operations* (Amsterdam: North-Holland, 1954, and New York: Humanities Press, 1954); Wilfrid Sellars, "Counterfactuals, Dispositions and the Causal Modalities" in H. Feigl, M. Scriven and G. Maxwell (eds.), *Minnesota Studies in the Philosophy of Science*, Vol. II (Minneapolis: University of Minnesota Press, 1958), pp. 225–308, and Arthur Pap, "Disposition, Concepts and Extensional Logic", *ibid.*, pp. 196–224; G. Bergmann, "Dispositional Properties", *Philosophical Studies*, VI (1955), 77–80; and "Comments on Professor Hempel's 'The Concept of Cognitive Significance'", *Proceedings of the American Academy of Arts and Sciences*, LXXX (1951), 78–86; W. V. Quine, *Word and Object* (Cambridge: Massachusetts Institute of Technology Press, 1960), especially pp. 222–225; and J. J. C. Smart, "Dispositional Properties", *Analysis*, XXII (1961), 44–46.

6

Induction
and hypothesis

The philosophical problem of induction

In the previous chapter we sometimes remarked that certain theories have been shown to be false, and the thought naturally occurs as to whether we ever have any reasons to suppose that even the best corroborated theories will not one day suffer a like fate. That is, suppose that we test a theory T at n different times (and possibly even in n different ways), and it is never falsified by our observations. Does this really give us any reason whatever, or even a nonzero probability, that no subsequent test will falsify the theory? Have we any reason whatever for supposing that even the *next* test will not falsify the theory? It is clear that we do usually regard well tested theories as probably true, but the theoretical justification of this attitude presents extraordinarily difficult problems. The problem of confirming a theory is a special case of the general question (the traditional problem) of induction: if we have observed n A's and we have observed all of them to be B's, and we have never observed an A which is not a B, does this give us any reason to suppose, or even a nonzero probability, that all *A*'s are *B*'s, or even that the next *A* will be a *B*? (In the special case take the property of being an *A* as the property of being a test of a particular theory, and the property of being a *B* as the property of being a confirming or nonrefuting test of the theory.) These considerations suggest that the traditional problem of induction can not be solved simply by pointing to the fact that science does not consist of generalizations from observations but makes use of the hypothetical-deductive method: the problem simply arises at another level when we generalize from the past success of a theory to its probable truth. Thus even though the terms in which the philosophical problem of induction have usually been discussed (namely by reference to natural history type generalizations, like "All ravens are black") are out of harmony with the picture of science which so far as been drawn in this book, it will not be so much of an irrelevance as might appear at first sight if we begin by discussing the matter in the way in which the problem has emerged from the writings of David Hume.[1]

The problem of induction has traditionally been discussed as arising in the following way. Suppose that we have a number of laws of the form "All *A*'s are *B*'s". Such laws are asserted either because a great number of examined *A*'s have been *B*'s and no examined *A*'s have failed to be *B*'s, or because the laws have been deduced directly or indirectly from laws which have been established directly in the just mentioned way. For example it would be reasonable to suppose that all samples of a certain chemical substance have a spectrum just like that observed in the case of one particular sample, but it is held that our confidence here in extrapolating from a single case rests on the induction that all samples of the same chemical substance show the same sort of spectrum, which will be based on many inductions about what always is observed to happen with many different substances. Ultimately, it will be said, we get back to direct inductions, to propositions of the form "All A's are B's", and these inductions rest on many observations of A's in which we always find them to be B's. To this should be added the qualification that inductions may also be made to laws which are statistical in nature, in which case our inductions are from propositions of the form "m out of n observed A's have been B's" to propositions of the form "The probability of an A being a B is m/n". This probability is usually interpreted as a limiting frequency. In Chapter 2, I have advocated Popper's propensity interpretation of probability. This gets over certain physical and mathematical objections to the notion of a probability as a limiting frequency, but it makes very little difference to the present discussion, since both propositions about propensities and propositions about limiting frequencies are tested in exactly the same way, namely by observations of observed frequencies over a fairly long run. (Unless, of course, they constitute axioms of a theory, in which case they may be tested indirectly by testing the theory. This consideration does not arise in the present context.)

Hume showed conclusively that our belief that all past, present, and future A's are B's can not depend on a valid deductive argument from the fact that all hitherto observed A's have been B's. We can not even deduce the much weaker proposition that the *next* observed A will be a B. His reason is a very simple one: there is no *contradiction* in asserting the proposition "All observed A's are B's but some not yet observed A's are not B's". Similarly there can be no valid deductive argument from observed frequencies ("m/n of observed A's have been B's") to any factual proposition about the frequency of A's among future B's. There is no inconsistency whatever in asserting that m/n of hitherto ob-

177

served A's have been B's and that none, all, or any intermediate proportion you like to mention, of future A's will be B's.

Nor, as Hume also noticed, can the reliability of induction be supported by an inductive argument. Suppose that we have noticed that most inductive arguments in the past have proved reliable. We then argue that most inductive arguments, now and in the future, will be reliable. This last argument, which is an inductive argument about inductive arguments, can be called a "second order" inductive argument. Suppose that its conclusion is stated in the form: the inductive principle is reliable in first order arguments. The argument makes use of a second order inductive principle, which is a *principle* or *rule* of the argument and not a *premise* in it. Hence, as Max Black [2] and R. B. Braithwaite [3] have pointed out, there is no formal *petitio principii*. Nevertheless, anyone who doubted whether first order uses of the inductive principle were justifiable would also be liable to doubt the justifiability of the second order use of the principle. If the past uses of the principle were cases of arguments from "All observed A's have been B's" to "All A's are B's", how could we ever know that past uses of the inductive principle were justifiable or not, since *ex hypothesi* we do not know whether or not the unexamined A's are B's? We must consider, therefore, our second order argument to be concerned with first order arguments of the form: "All hitherto examined A's have been B's; therefore the *next* examined A will be a B". We can indeed verify that in certain cases the inference has been justified by success: the *next* examined A has indeed turned out to be a B. We might then propound the second order argument that since (perhaps) most first order arguments of the form "All A's are B's; therefore the next A will be a B" have been successful, so also the next use of the first order inductive argument will itself be successful. This argument would certainly not be circular in the sense that its conclusion was one of its premises, but it would nevertheless fail to carry conviction to someone who was skeptical of the value of the inductive principle, since he would be just as skeptical of its second order use as of its first order use.

We might add that even if a second order inductive argument for the reliability of inductive arguments in daily life is accepted, there seems to be little prospect of producing an inductive defence of *scientific* inductions, in the sense of arguments for the reliability of well tested theories. For nearly all well tested theories in the past have been shown, later on, to be strictly incorrect. The most that a second order inductive argument could achieve would be the reliability of theories as instruments of prediction in certain types of circumstance. (Thus even though Newton's theory of gravitation is false, it is still quite a useful instrument of prediction for makers of nautical almanacs.) The inductive support of science would therefore seem to be a more attractive policy to the scientific instrumentalist than it would to the realist, since though most scientific theories have not turned out to be strictly true, they have nearly all continued to be useful predictive devices.

Another way in which philosophers have tried to get around Hume's argument is by proposing some factual assumption about the universe which, if it were true, might justify induction. The most famous of these is J. M. Keynes' Principle of Limited Variety.[4] To see how this would work let us first of all replace induction by simple enumeration through eliminative induction. We consider the property of being an A as one member of a finite set of properties $P_1, \ldots P_m, A$, each of which *might* be a sufficient condition of a thing's being a B. It is also supposed that there is no *other* property, outside the set, which could be a sufficient condition of a thing's being a B. Then by finding a P_1, which is not a B, then a P_2 which is not a B, and so on we exhaust all possibilities except A, which enables us to fix on being an A as a

179

sufficient condition of being a B, that is, to assert "all A's are B's". This technique can obviously be extended to deal with necessary conditions too, since "A is a sufficient condition for B" is equivalent to "B is a necessary condition for A".

It is clear that this technique of eliminative induction depends on factual assumptions about the universe. We need to know that the finite set P_1, P_2, . . . P_m, A exhausts all the relevant properties which need to be considered. It might be argued, however, that so long as the set P_1, P_2, . . . P_m, A does not contain a *vanishingly small* proportion of the total of relevant properties, the procedure of eliminating P_1, P_2, . . . P_m gives some nonzero probability that A is a sufficient condition of B. This is roughly J. M. Keynes' approach. He postulates a Principle of Limited Variety which ensures that the set of properties to be eliminated is finite. But once more Hume's dilemma rears its ugly head. The Principle of Limited Variety is clearly a factual assumption about the world, and so it can not be known to be true *a priori*, by pure reasoning. On the other hand it is needed to justify induction, and so it can not itself be justified by inductive argument.

The same difficulty attends other possible principles of inductive reasoning. Thus suppose that it is said to be a "necessity of thought" that the same cause produces the same effect. Actually it is *not* a necessity of thought, since it is rejected in quantum mechanics. This consideration shows that the alleged necessity of thought is an empirical principle, and a refuted one at that (if we believe quantum mechanics to have been established) In order to be established it would have to be established inductively, and in this case it could not be a principle on which all inductive reasoning rests. It might be regarded as a heuristic principle: an injunction to go on looking for causes when no causes have as yet been discovered. If so it is factually vacuous: indeed if quantum mechanics is correct the injunction is one which may in some cases never lead to success.

In response to the Humean dilemma some modern philosophers have taken the line that induction does not *need* to be justified. For example, Paul Edwards, in a well known paper "Bertrand Russell's Doubts about Induction",[5] argues that in science "good reasons" just *means* "good inductive reasons", that is, that ultimately science rests on the principle that if all and only A's have been observed to be B's it is legitimate to take this as *some* reason for asserting "All A's now and in the future are B's". Suppose that a philosopher questions whether scientists have good reasons to think that the future will be like the past in certain relevant respects, for example that if you jump without a balloon or other aid from a high floor of the Empire State building you will, like any one else who has jumped from high buildings in the past, fall rapidly towards the ground. What better reason, Edwards asks, could be given than that this sort of thing has happened in the past? We might point to the theory of gravitation, but this merely brings us back to an extrapolation from past successful predictions of the theory of gravitation to the theory's being successful in the future. The sorts of reasons which scientists *do* give for supposing (in some concrete case) that the future will conform to past experience just *are* what we commonly mean by "good inductive reasons".

Edwards illustrates this point by means of an analogy.[6] Ordinarily the word "physician" is used a bit vaguely: it may for example be taken to mean "person who possesses a medical degree" or it may be taken, perhaps more broadly, as "person who possesses a skill in curing diseases considerably above that of the average layman". However, though it is used a little bit vaguely, it *is* used within well defined limits: for example it would be incorrect to call a skilled bicycle repairer "a physician". Edwards now imagines that someone makes the paradoxical remark that really there are no physicians in New York. Although he believes that he is contradicting received opinion on the matter, it turns out that by "physician" he does not mean something like "person who has a medical degree and who has above-average skill in curing diseases", but that he means "person who has a medical degree and who can cure any conceivable disease in less than two minutes". We might at first take such a person as making a factual claim which disagreed with our own factual claims, but if it turned out that this person would refuse to call a someone "a physician" even if he were to cure all conceivable diseases within a few months, or in any period as long as two minutes or more, then we should see that our interlocutor was merely using the word "physician" in a nonstandard way. Edwards also says that Russell, in saying that we have no reason to suppose that the future will resemble the past, is making no real claim. It is clear, from what he says, that nothing short of a valid deductive argument from the premises to the conclusion will satisfy him, and, as Hume has shown, no such valid deduction is possible. Russell has merely shifted the use of the expression "good reasons" so that what the ordinary scientist calls "good reasons" no longer count as such, just as the person who uses "physician" in the odd way that we explained above, does not allow any of the people *we* would be happy to call "physicians" to count as physicians. Neither this person nor Russell has made a startling claim but has made a mere shift in his use of words.

Such a "dissolution" of the problem of induction looks attractive at first sight, and even at second sight we must concede that it does help to illuminate the problem and to dispel certain confusions which might make us think of the philosophical skeptic about induction, who can be satisfied by *no* empirical considerations, as a kind of ultra-cautious scientist, who can be satisfied by *hardly any* empirical considerations. The ultra-cautious scientist does not even approximate to the position of the philosophical skeptic any more than a large number, 10^{100} say, even approximates to the transfinite number $\aleph_0$. So far so good. Notice, however, that non-scientific methods of predicting the future, or of attempting to obtain truth about the world, could equally well be defended by a linguistic dissolution of the problem of their validity. Thus if we say that good scientific reasons are what scientists ordinarily call good reasons, so, equally, good magical reasons are what magicians ordinarily call good reasons.

Even though we may agree with Edwards, and like-minded post-Wittgensteinian philosophers, that the skeptic about induction who wishes for a deductive justification is asking for the logically impossible, we need not agree that once we have seen this we have to let the matter rest there as a pseudo-problem born of linguistic confusion. Perhaps there is another approach to the problem of justifying induction. This brings us to an important distinction. We may agree that induction can not be "validated"; that it is logically impossible to show that the conclusion of an induction follows logically from the empirical evidence. We might as well give up trying to show this, just as mathematicians have given up trying to square the circle, on account of an algebraic proof of the impossibility of such a task. Nevertheless we can perhaps "vindicate" induction, to use Herbert Feigl's terminology. Feigl,[7] following Hans Reichenbach,[8] points out the possibility of a form of argument whose conclusion is not the proposition "The inductive method of predicting the future works" but rather the weaker proposition "If any method of predicting the future works then induction works". Note that the argument would claim to show not that if any method works then induction is the *best* method, but merely that *if* any method works (and we do not know whether this is so or not) *then* induction is *one* such method. (Or equivalently, by contraposition, to show that 183 if induction does not work then no other method will do so.)

Hume's dilemma does not show that the attempt to vindicate induction is doomed to failure, since a vindicating argument is not designed to show that induction is a successful policy. It is merely meant to show the reasonableness of induction in the sense of being as good a bet as any. The argument is rather like that of Pascal's wager, which is designed not to show that Christianity is true but that it is reasonable to act on the assumption that it is true.[1] If Edwards' argument shows that someone who tries to *validate* induction is in the position of a would-be circle squarer, this will not by itself (in a sense) solve the problem of justifying induction unless we also show the mathematical impossibility of a *vindication* of induction too. If we could show that both validation and vindication of induction is impossible this might be held to solve the problem of induction in the same sort of way that the algebraic proof of the impossibility of squaring the circle by ruler and compass alone was taken as disposing of this problem. Jerrold J. Katz has recently pursued this line of thought.[12] But even if the possibility of a vindication of induction could be disposed of in this way, one might still wonder whether there might turn out to be something which could be regarded as a justification but which was neither a proof of validity, nor a proof of vindication. It might be a kind of justification which no one has thought of yet. After all, it was only comparatively recently that the idea of vindication was put forward. How can we be sure that the whole question of justifying induction may not be given a completely new twist one of these days? This is always at least a possibility to be borne in mind, since the question is not one which can

[1]I do not wish, of course, to defend Pascal's argument, which is fallacious. See Antony Flew, "Is Pascal's Wager the Only Safe Bet?"[9] and James Cargile, "Pascal's Wager".[10] For differences between Pascal's Wager and the attempt to vindicate induction, see a paper by Isabel Creed.[11]

be precisely formulated, as was the case with the problem of squaring the circle.

In order to assess the possibility of vindicating induction, it will be convenient to make the discussion concrete by having a look at some of the arguments of Wesley Salmon, who has been one of the strongest supporters of the idea of vindicating induction.[13] He has put the matter in the following form. Consider a sequence of events of a certain sort, and let us suppose that we have observed that a proportion f_n of the first n of these events possesses a certain property. Our problem is to discover what is the proportion to which f_n tends as n tends to infinity. If we adopt the usual inductive policy we shall conjecture that $\lim_{n \to \infty} f_n = f_n$. This is the so-called "straight" rule, and it is a "convergent" rule. Other "convergent" rules are of the form: If f_n is the observed frequency for n observed events, conjecture that $\lim_{n \to \infty} f_n = f_n + c_n$, where c_n is some specified function of n (other than the function $c_n = 0$) such that $c_n \to 0$ as $n \to \infty$. Such rules are called "crooked" rules. If we assume that the purpose of induction is to obtain limiting frequencies (which can of course be questioned) then we can show that the policy of adopting any of the above convergent rules can be vindicated, at least as a policy for immortal beings, for we can show that if a limiting frequency exists, the adoption of such a convergent rule, whether straight or crooked, will lead us eventually to get within any preassigned interval (however small) which surrounds this limiting frequency.

It is easy to see the superiority of any of these convergent rules as against certain other rules. Consider for example the "counter-inductive" policy of supposing that $f_n \to \dfrac{n - m}{n}$ (where as before m is the number of positive instances in n observations). People often *do* think rather nearly in accordance with this rule. If I toss pennies against someone and win the first four tosses my opponent may be confident of winning on the fifth occasion. (In Australia some sports writers have seemed to think in this way, when predicting the outcome of the toss for choice of first innings in cricket matches, which is so important in this game.) It is true that people who make such counter-inductive predictions do not actually follow the counter-inductive rule, but argue rather from a confused idea of "luck evens out". Actually, of course, if we are tossing a well balanced penny, then the probability of my winning on the fifth throw is one half, whatever may have happened in previous tosses, but of course if we do not know that the pennies are well balanced, and if the outcome of previous tosses constitutes all our evidence, the evidence of four successive "heads" turning up suggests, according to the usual inductive policies, that the penny is unbalanced and that we are more likely than not to get "heads" on the fifth occasion too. The superiority of the inductive policy to the counter-inductive one can be seen as follows. If the sequence (f_n) has a limit l then following the inductive policy will enable us eventually to get nearer and nearer to it, whereas the counter-inductive policy will get us arbitrarily near to a different value, namely $1 - l$. Another difficulty with the counter-inductive policy is that it can lead to contradiction in the following way. Suppose that we repeatedly throw a well balanced die. The ordinary inductive rule would of course lead us to the value $\frac{1}{6}$ as the limiting frequency of one particular face of it (say, a "two") turning up. The counter-inductive rule would lead us to postulate $\frac{5}{6}$ as the limiting frequency of this face turning up. Now since there are six faces, and the limiting frequencies postulated for each of them would be the same, namely $\frac{5}{6}$, we should have to assert that the frequency for any one of the six faces turning up would be $6 \times \frac{5}{6} = 5$. This is absurd, since no meaning can be given to a frequency greater than one. In any case it is a matter of pure logic that the frequency of throws in which one or the other face comes up is equal to one. (We can take it that freak throws in which the die lands in a crack in the floor, say, and balances on one edge or on one corner do not count as legitimate throws.)

Now consider the following non-inductive convergent rule, which does not lead to contradiction in the way which was described in the previous paragraph. Suppose that we distinguish six possible outcomes of the operation of tossing a die, and as a result we conjecture a limiting frequency of $\frac{1}{6}$ for each of the possible outcomes (a "one", a "two", a "three", and so on). Salmon calls this the "*a priori*" rule. It is clear that this rule is convergent (to $\frac{1}{6}$) but that it does not converge to the actual limiting frequency except in the case of a well made die. An interesting rule which can be shown to give convergence to the limiting frequency, if this exists, in all cases, is to assign a frequency $\dfrac{1}{n+1} \cdot \left(m + \dfrac{1}{k}\right)$ where k is the number of logically possible alternatives (e.g., 6 in the case of the throw of a die). Notice that for $n = 0$, that is, prior to all experience, it assigns the value $\dfrac{1}{k}$, as with the *a priori* rule. This rule is a compromise between the *a priori* rule and the straight inductive rule. Indeed it is one of the crooked rules, since it is of the form "assign $f_n + c_n$ as the limiting frequency" where $c_n \to 0$ as $n \to \infty$. The expression $\dfrac{1}{n+1} \cdot \left(m + \dfrac{1}{k}\right)$ can be written in the form

$$\frac{m}{n} + \frac{n - mk}{kn(n+1)} \text{ and } \frac{n - mk}{kn(n+1)} \to 0 \text{ as } n \to \infty.$$

Assuming that all the above remarks are in order, Salmon's residual problem is to justify the use of the rule which assigns f_n (the straight rule) instead of the infinity of crooked rules which assign $f_n + c_n$ where $c_n \to 0$ as $n \to \infty$. It turns out that all the assignments of functions c_n of the crooked rules have the property of being language dependent. For example the compromise rule of the previous paragraph depends on the number of alternative possibilities k. But suppose we had a language which just distinguished three faces on the die, so that "a 'one' or a 'two'", "a 'three' or a 'four'", "a 'five' or a 'six'" corresponded to ultimate predicates of this language. Speakers of this language would distinguish not six but three possible outcomes of a throw of the die, and we would have $k = 3$, not 6 as before. Salmon uses the criterion of linguistic invariance to rule out all functions c_n except that for which c_n is always equal to zero. However Stephen Barker[14] has objected that even the rule of induction (for which $c_n = 0$) violates the requirement of linguistic invariance. Here he brings up the case of the Goodman[15] predicates "grue" and "bleen". (See p. 62 above.) It will be recalled that we could define "grue" as meaning "green prior to A.D. 2000 and blue thereafter" and "bleen" as meaning "blue prior to A.D. 2000 and green thereafter". Then up to now all emeralds have been both green and bleen, and so Salmon's rule justifies the induction to "all emeralds are bleen" every bit as much as to "all emeralds are green".[2] As we have already noted (p. 62) it will not do to deny that the predicates "grue" and "bleen" are not proper scientific predicates because their definitions mention the specific date A.D. 2000. It can be said that "grue" and "bleen" could be regarded as the undefined predicates, in which case "blue" defined as "bleen until A.D. 2000 and grue thereafter", and "green", defined as "grue until A.D. 2000 and bleen thereafter", would be the ones whose definition involved a specific time reference. Salmon therefore suggests a further restriction, which is that the basic predi-

[2] Strictly speaking Salmon's rule can not justify an inference to a universal conclusion, since a few A's could be B's and the frequency of B's among the A's still tend to 1 as the number of A's tends to infinity. However this does not matter, since we can either give up asserting "All A's are B's" and say simply that the limiting frequency of B's among the A's is 1, or else modify the rule by specifying that a universal conclusion can be drawn only if *no* A's have been observed to have been B's.

cates of a scientific language must be "purely ostensive" predicates, i.e., predicates which can be defined ostensively and such that the similarity between their instances lies open to direct inspection.

This reply to the Goodman paradox will not do for those who accept the general standpoint of this book, according to which there is no basic observation language, and according to which observation sentences can not be distinguished from nonobservation sentences just by looking at their vocabularies. Indeed from the standpoint of this book the appeal to scientific inductive practice by means of vindicating the method of induction by simple enumeration seems artificial from the first, unless perhaps it is applied to the metatheory of science, i.e., to arguing from the past predictive success of well tested theories to the future predictive success of well tested theories. (It is hard to see how it could be used to argue for the *truth,* as opposed to the general predictive success of theories, since nearly all theories in the past have turned out strictly speaking to be false.) However Salmon's attempt is still of great interest, because it provides an example of a serious and carefully thought out attempt to vindicate induction: it shows the sort of thing one has in mind when one talks of an attempt to *vindicate* induction, in the face of Hume's proof of the impossibility of *validating* it. Indeed Salmon has shown a way of progressing beyond Hume's position which would probably have been very attractive to Hume himself, if he could have known of it, since Hume did himself believe that science rests ultimately on induction by simple enumeration and he did think that there was a set of basic predicates which could be defined only ostensively.[3]

[3]This reliance on ostension suggests that Salmon here believes that one can single out a special set of observation predicates. Even if this is so, he certainly rejects this in a more recent paper,[16] which I was able to see only when it was too late to discuss it in the present volume. In more important respects this paper shows that Salmon has modified his views, partly in response to criticism by Ian Hacking.[17]

Having observed some of the details of an important attempt to vindicate induction, let us stand back and consider the idea of vindication more generally. Consider any policy *P* for attaining a certain type of result *R*. We may not be able to show that *P* works, i.e., that it does attain *R*, but we may be able to show that if *P* does not attain *R* then no other policy does either. In which case, hoping for the best, we may judge it sensible to adopt *P*. Applying this to science, Salmon has taken *R* to be the prediction of limiting frequencies, over infinite sequences of events. But we are not immortals, and we can not apply the inductive method for more than a certain limited time span. To prove that if any method works *eventually* then induction does is by no means to prove that if any method works within a certain fixed time span (say 100 years) then induction does.[18] It is true that Salmon has considered the problem of "The Short Run" in a paper of that title,[19] but here he is concerned simply with the problem of predicting short run frequencies, whereas our present problem is a different one: that of predicting long run frequencies when we have only short run frequencies to go on.

Perhaps we can be more successful if we attempt to vindicate something other than induction by simple enumeration. After all, if we look at actual scientific practice we do not find scientists involved in conjecturing limiting frequencies on the basis of observed short run frequencies. Salmon is of course quite aware of this: he justifies his own approach as a useful "idealization".

Let us look at actual scientific inductive practice. As Brian Ellis has remarked in a very interesting article,[20] even though we had never tossed a die before, if we tossed a homogeneous and symmetrical die 100 times and got 55 "heads" we should not expect the frequency after many further trials to approach 0.55. We should put the discrepancy of 0.05 down to chance, and predict a frequency of 0.50. To do otherwise would be to conflict with well established theories of geometry and mechanics. In practice, therefore, our predictions are "theory involved", and we never find ourselves applying the straight rule, except possibly in the light of theoretical considerations with which we can see that it does not conflict. Even such a generalization of natural history as "All ravens are black" is not the result of simple induction from "All observed ravens are black", but depends on background assumptions about the inheritance of characteristics in animal species, and of consequent similarities of bird coloring within a single species. This is where Salmon's remarks about his system being based on an "idealization" may come in. Developed science, it might be said, depends on a concatenation of applications of the straight rule. Ellis replies that if science were a matter of applying the straight rule, then the making of scientific hypotheses would be a purely mechanical business and could be done by computers, whereas experience suggests that it requires noneffective[4] methods, depending on imagination and guesswork. I am not sure that his argument here is formally cogent, since a method which depends on a concatenation of effective procedures need not be effective if there is no effective rule for deciding in what order these effective procedures are to be applied. However, even so, the making of scientific hypotheses certainly does not look in the least like a concatenation of applications of the straight rule of induction, if only because it involves the invention of new concepts.

Ellis' view that theoretical involvement is a necessary condition for scientific induction enables him to give a simple answer to the Goodman paradox. Most of us would reject the use of the predicates "grue" and "bleen" because our theories do not lead us to suppose that there is anything specially significant about Janu-

[4] In the technical sense of mathematical logic. In the ordinary sense, of course, science is quite effective! In the technical sense, to say that scientific procedures are effective would be to say that they can be applied moronically, like a decision procedure in logic.

ary 1st A.D. 2000, and moreover if all emeralds *did* change from green to blue and vice-versa on that date this would be contrary to our present theories of optics and of physical chemistry. This idea of universal theoretical involvement is in harmony with the position taken in this book, and with K. R. Popper's idea that before any hypothesis is invented there must be some earlier hypothesis, because observation always presupposes some hypothesis in the light of which it is made. Popper[21] has compared the question "Which comes first, hypothesis or observation?" to the question, "Which comes first, the hen or the egg?" The answer to the latter is "an earlier egg" and to the former is "An earlier kind of hypothesis". Popper has argued that even much animal psychology is best understood as a matter of rudimentary hypothesis forming rather than as a matter of conditioned reflex learning (which corresponds to induction by simple enumeration).

In essence, and without doing full justice to the complexities with which it is worked out, Ellis' argument seems to come to this: scientific prediction requires theoretical involvement, and so there is no better way than to use existing theories, or, should these theories be shown by further observation to lead to incorrect predictions, to then use new theories which can be shown to be at least as successful as the old ones have been. Now it does seem to me that Ellis has given a good reason for theoretically involved prediction, rather than recourse to Salmon's straight rule. Nevertheless, it also seems that he has done nothing to justify scientific method against a radical skeptic: one who wishes to know why scientific methods should *continue* to be successful, and why, from midnight tonight onwards, say, witchcraft or soothsaying should not be better. It is true that if witchcraft or soothsaying did begin to be predictively superior to science, there would be great difficulties, on the basis of existing scientific theories, in explaining why things suddenly began to behave so differently. But this consideration could surely not be expected to carry any weight with someone who already was prepared to consider the possibility that quite nonscientific methods should have superior predictive efficacy.

A further consideration is this. We have noted that vindication is always relative to an aim or intended result. Ellis, in common with Salmon, assumes that this is *prediction*, though he does go on at the end of the paper to deal with the fundamental question of the acceptance of theories. He makes the point that it would be irrational to accept or reject any theory solely on the basis of what *might* happen. (But the skeptic about induction will question this: he will *reject* or at least *refuse to accept* theories because of his worry that contrary instances might happen.) Then if experience has caused us to reject a theory T_1 (e.g., the caloric theory) whereas another theory T_2 (e.g., the kinetic theory of heat) *can* still be accepted, and there is as yet no other theory which has been proposed which can be accepted, Ellis holds that it must be rational to accept T_2. This suggests a policy similar to that which has been proposed by Hilary Putnam.[22]

Putnam's account involves an oversimplification of actual scientific practice, but it comes nearer to real science than does the sort of view of science suggested by Reichenbach's and Salmon's discussions. Putnam's idea comes to this. We consider only "effective" hypothesis. Slightly simplified, Putnam's method is the following. Suppose that M is a property of a certain class of individuals. Then "an effective hypothesis on M" is one from which we can calculate in a routine way whether or not an individual has the property M. Let the hypotheses on M which survive at a time t be called "the alternatives". (If during the tests of the alternatives at any particular time t_0, further hypotheses on M are suggested, these are added to the set of alternatives.) We calculate whether or not the next observed individual has the property M. We keep the alternatives which predict the result (M or not M as the case may be) and reject those which predict the contrary result. We continue until all alternatives but one have failed or until all have. If exactly one remains then we accept it as true.

Notice that we may be wrong in accepting the one remaining hypothesis as true. Further tests may lead us to reject it also. Nevertheless the method has the following desirable property: if we make a hypothesis which is both effective and true, then the method will lead us to accept the hypothesis if it is true.[5] Putnam's idea does seem to constitute a partial vindication of induction, since it is presumably impossible for the proponent of quite nonscientific methods (which will presumably not involve the observational tests of hypothesis) to prove that *his* methods have any comparable property. Nevertheless it does not constitute a full vindication of induction, in that it does not enable us to prove that if any method whatever succeeds in enabling us to find true hypothesis, this method will. We have no assurance that we will ever think of the true hypothesis on M, and we have no assurance that we shall be able to settle on the true hypothesis in a reasonable time, even on the conditional assumption that some method or other will enable us to do these things. Obviously it would not do if the observation which was to eliminate an alternative will occur only after millions of years. In remarking that Putnam's method does not show us how fully to vindi-

[5]In the case of statistical hypotheses on M, a rejected hypothesis can be reinstated. If we got a run of 550 "heads" from 1000 trials of tossing a penny, we might reject the hypothesis that the frequency is $\frac{1}{2}$ as "too improbable". But 5001 "heads" out of the next 10,000 would lead us to reject our previous rejection. Nevertheless I think that Putnam's method would work for probabilistic hypotheses as well as for nonprobabilistic ones, in the sense that *if* the true hypothesis were ever produced it would be retained. (On conditional rules of rejection for frequency hypotheses, see R. B. Braithwaite, *Scientific Explanation*, Chapter 6 [23].)

cate induction, I am not however putting this forward as a criticism of Putnam's paper, since his method is thrown out in the course of a discussion in which he is concerned about other things.

In any case, hypotheses in real science are not always effective. (Remember that Putnam himself claimed to be suggesting only a simplification of scientific method.) Apart from the fact that there is in general no assurance that we will ever discover a proof of a provable theorem in a physical theory (though this sort of noneffectiveness is not in practice very important) there is no assurance that the presence of an apparent case of not-M can be taken as refuting even a nonprobabilistic hypothesis on M. This is because, as Pierre Duhem pointed out,[24] in science a theory can be saved in the face of apparent refutation by means of a change in some auxiliary hypothesis. That is, when we test a hypothesis H by investigating some observational consequence O, the situation usually is that O does not follow from H alone, but from H together with certain auxiliary assumptions A. In planetary astronomy for example, H may be Newtonian mechanics, while A will contain statements of "initial conditions" (previously observed positions of the planets), and also statements of optics, since it is by optical means that planetary positions are found. Thus if we find a planet in a position where according to our theory of mechanics it should not be, it is formally possible to retain the laws of mechanics and reject our optical assumptions and to explain the discrepancy by postulating some optical effect involving the bending of the light rays from that planet. Of course this would not be done, but it requires tact and expertise to know whether or not to reject auxiliary hypotheses, and this feature of science prevents actual hypotheses from being "effective". On the other hand, as Ellis has pointed out, [25] continual abandonment of auxiliary hypotheses would lead to intolerable complications in practice, and it is often not too far off the mark to regard scientific hypotheses as if they were effective in Putnam's sense.

Putnam's method, described above, is pretty well a formalization of scientific method as described by K. R. Popper. Popper, however, seems to regard any attempt to justify induction as misguided.[26] In fact he regards induction as a myth. If "induction" here means the inductive inference of the logic books, perhaps he is right, but if "induction" means predicting the future on the basis of the past, by means of scientific theories, it is clearly not a myth but something we do all the time. I shall therefore continue to avail myself of the concepts of "induction" and "inductive procedure" in discussing Popper's views. Popper in effect holds that if we change our aim from that of the inductivists, who wish to justify inductive procedures, to another one, namely *criticism*, it is clear that if false hypotheses are refutable by suitable experiences, then scientific method can be vindicated by means of considerations of deductive logic alone. In fact one might say that it can even be validated, since the falsity of a hypothesis can be deduced from a suitable observation simply by *modus tollens*, that is, an argument of the form "$H \supset O$ and $\sim O$; therefore $\sim H$".

Popper rejects the theories of confirmation given by Carnap [27] and like-minded philosophers. This is not surprising, since on such theories of confirmation the confirmation of a universal law h by evidence e is given by $c(h, e) = 0$. For example, suppose that h is "All A's are B's" and suppose that $c(h, e)$ is taken to be the ratio of the number of already observed A's to the number of all possible A's. If we take it that the number of all possible A's is infinite, then $c(h, e) = 0$. Carnap has a more complicated and subtle definition for $c(h, e)$ but it still gives the value 0 when h is a universal hypothesis. Carnap gets over this difficulty by introducing the notion of "instance confirmation". The instance confirmation of a hypothesis h is the confirmation of the hypothesis that the *next* observed instance of the phenomenon in question will be in conformity with h. Carnap's confirmation theory can give a nonzero value to the instance confirmation of a universal hypothesis even when the value of the confirmation function is itself zero. We can then say that the confirmation of a law is to be taken as its instance confirmation.

However this resort to instance confirmation seems to presuppose an instrumentalist or positivist philosophy of science. If a theory is regarded merely as a useful prediction tool, then instance confirmation will be what is of value to us. If we are interested mainly in understanding the universe, then the case would appear to be otherwise, since it is possible for a false hypothesis to have high instance confirmation. Consider a law "All A's are B's" and let us suppose that up to a hundred million years hence there are no A's which are not B's, but that after a hundred million years hence there are some A's which are not B's. Let us suppose that the instance confirmation of the hypothesis is high, as on the assumption it probably would be. A pragmatist would not really need to know any more, since high instance confirmation could lead him to false expectations only a hundred million years hence, and he is unlikely to be around at that remote date in the future. The realist, however, will not be satisfied, since he will want to know whether *all* A's are B's, even including ones which are remote from us in space and time. It should also be noted, as a serious criticism of Carnap's confirmation theory, that it can be applied only to rather simple languages, which are not rich enough to express actual science.

Now Popper also wishes to hold that the confirmation[6] of h given e is zero when h is a universal hypothesis. Nevertheless he wishes to hold that some hypotheses

---

[6]Confirmation is a metalinguistic notion. It is closely related to the metalinguistic concept of probability. (See Chapter 2, p. 41.)

are better *corroborated* than others, and by "corroboration" he does not mean "confirmation" in the sense of
"making more probable". (Neither does Carnap, by the
way, wish to identify his "confirmation" with "making
more probable", since if *h* is a universal law no amount
of evidence *e* will make c(*h*, *e*) other than zero. For
Carnap it is *instance* confirmation which can be made
greater by further evidence.) Popper wishes to hold
that one hypothesis may be better corroborated than
another even though their probabilities are both zero.
That is, the one hypothesis may have been put to *more
severe tests* than the other. The severity of a test is a
concept that can not be formalized: it is not just a matter
of the mere number of tests of a hypothesis. It involves
the notion of the *sincerity* of the experimenter or observer and of his theoretical colleagues who ask him to
perform certain observations: they must be actively and
sincerely trying to test the theory in those circumstances
in which they judge it least likely to succeed, as well as
in those cases in which success is expected. They must
be trying to find refutations of the hypothesis, not just
"verifications" or "confirmations"[7] of it. Corroboration
is unlike confirmation in that the more improbable a
hypothesis is the better it can be corroborated. In other
words, to survive a difficult test is worth more than to
survive an easy one. Popper has suggested that certain
psychoanalytic hypotheses can be corroborated very
little (if at all) because it is difficult or perhaps impossible to devise experiments or observations which, if they
turned out in a certain way, would be regarded by the
psychoanalyst as refuting his theory.[28] Physical theories are usually highly corroborated: they stick their
neck out a long way, so to speak, and it is often possible
for the physicist to specify some antecedently surprising
results which can be checked experimentally. Popper
gives the example of Einstein's general theory of rela-

[7]I put these words in shutter quotes, because of course according to Popper
there can not really be a verification or confirmation of a scientific hypothesis.

tivity, which predicted a bending of a light ray from a distant star, as the ray passed close to the sun. These predictions were tested during the eclipse of 1917 in expeditions to Sobral, Brazil, by A. C. D. Crommelin and C. Davidson, and to Principe, in the Gulf of Guinea, by A. S. Eddington and E. T. Cottingham. (Special relativity also predicts a bending, but only half that of general relativity.) Einstein's theory took a *risk* in predicting this effect, since if the effect had been absent Einstein would have had to abandon the general theory of relativity. Perhaps Popper has not chosen the best example here, in view of the considerable difficulties in evaluating the tests of general relativity (both those mentioned above and others, such as that of the advance of the perihelion of Mercury, which is predicted by the theory). In fact it is the difficulty of testing the general theory of relativity (hitherto at least) which has caused it to be regarded as rather a speculative or metaphysical theory unlike Einstein's special theory of relativity, of which there are abundant tests, both optical and dynamical (such as the observations of collisions among, and trajectories of, fast particles).

It might be asked how Popper can talk, as he does, of the *more improbable* hypothesis being corroborated by a successful test, if all universal hypotheses have the same (zero) probability. The answer is that Popper has a theory of *fine structure* of probability,[29] so that if a hypothesis h_2 is deducible from another hypothesis h_1, but h_1 is not deducible from h_2, we can then say that h_1 is more probable than h_2, even though $c(h_1, e) = c(h_2, e) = 0$.

The question remains, nevertheless, why we should be interested in testing (and perhaps corroborating) theories, if we can not justify the ascription of a probability greater than zero to even the best corroborated theory. One answer which Popper has given is the following. If a theory h_1 is better corroborated than h_2, in that it has survived all the tests to which h_2 has been subjected and also some tests which h_2 has failed, then it is a *stronger* theory than the h_2. Hence the strengthening and continual testing of our theories always leads to more observational truths. Indeed even if we devise a new test which falsifies our present theories, the outcome of this experiment increases our knowledge of what happens in various circumstances.[30] This certainly is a good justification for seeking corroborations, but only from an instrumentalist point of view, which is fundamentally as unacceptable to Popper as it is to me. If we are not much interested in observational consequences, save insofar as they are tests of theories, then do we not need some justification of corroboration in terms of the truth, or at least the probability, of theories? It would seem, therefore, that Popper has not dispelled the apparent necessity for a vindication of induction on the general lines of the attempts discussed earlier in this chapter.

Duhem's objection to the asymmetry between confirmation and refutation

Popper's philosophy of science leans heavily on an asymmetry between verification and refutation. No observed consequence of a theory can verify the theory, since this would commit the logical fallacy of arguing from $A \supset B$ and B to A. On the other hand refutation of a theory is possible, since the argument from $A \supset B$ and $\sim B$ to $\sim A$ is valid. We noted on p. 195 above, however, that Duhem has in effect contested this asymmetry, since he held that in the face of apparently refuting evidence, a theory can be saved by rejecting certain auxiliary assumptions. If H is a theory and O an "observational consequence", O does not follow from H alone, but from $H \cdot A$ where A are certain assumptions extraneous to H itself. Then, so far as logic is concerned, in the face of $\sim O$ we have the choice of rejecting H or of rejecting A. Thus when the planet Uranus was observed to deviate from the orbit calculated from Newtonian mechanics, taking into account the perturbations due to the then known planets, this was not taken as a refutation of Newtonian mechanics. The auxiliary assumptions A (including data about the perturbing bodies in the solar system) were modified by J. C. Adams and U. J. J. Leverrier (independently) to include the supposition of the existence of an as yet unknown planet with an orbit exterior to Uranus. They then predicted the position of this planet, which was subsequently observed to exist.

Popper's answer here is that all our assumptions can be challenged, but that we cannot challenge them all at the same time. We can test H, assuming A to be unproblematic, but at another time we can test A. This will involve auxiliary assumptions B, which can themselves be challenged with the aid of auxiliary assumptions C, which can themselves be challenged, and so on. In fact for Popper these considerations in a way confirm his fallibilist position. Everything in science is risky, even the acceptance of a set of background assumptions (and this also includes acceptance of the deliverances of our memory and of our sense perception).

Adolf Grünbaum has pointed out[31] that the schema $(H \bullet A) \supset O, \sim O, \therefore H \lor \sim A$, is of interest only if it is possible to think of some nontrivial hypothesis A' which implies $\sim A$. Otherwise it will not be possible for us to modify our auxiliary hypothesis in a suitable way. It is not obvious that any such nontrivial alternative exists. (A *trivial* A' can of course always be found. Thus $H \supset \sim O$ would do since $[(H \bullet H \supset \sim O) \supset \sim O]$ is true.) For example consider the case of the advance of the perihelion of Mercury, which could not be explained by Newtonian mechanics plus the usual background assumptions. At one time it was proposed to save Newtonian mechanics by means of the postulation of a planet (which was even tentatively named "Vulcan") in between Mercury and the Sun. However it was shown that such a hypothesis would not work. In this case, therefore, it is not obvious that a nontrivial modification of the auxiliary assumptions, which would save Newtonian mechanics, is possible. (I am oversimplifying the case, and neglecting certain difficulties which exist in evaluating the significance of the observational data. On the whole, however it would appear that *probably* the data can not be explained away by assumptions in accordance with Newtonian mechanics.) Grünbaum even argues that he can show a case in which it is not even *logically* possible that there should be such an A'. If the notion of "logically possible" meant simply "not contradicting the laws of classical logic" it would be a clear enough notion, but in fact Grünbaum requires for his argument a distinction between fact and convention in geometry which would probably be rejected by most defenders of the Duhemian position, for example W. V. Quine, against whom Grünbaum is specifically arguing.

Conclusion

It would appear that scientific method, even as a means of prediction, does require vindication, if not validation. Of course if proofs, such as those suggested by Katz, of the mathematical impossibility of this were accepted, we should have to give up the search. Nevertheless, would we not feel certain dissatisfaction, which would *not* be felt by the man who sees the mathematical impossibility of squaring the circle? We can get on in life without squaring the circle, but we can not get on in practice without science as a means of prediction and some of us can not be happy without science as a means of attaining truth about the world. Mere rejection of falsehoods does not seem as satisfying to some of us as it does to Popper, and we would like some account of the way in which successive scientific theories, even though they in turn have to be rejected, not only become more successful as a means of prediction, but somehow give us a "more correct picture of reality". We seem far from this. With some relief then, let us now turn from these skeptical doubts and metaphysical worries, and accepting, whether justifiably or not, the general truth of present day theories, let us see whether science can aid us in discussing some of the problems which have exercised philosophers.

SUGGESTIONS FOR FURTHER READING

Good philosophical introductions to the problem of induction are G. H. von Wright, *The Logical Problem of Induction*, second revised edition (Oxford: Blackwell, 1957, and New York: Barnes and Noble, 1965); William Kneale, *Probability and Induction* (Oxford: Oxford University Press, 1949); and Stephen Barker, *Induction and Hypothesis: a Study of the Logic of Confirmation* (Ithaca, N. Y.: Cornell University Press, 1957). In his *Treatise on Probability and Induction* (London: Routledge and Kegan Paul, 1951), von Wright is more concerned with formal logical analysis than in his other work mentioned above. A view of some current points of view can be got from the symposium edited by Henry E. Kyburg, Jr., and Ernest Nagel, *Induction: Some Current Issues* (Middletown, Conn.: Wesleyan University Press, 1963). A most useful survey of work in inductive logic since 1951 is given by Henry E. Kyburg, Jr., "Recent Work in Inductive Logic", *American Philosophical Quarterly*, I (1964), 249–287. It includes a detailed bibliography which is a useful supplement to the bibliography in von Wright's *The Logical Problem of Induction, op. cit.*, which includes a good listing of earlier work on the subject. A useful selected bibliography on induction is to be found on pp. 167–171 of Paul Edwards and Arthur Pap (eds.), *A Modern Introduction to Philosophy*, revised edition (New York: Free Press, 1965). Some criticisms of details in Kneale's book (*op. cit.*) are made by Jonathan Bennett, "Some Aspects of Probability and Induction" I and II, *British Journal for the Philosophy of Science*, VII (1956–57), 220–230 and 316–322.

For the view that induction requires a limitation of the variety of nature, see C. D. Broad, "On the Relation between Induction and Probability", *Mind*, XXVII (1918), 389–404 and XXIX (1920), 11–45, and J. M. Keynes, *Treatise on Probability and Induction* (London: Macmillan, 1921 and paperback, New York: Harper and Row, 1962). Other metaphysical postulates to justify induction are suggested by Bertrand Russell in his *Human Knowledge* (New York: Simon and Schuster, 1948, and paperback, 1962).

Between science and philosophy

On vindication of induction, see H. Reichenbach, "On the Justification of Induction", *Journal of Philosophy*, XXXVII (1940), 97–103, and *Experience and Prediction* (Chicago: University of Chicago Press, 1938), pp. 348–363; H. Feigl, "De Principiis Non Disputandum . . . ?", in Max Black (ed.), *Philosophical Analysis* (Englewood Cliffs, N. J.: Prentice-Hall, 1950), pp. 119–156, and "On the Vindication of Induction", *Philosophy of Science*, XXVIII (1961), 212–216; many papers by Wesley Salmon, especially "Inductive Inference" in Bernard Baumrin (ed.), *Philosophy of Science, The Delaware Seminar*, Vol. 2 (New York: Interscience, 1963), pp. 341–370, and "The Foundations of Scientific Inference" in R. G. Colodny (ed.), *Mind and Cosmos* (Pittsburgh: University of Pittsburgh Press, 1966), pp. 135–275. In this latter paper, Salmon acknowledges a criticism by Ian Hacking of his attempts to vindicate the straight rule. See Ian Hacking, "Salmon's Vindication of Induction", *Journal of Philosophy*, LXII (1965), 260–266, which is written largely from the point of view of mathematical statistics. A discussion of Hacking's paper is given by I. Levi, "Hacking Salmon on Induction", *ibid.*, 481–487. A rather different approach to the vindication of induction is to be found in Brian Ellis, "A Vindication of Scientific Inductive Practices", *American Philosophical Quarterly*, II (1965), 296–304.

J. J. Katz, *The Problem of Induction and Its Solution* (Chicago: University of Chicago Press, 1962), argues that the problem of induction can be dissolved by showing that a justification of induction, whether by validation or vindication, is mathematically impossible. Arguments to the effect that the so-called problem of induction is a pseudo-problem, to be dispelled by "linguistic" or "conceptual" analysis, are to be found in a number of chapters of Max Black's *Language and Philosophy* (Ithaca, N. Y.: Cornell University Press, 1954), and *Models and Metaphors* (Ithaca, N. Y.: Cornell University Press, 1962). In the same philosophical tradition are Paul Edwards' "Bertrand Russell's Doubts About Induction" in A. Flew (ed.), *Logic and Language,* First Series (Oxford: Blackwell, 1951, and paperback, New York: Doubleday Anchor Books, 1965), pp. 55–79, and Chapter 9 of P. F. Strawson's *Introduction to Logical Theory* (New York: Wiley, 1952, and paperback, New York: Barnes and Noble, 1952). J. O. Urmson, "Some Questions concerning Validity", in A. Flew (ed.), *Essays in Conceptual Analysis* (London: Macmillan, 1956, and New York: St. Martin's Press, 1956), pp. 120–133, is both sympathetic to and critical of the attempted dissolution of the problem by linguistic analysis of the above-mentioned sort. See also F. I. Will, "Will the Future be like the Past", in A. Flew (ed.), *Logic and Language,* Second Series (Oxford: Blackwell, 1953, and paperback, New York: Doubleday Anchor Books, 1965), pp. 32–50, with criticism by D. Williams, "Induction and the Future", *Mind*, LVII (1948), 226–229. David Hume's "Sceptical Doubt concerning the Human Understanding", which is Section IV of his *Inquiry Concerning Human Understanding* (first published in 1748), is discussed from the point of view of modern analytic philosophy in Chapter 4 of A. Flew's book, *Hume's Philosophy of Belief* (London: Routledge and Kegan Paul, 1961, and New York: Humanities Press, 1961).

204

A priori justifications of induction are attempted by Donald C. Williams, *The Ground of Induction* (Cambridge: Harvard University Press, 1947), and Roy Harrod, *The Foundations of Inductive Logic* (New York: Harcourt, Brace and World, 1956).

For Rudolf Carnap's philosophy of induction see especially his *Logical Foundations of Probability*, second edition (Chicago: University of Chicago Press, 1962), as well as pp. 966–979 of his "Replies and Expositions" in P. A. Schilpp (ed.), *The Philosophy of Rudolf Carnap* (La Salle, Ill.: Open Court, 1963). This last volume also contains valuable essays by J. G. Kemeny, A. W. Burks, H. Putnam and E. Nagel on various aspects of Carnap's work on inductive logic, and replies by Carnap. See also G. H. von Wright, "Carnap's Theory of Probability", *Philosophical Review*, LX (1951), 362–374. For K. R. Popper's views, see his *Logic of Scientific Discovery* (London: Routledge and Kegan Paul, 1959, and paperback, rev. ed., New York: Harper and Row, 1965) and his *Conjectures and Refutations* (London: Routledge and Kegan Paul, 1963, and New York: Basic Books, 1963), especially Chapter 1. On the interpretation and criticism of Popper there is a lively interchange between D. C. Stove (criticizing Popper) and J. W. N. Watkins (defending Popper) in articles in *Australasian Journal of Philosophy*, XXXVII (1959), and XXXVIII (1960). The latter volume also includes a critical notice by Stove of Popper's *Logic of Scientific Discovery, op. cit.* See also J. A. Passmore, "Popper's Account of Scientific Method", *Philosophy*, XXXV (1960), 326–331. A treatise written from a point of view sympathetic to Popper is J. O. Wisdom's *Foundations of Inference in Natural Science* (London: Methuen, 1952).

Nelson Goodman is much concerned with the problem of induction in his *Fact, Fiction and Forecast* (Cambridge: Harvard University Press, 1955, and paperback, New York: Bobbs-Merrill, 1965), and in particular brings up his puzzle about "grue" and "bleen". This has been much discussed in the literature. A recent discussion is the symposium, "The New Riddle of Induction", with papers by Richard C. Jeffrey, Judith Jarvis Thomson, John R. Wallace, and foreword and comment by Nelson Goodman, *Journal of Philosophy*, LXIII (1966), 281–331. See also R. J. Butler, "Messrs. Goodman, Green and Grue", in R. J. Butler (ed.), *Analytical Philosophy*, Second Series (Oxford: Blackwell, 1965), pp. 181–193.

On Pierre Duhem's position on the falsifiability of scientific theories see his *Aim and Structure of Physical Theory* (Princeton: Princeton University Press, 1954, and paperback, New York: Atheneum, 1962) and Armand Lowinger's *The Methodology of Pierre Duhem* (New York: Columbia University Press, 1941). Duhem's argument is revived by W. V. Quine in his *From a Logical Point of View*, second edition revised (Cambridge: Harvard University Press, 1961, and paperback, New York: Harper and Row, 1963), Chapter 2. For criticisms, see A. Grünbaum, *Philosophical Problems of Space and Time* (New York: Alfred A. Knopf, 1963), Chapter 4; and A. Grünbaum, "The Falsifiability of a Component of a Theoretical System", in P. K. Feyerabend and G. Maxwell (eds.), *Mind, Matter and Method, Essays in Philosophy and Science in Honor of Herbert Feigl* (Minneapolis: University of

Minnesota Press, 1966), pp. 273–305. Some apparent paradoxes which arise in connection with induction are lucidly discussed by Carl G. Hempel, "Recent Problems of Induction", in R. G. Colodny (ed.), *Mind and Cosmos, op. cit.*, pp. 112–134.

7

Space
and time

Some philosophical theories about space

Of what sort of thing are we talking when we talk about space and time? Are they, or the combination of them, a substantial entity, or are they sets of relations among things other than themselves? Or are they perhaps forms which the mind imposes on a non-spatial and non-temporal world, as Immanuel Kant held? In this chapter let us see how some of these old philosophical problems appear when they are seen in the light of scientific ideas. We shall begin by discussing space, insofar as this can be done without bringing in time.

Some of the Greeks tended to think of things in space as fish swimming in a sea. Thus Plato in the *Timaeus* spoke of space as a "receptacle". This foreshadows what later came to be called the "absolute" theory of space. Roughly, as fish are to sea, so things are to space. Space is the ultimate stuff in which exists water or air or heavy matter. The void between bits of matter is empty space, and so is not truly nothing, any more than the sea between different fish is nothing. As the sea between fish is water, so the "void" between lumps of matter is space. Indeed space is more pervasive than the water of the sea, for water does not penetrate fish, and yet, in the absolute theory of space, it is not only that lumps of matter are in space but bits of space are in the lumps of matter: space thoroughly pervades that which is *in* space. The absolute theory of space appears in a very pure form in the philosophy of René Descartes. According to Descartes the essence of matter is extension, and in consequence the problem for him was to distinguish between matter and empty space. If the essence of matter is extension, then, since apparently empty space is extended, it follows that there is no true vacuum and every part of space is filled with matter. This raises a further problem: how could Descartes distinguish between ordinary matter and the more subtle matter of apparently empty space? What account, again, could he give of the motion of matter *in* space? We shall see later that Descartes' difficulties here can, at least partially, be overcome by means of mathematical ideas which had not been developed in his time.

Against the absolute theory of space held by Descartes, Gottfried Leibniz propounded a relational theory. According to Leibniz the world was made up entirely of non-spatial entities, called "monads", and space is analyzed in terms of the relations among these monads. Since Leibniz, the relational theory of space has usually been propounded without the theory of monads or of other non-spatial bearers of spatial relations. According to this version space is analyzed in terms of relations among things which are themselves *in space*. Now if these things which are in space are spatial and have extension and shape, then there is a difficulty in understanding the relational theory which was not present in Leibniz's version of the theory. It is easy enough to consider, for example, a set of kinship relations: father, mother, son, daughter, nephew, niece, cousin, grandson, granddaughter, etc. The bits of a father or grandson do not have kinship relations to one another. According to the relational theory, the relations that make up space are relations among things, the bits of which are themselves related by relations in the set. I am unsure whether this is a real difficulty in the relational theory of space. Perhaps it is more a difficulty if our physics is one of continua, whereas with a modern particle theory the ultimate particles are not spatial in any simple sense. Nor, however, do they appear to be simply nonspatial, like Leibniz's monads. At any rate the relational theory of space is, in this respect at least, easier to state if we suppose with Leibniz that in the last resort spatial relations hold between nonspatial things.[1]

Despite this metaphysical doubt about whether the relational theory of space needs nonspatial entities as the ultimate *relata*, the relational theory is in many ways very plausible. Thus the distance between two stars is easily thought of as a relation between the stars and some standard of length. We shall come across other arguments in favor of a relational theory of space and time, but to set them in their context it will be convenient to have a look at Isaac Newton's views about space and time.

Newton's theory of space and time

In the Scholium to the Definitions of the *Principia*,[2] Newton distinguished "absolute, true and mathematical time" from "relative, apparent, and common time", which he said is "some sensible and external (whether accurate or unequable) measure of duration by the means of motion, which is commonly used instead of

---

[1]We need not concern ourselves here with a special difficulty in Leibniz's theory. Because of his subject-predicate logic he is not consistently able to hold that there are relations at all. Thus if a and b are monads, we do not have $R(a, b)$, where R is a relation, but rather $R_b(a)$ and $R_a(b)$, where R_a and R_b are relational properties. Eventually, as Bertrand Russell has argued, [1] Leibniz's refusal to admit relations leads him into inconsistency.

true time". In similar vein he said that "absolute space, in its own nature, without relation to anything external, remains always similar and immovable", but that on the other hand, "relative space is some movable dimension or measure of the absolute spaces, which our senses determine by its position to bodies, and which is commonly taken for immovable space".

All this is couched in rather metaphysical language, and part of what Newton meant is no doubt really metaphysical. Nevertheless his problem was essentially a mathematical one which can be stated neutrally as between absolute and relative theories of space and time. For example part of what Newton meant by absolute time flowing equably, as contrasted with relative time, was simply the following. If we use as a measure of time the apparent rotation of the fixed stars round the earth, due to the fact that the earth is revolving on its axis, we find that the predictions from Newtonian mechanics of the positions and motions of the planets are not accurately borne out by observation. However if one assumes that the rotation of the earth is slightly irregular we can change to a new measure of time, t', which is related to the old one t, by a function $t' = f(t)$. (To a rough approximation only, $t' = t$.) If the new time scale t' is applied to the equations of Newtonian mechanics we find that the predictions of the positions and motions of the planets become accurate. In Newton's terminology we would say that t' is a measure of absolute time whereas t is a measure of relative time. It can be seen that the issue is not a metaphysical one, but merely a search for a suitable function $f(t)$. We need not think of t' as defined in terms of rotation in absolute space, since it can be defined, and in practice has to be defined, by means of the function $f(t)$, of which the argument t is defined by means of relations to the fixed stars.

The same lesson, here illustrated with respect to time, can be learned, with respect to space, from Newton's experiment of the rotating bucket, which is also discussed in the Scholium to the Definitions of the *Principia*. Suppose that a bucket is hung from a twisted cord, so that as the cord untwists it rotates rapidly. The water in the bucket will also, through viscosity, begin to rotate, and its surface will become concave. Eventually this concavity will reach a maximum when the water in the bucket is rotating with the same angular velocity as the bucket itself. Newton points out that the water then has zero angular velocity relative to the sides of the bucket. Nevertheless from the concavity of the water and from the laws of motion and of gravitation we can deduce that the water must have a considerable angular velocity (equal to that of the bucket). In relation to what is this angular velocity an angular velocity? Newton's answer is: "absolute space".

Another answer, however, is equally consistent with the principles of Newtonian mechanics. Why could Newton not have said that the rotation was relative to a set of axes determined by the general distribution of matter in the universe? For Newton this determination of axes would have been by reference to the system of the fixed stars; today we might do so by reference to the galaxies. Such a system would be suitable for expressing Newtonian mechanics, without the necessity to postulate additional forces; centrifugal forces, for example. Such a set of axes is called an inertial system.

It might be asked, however, what would have to be said if Newton's bucket experiment were performed by physicists who lived on a planet which, like Venus, was surrounded by dense clouds, beyond which they never penetrated, so that they had no knowledge of bodies, such as the fixed stars, external to their planet. In this case they might at first specify an inertial system by relation to the surface of their planet. This would be only an approximate expedient, as would be apparent if their physical techniques improved so that instead of the crude bucket experiment they could do the experiment of Foucault's pendulum. In this experiment a pendulum is allowed to swing in a vertical plane from a fulcrum which is able to rotate about a vertical axis as near as possible without friction. When this experiment is done on Earth it is observed that the plane of oscillation of the pendulum rotates once every twenty-four hours. The physicists on the cloud covered planet, similarly, would be able to deduce from the experiment of Foucault's pendulum that they were on a rotating planet. Now what will they say are the axes relative to which their planet rotates? They can not refer the rotation to the surface of the planet itself, as they might have done with the bucket experiment. They would see that they would be wrong in taking axes which were fixed with respect to the surface of the planet as determining an inertial system. (The bucket experiment, unlike the Foucault's pendulum experiment, would have simply been too inaccurate to have shown them their error.) So they might be tempted to say that the axes which they have discovered as determining an inertial system, and relative to which the plane of oscillation of the Foucault's pendulum would not rotate, are axes fixed in absolute space.

Nevertheless these physicists *need not* say this sort of thing. Why could they not just as well say that an inertial system was determined by a set of axes which rotated relative to their planet? They could even have retained the set of axes which were fixed relative to the planet and suitably modified the laws of mechanics. In their cloud infested state, this could well have seemed a reasonable course to take. It is not so reasonable from our present point of view, since it would arbitrarily single out one point of space as of cosmic importance (the center of the planet), and, if everything in the universe were rotating around a point, very distant objects would have to have a velocity greater than light. (We shall return to some of these considerations on pp. 237–239 below.) But these difficulties would not be apparent to our cloud surrounded astronomers, since if their planet were the only part of the universe which was known to them, it would appear quite reasonable that the center of the planet should be of cosmic importance and that there should be a law of centripetal forces depending on it. (Compare Aristotelian physics in which the center of the earth entered into the laws of nature.)

It would also be possible for the physicists on the cloudy planet to take another course. They could postulate that inertial systems depend on the general distribution of matter in the universe, and from this they could deduce that if they were to rise above their clouds they would get visual evidence of such a system, with respect to which their planet would be seen to be revolving with such and such an angular velocity.

It can be seen, therefore, that there would be various courses open to physicists on the cloudy planet whereby they could perfectly well avoid an absolute theory of space. Like Newton's bucket, Foucault's pendulum gives evidence which is quite neutral as between absolute and relational theories of space. Ernst Mach,[3] who discussed Newton's bucket very much in the manner in which I have in the previous pages, concluded that assertions about the motions of a body "in space" should be construed as containing a reference not to absolute space but to the whole material universe. The principle that the inertia of a body is determined by the distribution of matter in the universe has therefore been called by Einstein "Mach's Principle" and is a controversial question in modern cosmology, since it is by no means easy to modify the equations of the general theory of relativity so that Mach's principle is obeyed. (See pp. 237–239 below.)

In fact the concept of the general distribution of matter in the universe is not precise enough for us to determine an inertial system with enough accuracy for celestial mechanics (the theory of the motions of sun, planets,

and other members of the solar system), which was
Newton's chief concern. Suppose that we have a number of particles $P_1, P_2, \ldots P_n$. (The sun, planets, moon,
etc., are not particles, but since they are spherical, it is a
consequence of Newton's law of gravitation that they
behave gravitationally as if all their masses were con-
centrated at their centers.) Then our problem is to assign numbers $m_1, m_2, \ldots m_n$ to these particles (also see
p. 165 above) and a suitable set of axes such that if f_{kl} is
the component of acceleration of P_k towards P_l, we
have in every case $m_k f_{kl} = m_l f_{lk}$. (The numbers $m_1,
m_2, \ldots m_n$ of course measure the masses of the parti-
cles.) This problem has no analytic solution but it can be
solved by approximative methods. The set of axes as
thus determined is an inertial system. Now if Newton
had been asked whether his notion of absolute space
was really necessary, or whether an inertial system as
defined relationally in the above manner was what he
was really demanding, it is quite likely that he would
have said that this was essentially all that he had in
mind. At any rate he might well have conceded that,
apart from theological and metaphysical considerations,
all that *physics* requires is an inertial system which can
be defined relationally.

Even though Newtonian mechanics is quite compatible with a relational theory of space and time, it is also
compatible with an absolute one. However if we wish to
follow Newton's own words literally and hold that space
and time are absolute, we have to put up with one awk-
ward consequence. This is that we can never know
which inertial system corresponds to a set of axes at rest
in absolute space. This is because there is an infinity of
inertial systems. If S is a system of inertial axes, then
any other system S' which moves with uniform velocity
relative to S will also be an inertial system. All that
procedures of the sort which were described in the previous paragraph could determine for us would be absolute *accelerations*. No *velocity* with respect to absolute

space could possibly be determined by observations in mechanics. Since the special theory of relativity, we now also know that a velocity with respect to absolute space can not be determined by any means whatever: for example, by optical experiments. A verificationist[2] or operationalist philosopher would therefore deny all meaning to talk of absolute space. Nevertheless if we are not verificationist about meaning (and we must bear in mind the failure of logical positivists to supply an adequate verificationist criterion of meaning), then we can allow Newton's assertion of the existence of absolute space to be both meaningful and consistent with his assumptions. We might still, however, regard the assertion of the existence of absolute space as pointless, as an assertion which does not make an interesting (because testable) scientific hypothesis.

One may interpret Leibniz's criticisms of Newton's theory of absolute space and time in the spirit of the previous paragraph. Leibniz appealed to a "principle of sufficient reason", which, shorn of the theological overtones with which it occurs in Leibniz, we might interpret as a "principle of testability". Leibniz points out that in the absolute theory of time we might ask why God did not create everything a year sooner than he did. This leads to difficulty, since God would have no reason for creating the universe at one instant of absolute time rather than at another, and presumably everything that God did would have to have a reason. (Even if we suppose the world to have existed from an infinite past, we could still ask why God created the world as it is, rather than with everything shifted a year,

[2]By a verificationist is meant roughly someone who holds that the meaning of a sentence is a function of the method of verifying the proposition which it expresses. If there is no means of verification, then the sentence has no meaning. One can sense an incoherence here, since if a sentence has no meaning, and does not express a proposition, what is it that one is not able to verify? (Ryle has criticized the verification theory of meaning in this way.[4]) The difficulty is often glossed over by proponents of the verification theory by using the word "proposition" ambiguously to mean both "sentence" and "what a sentence expresses".

earlier or later.) There would be no observable difference. Similarly with space, we can ask why everything is where it is in absolute space, instead of everything being a yard to the right, say, of where it in fact is. Leibniz's idea is that nothing in the world (or nothing that God does) is arbitrary or without a reason. The principle of sufficient reason does not appear to be analytic (true by definition) but it can possibly be interpreted as an anticipation of the verificationist objection to the meaningfulness of the notions of absolute space and time. I have preferred to reinterpret Leibniz's theological form of the principle differently, as a principle of testability, not of meaning.

We may conclude at least that in the context of Newtonian mechanics the theory of absolute space and time is scientifically otiose. Newton could have said all that he really needed to say from a scientific point of view by talking of the necessity for determining inertial systems, and inertial systems can be discussed consistently within a relational theory of space and time. This does not mean, however, that the theory of absolute space-time (we can no longer talk of space and time separately) is necessarily otiose in modern physics. We shall see that it is not easy for the *general* theory of relativity to dispense with absolute space-time, and the cosmologist J. A. Wheeler has even aspired to make space-time the whole stuff of the world, quite in the tradition of Descartes. Modern mathematical ideas enable an essentially Cartesian position to be developed in a way which is at least not open to the simple objections to Descartes' own position. It is true that in the *special* theory of relativity a relational theory of space-time seems quite plausible, though even here it is not necessary. We do of course have to give up an absolute theory of space and time taken separately, but this does not mean that we are forced into a relational theory of space-time as a whole. Admittedly, if we do not go beyond the *special* theory, such a postulation of absolute space-time is pointless, just as the Newtonian theory of absolute space and time is pointless, but it is not inconsistent with the theory. A brief discussion of space-time as it appears in the special theory of relativity will not only be useful on its own account but will be a preparation for discussing the issue between absolute and relational theories of space-time in modern cosmology. It is worth adding, moreover, that in the present state of knowledge special relativity is philosophically important in its own right: it should not be regarded as an incorrect theory which gives an approximation to the predictions of the true theory, which was the line we took (in Chapter 3) with phenomenological thermodynamics in its relation to statistical thermodynamics. In fact *general* relativity is by no means a well established theory, even for gravitational phenomena, and it is good only for discussing gravitational phenomena. It is the special theory that is widely used, as for example in microphysics.

Kant's example of the left hand and the right hand

In his *Prolegomena to Any Future Metaphysics* (Section 13)[5] Kant brings up the case of such things as a left hand and a right hand. Suppose that the universe contained only one thing, a left hand. All the relations between its parts would be the same as they would have been if it had been a right hand. Hence the relational theory of space can not do justice to the difference between a left hand and a right hand. The relationist, however, has an easy reply. He can reply that if there were only one thing, a hand, in the universe, it would be meaningless to call it either a left hand or a right hand. Or at least, the relationist would say that this is what would be said on the assumption that the laws of nature are symmetrical with respect to mirror reflections. The recent discovery in physics of the non-conservation of parity suggests that, provided that we knew whether the hand consisted of matter or anti-matter, there would be a meaning in saying whether it was a left hand or a right hand. But this, once more, would con-sist of a *relation* between the "handedness" of the elementary particles of which the hand was composed and the "handedness" of the hand as a whole. Once more, there would be no need for absolute space. Moreover there would be some difficulty about the meaningfulness of saying whether the hand consisted of matter or anti-matter if it were the only thing in the universe. Let us call matter "the most common kind of particles in the universe (or in our region of the uni-verse)". Thus electrons are more common than posi-trons. Then by definition, our single-hand universe would consist of matter, not of anti-matter.

Space-time in special relativity

Consider the set of axes $O'x'$, $O'y'$, $O'z'$ in Figure 4 which move with constant velocity v in the direction Ox of a parallel set of axes Ox, Oy, Oz. According the pre-relativistic or "Galilean" transformation the new coor-dinates are related to the old ones by means of the equations

$$x' = x - vt$$
$$y' = y$$
$$z' = z$$

to which for completeness we may add

$$t' = t$$

If we apply the above transformation $(x, y, z, t) \rightarrow (x', y', z', t')$ to Maxwell's electromagnetic equations, we find that these equations change their mathematical form, and moreover that they imply (as common sense would expect) that the velocity of light relative to the one system of axes will differ from that relative to the

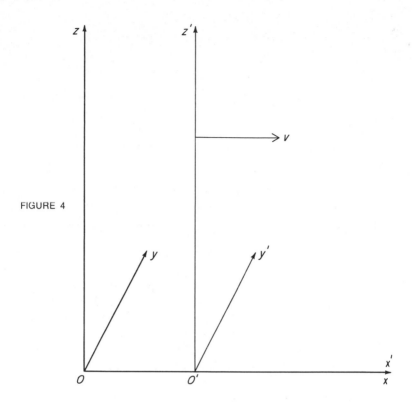

FIGURE 4

other system by v. The outcome of the Michelson-Morley and other optical experiments suggested on the contrary that, whatever the system of axes, the velocity of light will be discovered to be exactly the same by experimenters who are at rest relative to these axes. This fact, surprising to commonsense ideas, is explained by Einstein's special theory of relativity.

According to this theory the Galilean transformation is replaced by the following (assuming once more that the velocity v of the one system with respect to the other is parallel to Ox and where c is the velocity of light):

$$x' = \frac{x - vt}{\sqrt{1 - \dfrac{v^2}{c^2}}}$$

$$y' = y$$
$$z' = z$$

$$t' = \frac{t - \dfrac{vx}{c^2}}{\sqrt{1 - \dfrac{v^2}{c^2}}}$$

Notice how much more symmetrical these equations look if we choose units of space and time so that c = 1. Notice also that these equations approximate to the Galilean ones when v is small.

When the transformations of special relativity are used instead of the Galilean ones, Maxwell's equations of electromagnetism retain their form, and imply the same value for the velocity of electromagnetic waves (light) whatever the system of axes. The negative result of the Michelson-Morley experiment follows as a consequence, as also the results of other optical experiments (Ives-Stilwell and Kennedy-Thorndike) which are incompatible with pre-relativistic ideas. Similarly other experimental results of optics, such as aberration and the Doppler effect can be deduced from Maxwell's theory together with the new transformations.

H. A. Lorentz had endeavored to explain the negative result of the Michelson-Morley experiment by means of a theory which implied that moving bodies are contracted in the direction of motion. That is, the velocity of light does vary from one system to another, but this change is undetectable because of an exactly compensating contraction of our laboratory instruments in their direction of motion. Though this theory looks rather *ad hoc* it is not in fact so unplausible, considering that matter consists largely of electrically charged particles (and at the time was thought to consist entirely of electrically charged particles), and so Lorentz was able to argue with some success that the same laws which led to a change in the velocity of light as measured in one system or another would lead also to a contraction of material bodies which would render the change in velocity undetectable. So even if Lorentz's hypothesis were untestable it would gain indirect support from the theoretical considerations whereby he strove to justify it. As a matter of interest, however, Adolf Grünbaum has pointed out [6] that the Lorentz hypothesis is *not* untestable and so the hypothesis is not *logically ad hoc*, even though, because Lorentz had not known of these tests, it could be said to be *psychologically ad hoc*. In fact the hypothesis of the (ether-theoretic) Lorentz contraction can be refuted by the Kennedy-Thorndike experiment. This is similar to the better known Michelson-Morley experiment, except that instead of the two interferometer arms (which are at right angles to one another) being made equal in length, they are made very much unequal to one another.

Let us go back to the so-called Lorentz transformations as they appear in the special theory of relativity (the transformations on p. 220 above). Here they are merely a mathematical transformation from one coordinate system to another and do not represent real contractions (caused by motion) as in Lorentz's theory. As was discovered by Minkowski, Einstein's transformations represent merely a rotation of axes in space-time. If we slice a cylindrical cake at different angles we get different cross-sections of the cake, some more elliptical or elongated than others, but of course there is no physical expansion or contraction of the cake. It is rather like this with special relativity: an instantaneous state of a ruler at rest relative to us corresponds to a straight cut of the four-dimensional object which is the ruler throughout its history, whereas if we are moving relative to the ruler, what we see at an instant corresponds to an oblique cut. There is a difference from the case of the cylindrical cake, in which oblique cuts are more elongated than straight ones, since owing to the special geometry of space-time the oblique cuts of the ruler are *shorter* than the straight cuts. Hence the so-called "contraction".

Newton's equations of motion are invariant with respect to the Galilean transformation, but the equations of electromagnetism are not invariant with respect to this transformation. On the other hand, while the Lorentz transformations of special relativity leave the equations of electromagnetism invariant, they do not leave the laws of Newtonian mechanics invariant. To achieve this invariance Einstein had to modify the laws of mechanics. In the case of bodies which move at small velocities relative to our system of axes, the new equations predict the same results, within the limits of observational error, as do the Newtonian ones, but they lead to testably different results for high velocities, and the modified equations have been confirmed by observations of fast particles. It is important to stress that the testability of special relativity depends very strongly on these mechanical predictions, since critics of relativity are often content with attempting to explain the *optical* experiments in non-relativistic ways. The special theory of relativity is tested in many ways, and its predictions have to be taken into account even in engineering (in the design of cyclotrons, for example) and it does not rest simply on a few optical experiments.

Because the equation $t' = t$ of the Galilean transformation is replaced in special relativity by the equation

$$t' = \frac{t - \frac{vx}{c^2}}{\sqrt{1 - \frac{v^2}{c^2}}}$$

it can be seen that whether or not distant events are simultaneous depends partly on v. That is, if distant events are simultaneous in a system for which $v = 0$, then, in a system moving with velocity v relative to this system, one of the events will be earlier or later than the other. When $x = 0$, of course, events which are simultaneous according to the Galilean transformation will be simultaneous according to the Lorentz one.

In the laboratory we are dealing with things which are approximately in the same place, and so direct laboratory measurements of simultaneity are not affected by the change from Newtonian to relativistic ideas.

Now let us consider the fact, shown by Minkowski, that the Lorentz transformations can be regarded simply as a rotation of axes in space-time. We have to assume that the metric of space-time is given not by

$$ds^2 = dx^2 + dy^2 + dz^2 + dt^2$$

which would be the case if it were Euclidean, but by the semi-Euclidean[3] metric

$$ds^2 = dt^2 - dx^2 - dy^2 - dz^2$$

(For convenience I have supposed that we have chosen time and space units so that the velocity of light is equal to one. Otherwise in both the above equations we should have c^2t^2 instead of t^2.)

Now consider Figure 5, in which are shown the time direction Ot and the space direction Ox. (I can of course draw only two dimensions on a piece of paper.)

Let a particle move with constant velocity v relative to a particle at rest at O. Let all the successive space-time positions of the particle lie on the line Ot'. This line is called the world-line of the particle and clearly the particle, considered as a four-dimensional space-time body, lies along Ot'. Clearly also Ot is the world-line of a particle at rest in the original system of axes. It is natural, therefore, that we should take Ot' as the time axis for a system of axes for which the moving body would be said (thinking of it as an enduring three dimensional entity)

[3]It is semi-*Euclidean* because a three-dimensional slice at right angles to a time axis is Euclidean. It is *semi*-Euclidean because of the minus signs: slices the other way (along a time axis) are hyperbolic.

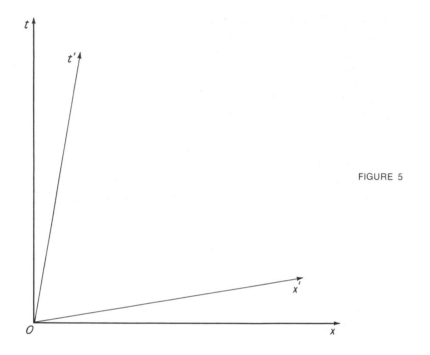

FIGURE 5

"to be at rest". Now if we rotate Ox as Ot rotates to Ot' it comes to lie along Ox'. This looks a bit counter-intuitive in the diagram, since Ox' goes *above* Ox, not below it as one might expect. This is because of the semi-Euclidean geometry of space-time, which makes diagrams drawn on Euclidean pieces of paper look rather odd. Notice that the velocity v is simply the tangent of the angle tOt'. It is a simple exercise in coordinate geometry to discover what are the equations for transforming from the tOx coordinate system to the $t'Ox'$ one. These turn out to be the same as those of the Lorentz transformation.

The special theory of relativity comes to be much more understandable than before when we see it in this light, in terms of the geometry of space-time. Indeed it becomes much more elegant than the old Newtonian

224

theory. For what happens in the Newtonian theory if, as seems plausible, we continue to take our time axis as a line along which coincides the world-line of a particle at rest in our system? In the Newtonian theory we then rotate Ot but do *not* rotate Ox. There is therefore as Minkowski pointed out,[7] a certain mathematical elegance about the Lorentz transformations which the Newtonian ones lack.

It may be worth pointing out that the asymmetry in the appearance of the diagram is misleading. It comes once more from trying to represent a non-Euclidean space on a Euclidean piece of paper. On our paper the rectangular coordinate system of $t'Ox'$ would appear rhomboidal. But equally we could have drawn $t'Ox'$ to make a right angle and tOx as oblique, as in Figure 6.

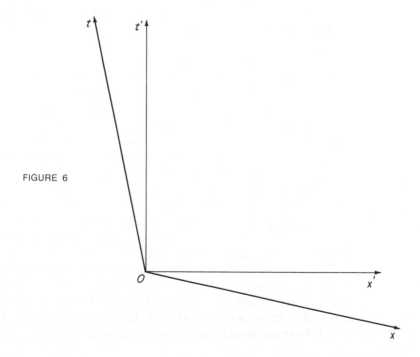

FIGURE 6

In Minkowski's eloquent words, "Henceforth space by itself, and time by itself, are doomed to fade away into mere shadows, and only a kind of union of the two will preserve an independent reality".[8]

It is important to learn to think in terms of the four-dimensional space-time picture of the world, since Minkowski has shown the indissoluble union between space and time. One trap must be avoided. It is one into which physicists often fall, especially in works written for the general public. Since time is already involved in space-time, we can not speak of change in space-time in any sense other than of some parts of space-time being different from others. In this last sentence "being" is of course not a true present tense, but is the tenseless "present" which we get in mathematics, as when we say that π is an irrational number. When we say that π is an irrational number we do not mean that it is *now* an irrational number. Instead of saying that a body changes from being red to being green we should say that an earlier spatial cross-section of the (four-dimensional) space-time body is (tenselessly) red and that a later one is (tenselessly) green. Again, it is clearly illegitimate to speak of a body or a signal moving through space-time. The concept of motion is now replaced by the notion of the relative inclinations of world-lines. Thus in Figure 7 the particles AB and CD are further away from one another at t_2 than they are at t_1. Similarly, instead of saying that the relative motion of the second with respect to the first is greater at t_1 than at t_2, we say that the inclination of one world-line with respect to the other is greater at t_1 than at t_2. We must not speak of change or motion in the ordinary way, since time is already in our representation.[9]

Of course it could be misleading to say that according to the theory of relativity the future is "already in existence". The future, for me as I write this book, contains such dates as A.D. 1970. To say that the events of A.D. 1970 are already in existence suggests that A.D. 1970

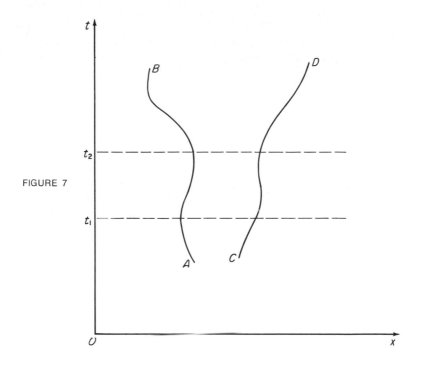

FIGURE 7

exists now, that is, in 1967, which is absurd. To think thus is to confuse the tenseless present of "is in A.D. 1970" with the tensed "is now in A.D. 1970". The four-dimensional world contains a place for all possible dates along the time axis, and clearly does not make everything simultaneous. Nor does it make any event eternal either: to think thus would be to commit the absurdity of trying to make one point in the space-time world cover an infinite line stretching from past to future. Furthermore, the four-dimensional world does not imply determinism. Determinism suggests that from a complete knowlege of everything at t_1 (say on the lower dotted line of Figure 7, if we can neglect all but one spatial dimension) we could, given a knowledge of all the laws of nature, deduce the complete state of the **227** world at t_2 (say, all events along the upper dotted line). There is nothing in the space-time picture which either implies this or is inconsistent with it. The view that the world is a space-time world is quite neutral between determinism and indeterminism.

The clock paradox

A discussion of the so-called clock paradox of special relativity will help to bring out the power and intuitive appeal of the four-dimensional world picture. Indeed, once one begins to think four-dimensionally, it is hard to imagine how anyone ever should have thought that there was anything really paradoxical about the clock paradox.

A consequence of the Lorentz equation

$$t' = \frac{t - \dfrac{vx}{c^2}}{\sqrt{1 - \dfrac{v^2}{c^2}}}$$

is as follows: Consider two clocks which are together at space-time point O. One is at rest in the system (Ox, Ot): in other words, considered as a four-dimensional object it lies along Ot. The other is moving with velocity v and considered as a four-dimensional object it lies along Ot'. See Figure 8. Consider an event at T in the history of the first clock. Obviously T lies on Ot. With reference to the (Ox, Ot) system the event in the history of the second clock which is simultaneous with T lies on the point T' on Ot', such that TT' is parallel to Ox. Now OT' is shorter than OT. (It looks longer in the diagram, which is drawn on a piece of paper with the Euclidean metric given by $ds^2 = dt^2 + dx^2$, whereas in space-time we have $ds^2 = dt^2 - dx^2$.) This is somewhat misleadingly put by saying that clocks in the moving system run slow relative to the rest system. Similarly, with reference to the (Ox', Ot') system the event on Ot which is simultaneous with T' is T'', where $T''T'$ is parallel to Ox'. OT'' turns out to be shorter than OT' just as OT' was shorter than OT. This is again sometimes misleadingly put by saying that clocks in the (Ox, Ot) system run slow compared with clocks in the (Ox', Ot') system. It is easy to see that there is no contradiction implied when it is said that clocks in the second system run slow compared with clocks in the first system, and that clocks in the first system run slow compared with clocks in the second system. There is no contradiction whatever in saying that $OT' < OT$ and that $OT'' < OT'$.

In fact let T' have the (Ox, Ot) coordinate (x_1, t_1). $OT = t_1$ and $OT' = t'_1$. Then by the fourth equation of the Lorentz transformation

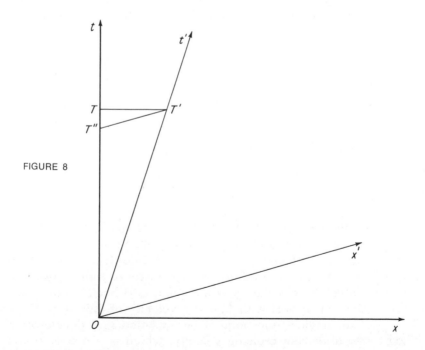

FIGURE 8

$$t'_1 = \frac{t_1 - \frac{vx_1}{c^2}}{\sqrt{1 - \frac{v^2}{c^2}}}$$

where v is the velocity of the second clock with respect to the first one. Clearly $v = \frac{x_1}{t_1}$. And so we have

$$t' = \frac{t_1 - \frac{vx_1}{c^2}}{\sqrt{1 - \frac{v^2}{c^2}}} = t_1 \sqrt{1 - \frac{v^2}{c^2}}$$

Similarly let T'' have the Ox' coordinate x'_2 (which will be a negative number). The Ot' coordinate of T'' is clearly t'_1. The velocity of the first system with respect to the second is $-v$ and so we have the Ot coordinate of T'' to be t_2 where

$$t_2 = \frac{t'_1 - \frac{(-v)\,x_2}{c^2}}{\sqrt{1 - \frac{v^2}{c^2}}} = \frac{t'_1 + \frac{vx_2}{c^2}}{\sqrt{1 - \frac{v^2}{c^2}}}$$

But $-v = \frac{x_2}{t'_1}$ and so

$$t_2 = t'_1 \sqrt{1 - \frac{v^2}{c^2}}$$

which confirms that both $OT' < OT$ and $OT'' < OT'$.

Now for the clock paradox itself. Suppose that there are two twins Jack and Jim. While Jack remains on earth Jim takes off on a space rocket to Alpha Centauri, which is four light years distant, and back again. Jim's rocket travels with half the velocity of light and (if we can neglect questions of acceleration and deceleration to and from cruising velocity, which is a matter that I shall discuss presently) the time in Jack's (Earth) coordinate system between Jim's departure and return is sixteen years. However Jim's coordinate system is moving with a velocity $\frac{c}{2}$ relative to Jack's, and so in Jim's system the outward journey takes $8\sqrt{1 - \frac{\frac{1}{4}c^2}{c^2}}$ $= 4\sqrt{3}$ years. On his return journey he moves with a velocity $-\frac{c}{2}$ relative to Jack, and so in his coordinate system the return journey also takes $4\sqrt{3}$ years. So his to and fro journey takes $8\sqrt{3}$ years. Jim is therefore slightly more than two years younger than Jack when he returns.

The clock paradox now comes from the following fallacious bit of reasoning. In our calculations we have taken Jack to be at rest and Jim to be moving with a velocity of either $+v$ or $-v$ relative to him. Equally, it is said, we could take Jim to be at rest, and Jack's velocity relative to Jim will also be $\pm v$. So after the journey Jack should be slightly more than two years younger than Jim. Putting the two sides of the argument together we have Jack younger than Jim and Jim younger than Jack, which is impossible.

The fallacy in the reasoning is that the first calculation (showing Jim to be younger than Jack) was correct, because Jack has been in the same inertial system throughout. However Jim had to be accelerated and decelerated at Alpha Centauri (and hence he would have had, for example, some very painful physiological experiences which Jack had not had!) and so the second half of the argument is invalid. In special relativity it is permissible to take a set of axes as at rest only if they are an inertial set of axes throughout.

Now we can show the power of the Minkowski space-time picture of the world. If we draw the world-lines of Jack and Jim the picture will show vividly the asymmetry which we noted in the previous paragraph, and the comparative youthfulness of Jim on his return will be seen to be a simple consequence of the geometry of space-time.

In Figure 9, Ot, Ox are Jack's axes. Jack is a four-dimensional "worm" lying along Ot. A is the space-time position of Jim's turn around at Alpha Centauri. He leaves Jack at O and returns to Jack at B, and so he is a bent space-time "worm" lying along OAB. The rest of the diagram does not matter much, but I have drawn in Ot', Ox', which are Jim's axes on the outward journey and Ot'', Ox'' which are his axes on the return journey, to show that, as noted previously, he is not in the same inertial frame throughout. The asymmetry, which the clock paradox argument tries to deny, between the situations of Jack and Jim is seen very clearly from the straightness of Jack (as a four-dimensional object) and the bentness of Jim. The time of aging of Jack between the events O (departure of Jim) and B (return of Jim) is OB. The time of aging of Jim is the length of his world line, which is $OA + AB$. Intuitively $OA + AB$ looks greater than OB, but this is because of the Euclidean paper on which this book is printed. In the geometry of space-time $OA + AB$ is less than OB. But allowing for the Euclidean nature of our paper, the diagram shows that there is nothing puzzling about the clock paradox: the relative youthfulness of Jim is simply a matter of two sides of a triangle adding up to a different length from that of the third side.

In the above discussion I have neglected the periods of acceleration and deceleration. However this does not matter greatly, since by choosing a far enough distant star (perhaps far more distant than Alpha Centauri, which was the one in our example) we can ensure that the periods of acceleration and deceleration are as small as we please in comparison with the total time. Thus if we redraw the triangle of our figure so as to show the periods of acceleration and deceleration it will

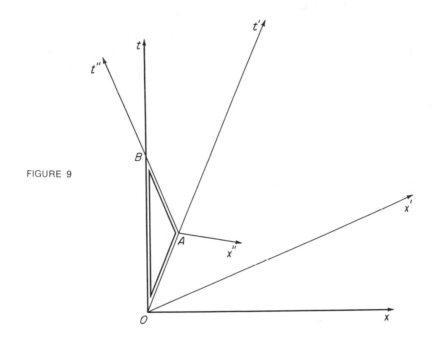

FIGURE 9

contain curved bits as in Figure 10, but these can be very small compared with the sides of the triangle, and our previous calculation can be approximately correct. In any case a more complicated calculation including a computation of the length of the curved bits will show that the to and fro journey is a shorter world line than the world line of the stay at home twin.

In fact we can tell a similar story about Jack and Jim even if we assume no accelerations or decelerations at all. Suppose that the universe were a finite (and nonexpanding) one of constant positive curvature. Suppose that Jack stayed at home and Jim was in a rocket which passed Jack with velocity v in a straight line. Then like a sailor circumnavigating the earth, Jim would return to Jack again. (We shall in this case of course have to suppose that Jack and Jim are practically immortal!) Jim

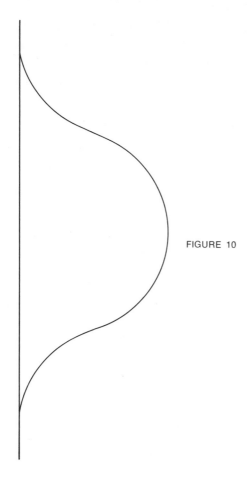

FIGURE 10

will be younger than Jack on his return since if Jack is

older by a time t then Jim will have aged by $t \sqrt{1 - \dfrac{v^2}{c^2}}$

(This case was put forward and discussed by E. A. Milne and G. J. Whitrow.[10]) We can show this on a Minkowski type diagram if we change the drawing slightly. Draw the diagram not on a plane sheet of paper but on a cylinder as in Figure 11. Then the line which

234

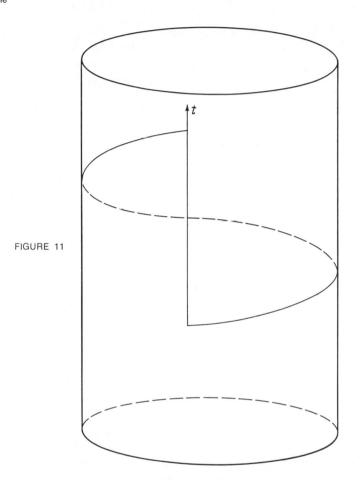

FIGURE 11

goes round the cylinder is shorter (though because
of our Euclidean intuitions it looks longer) than the
straight line Ot which is Jack's world-line. From the
diagram it can be seen in what sense Jack is at rest
relative to the universe as a whole whereas Jim is not.
The difference between the world-lines of Jack and Jim
is an absolute (topological) one—Jim circumnavigates
the cylinder whereas Jack does not. Even though calcu-   235

lations on these lines would use only the Lorentz transformations of special relativity, we are moving closer
to the cosmological ideas associated with the general
theory of relativity, since we need to consider the structure of space-time from a cosmological point of view.

It can be seen that the special theory of relativity is
inconsistent with Newton's theory of an absolute space
and time taken separately. On the other hand it seems
to be perfectly consistent with an absolute theory of
space-time. Is space-time an absolute plenum or is it
simply a four-dimensionally ordered system of relations
between events? The special theory of relativity is quite
neutral between these interpretations, just as Newton's
mechanics, as opposed to his metaphysics, is neutral between absolute and relational theories of space.
There is also the same arbitrariness as well. Just as we
have no particular reason for supposing any given inertial system to be at rest in absolute space, and just as it
makes no difference to physics whether we suppose
everything in the universe to be at a point in absolute
space one mile to the right or left, or front or back, or
up or down, so in the Minkowski world the same situation arises with regard to space-time. It would not matter whether everything in our Minkowski diagram were
pushed up or down, or right or left, or whether our
diagram rotated through a certain angle. All the physically significant relationships would remain the same.
So even though absolute space-time is consistent with
special relativity, it plays no physically significant role in
the theory. With the general theory of relativity, however, there is good reason for supposing that absolute
space-time may play an essential role in the theory. At
any rate cosmological hypotheses incorporating the
general theory of relativity may have to make use of
absolute space-time in an essential way.

Space-time in general relativity

At present the question of whether general relativity can be formulated in accordance with Mach's principle usually depends on the cosmological hypotheses which the investigator is prepared to make (together of course with his mathematical ingenuity). Suffice it to say that most relativistic cosmologies are unable to accept Mach's principle in its entirety, and whether *any* can be accepted is a difficult and controversial question for mathematical physicists. Let us look briefly at some of the difficulties which appear to beset a cosmologist who wishes to dispense with absolute space-time.[11]

It will be remembered that according to the relational philosophy of space espoused by Mach it is immaterial whether we say that the earth rotates relative to the fixed stars or whether we say that the fixed stars rotate around the earth in orbits determined by appropriate earth-centered forces. The special theory of relativity has nothing to say on this question, because it deals only with inertial systems, and the system of axes relative to which the rotation of the earth is zero does not qualify as an inertial system. Now the general theory of relativity does reduce to special relativity (within the limits of observational error) when we are dealing with systems of a rather small size and provided we are prepared to postulate additional forces if necessary. Thus to take a hackneyed example, consider an accelerating elevator. We can regard the accelerating elevator as a non-accelerating elevator, i.e., as an inertial system, if we introduce an appropriate gravitational force. Instead of thinking of the floor of the elevator as pushing with a force which accelerates us, we think of ourselves as dragged down against the floor by means of a gravitational force. It should be realized however that such a reduction to special relativity, which corresponds to a change from curved space-time to flat space-time, can be done only *locally*. The case is rather like that of smoothing out a badly fitting carpet. We can smooth out wrinkles in any small region, but this leads to wrinkles elsewhere. We can not make the carpet smooth everywhere.[4]

To accept parity of esteem between the two descriptions (a) accelerating elevator and (b) non-accelerating elevator, or between (a') rotating earth and (b') non-rotating earth, would be tantamount to supposing that wrinkles can be smoothed out *everywhere*. If we consider the earth to be at rest we have the difficulty that the transverse velocity of the stars would have to be greater than that of light, which is inconsistent with the special theory of relativity. We cannot, therefore, "smooth out the carpet" even as far as the nearest star. Grünbaum has remarked,[12] therefore, that the earth must be held to rotate not relative to an extensive system of axes reaching out to the fixed stars but relative to a local system formed by the stellar light rays as they approach rather near to the earth, where their paths are determined by the local metrical field.[5] Unless this local metrical field can be elucidated purely relationally, and it is not at any rate easy to see how this can be done, we

[4]To forestall possible misunderstanding it should of course be emphasized that "curved" and "flat" as applied to space-time are given a precise mathematical meaning which does not depend on intuition as does our analogy of the carpet. The metric in general relativity is given by:

$$ds^2 = g_{11} \, dx^2 + g_{22} \, dy^2 + g_{33} \, dz^2 + g_{44} \, dt^2$$
$$+ 2 \, g_{12} \, dx \, dy + 2 \, g_{13} \, dx \, dz + 2 \, g_{14} \, dx \, dt$$
$$+ 2 \, g_{23} \, dy \, dz + 2 \, g_{24} \, dy \, dt + 2 \, g_{34} \, dz \, dt$$

The g's are all functions of (x, y, z, t). To say that space-time is flat at a certain point is to say that x, y, z and t axes can be chosen so that at that point $g_{11} = g_{22} = g_{33} = -1$, $g_{44} = 1$, and $g_{12} = g_{13} = g_{14} = g_{23} = g_{24} = g_{34} = 0$. Note that the fact that for a particular system of axes g_{12}, etc., are *not* equal to 0 at a certain point does not show that the space is not flat. Thus 2-dimensional Euclidean space is "flat" everywhere because axes can be chosen such that always $ds^2 = dx^2 + dy^2$, but with oblique axes we have $ds^2 = dx^2 + dy^2 + kxy$. A space is flat if there is *some* system of axes for which g_{12}, g_{13}, etc., are zero. See also pp. 242–246 below.

[5]Talking about the "metrical field" is a matter of talking about a certain relationship among the g_{ik} (about the curvatures at the various points of space-time).

are not able to deal with the rotation of the earth relative to the fixed stars in a way that is in accordance with Mach's principle.

The reason why the general theory of relativity is so bound up with cosmology is that assumptions of a cosmological nature about boundary conditions have to be made before the equations of the theory can be solved. Of course assumptions about boundary conditions need to be made in the case of *any* theory, but in Newtonian mechanics, for example, these do not have to be so concerned with the universe at large, since in Newtonian theory very distant bodies have negligible effects on one another. One possible way of solving Einstein's equations is to suppose that space-time is flat "at infinity". This is like smoothing out all the edges of a carpet and concentrating the wrinkles at the center. Now to suppose that space-time has a definite ("flat") structure infinitely far from matter is obviously not in accordance with Mach's principle. Einstein's modified equations which give a finite but unbounded universe do not avoid the denial of Mach's principle either, since they imply a definite curvature to space-time even in the absence of all matter.

Indeed it is not at all clear that a reconciliation of general relativity with Mach's principle is necessarily desirable. Why should not space-time be a perfectly good "theoretical entity" of physics in its own right, and not merely a system of relations among other theoretical entities such as electrons and protons? There is a good tradition in mathematical physics which stems from Descartes, and which must be set against the relational philosophy which stems from Leibniz. Descartes' own theory foundered in inconsistencies, since he was unable to make a distinction between parts of space, and it was impossible for him to explain how some parts of space consist of bodies and how the other parts of space can be spaces *between* bodies. Since he held that the essence of matter is extension he had to deny the exist-   **239** ence of a vacuum, but his theory was unable to account for the fact that even if there is no vacuum there is a difference between parts of space in that some at least come nearer to being vacua than do others. Descartes was also handicapped by the fact that he had not welded space and time together into a unitary space-time. This made it hard for him to deal with motion. Since the mathematical discoveries of Riemann, however, the notion of a space of variable curvature enables us to give a real physical role to space, and we can even toy with the idea of material bodies as being nothing but singularities in such a space-time.

Another modern mathematical idea which was not available to Descartes was that of a multiply connected space. Consider the surface of a sphere. This is a two-dimensional space. Consider a closed curve on this surface. It can be shrunk down until it becomes a point. Now suppose that our two-dimensional space is the surface of a doughnut. It is evident that some closed curves in this space are such that they can not be shrunk down to a point. The surface of the sphere is said to be "simply connected". The surface of the doughnut is said to be "multiply connected". A surface is n-tuply connected if $n-1$ nonintersecting cuts are needed to make it simply connected. Now on this analogy try to conceive a multiply connected space of many dimensions. You can not *imagine* it but I hope you can *conceive* it. If you allow yourself as many dimensions as you like, any degree of connectedness, and variable curvature, you have a far more wonderful sort of space than the three dimensional Euclidean space which was available to Descartes.

J. A. Wheeler[13] has proposed a cosmological model on these lines, according to which electrons and protons are opposite ends of "worm holes" in a multiply connected space-time. (These worm holes need not themselves be asserted to exist at all. It is only from the standpoint of a three-dimensional space that we can assert that a doughnut has a hole through the middle. From the standpoint of a two dimensional being existing on the surface it is a two dimensional surface without holes but with the interesting topological property of being doubly connected.) Wheeler's cosmology is of course speculative and so must be all cosmologies, at least until after the day when there comes to be a unification of microphysics (a particle physics) with the field theory of general relativity. It is at present impossible to tell whether physics will come to elucidate space-time in Leibnizian fashion, in terms of the relations among particles or whether the Cartesian idea will be vindicated, and the universe will come to be seen as built, perhaps in the manner envisaged by Wheeler, of space-time points alone.

Geometry and physics

If the program envisaged by Wheeler were eventually to be carried out, physical theory would end up by being a fantastically complicated multiply-connected many-dimensional geometry of variable curvature. The complexities of the geometry, however, would be offset by the extreme ontological simplicity of the theory, since the world would be built up of space-time points alone. Even if physics is not fully geometrized, but if absolute space-time is needed in physical theory, geometry will still be an essential part of physical theory, and space-time points will be theoretical entities on par with such things as electrons and protons. And even if the relational theory of space-time should prove viable, the set of relations between physical particles which would be dealt with in a geometry would be describable only by means of laws of geometry which would have the status of theoretical laws of nature.

The above conception is in contrast with the operationalist account of descriptive geometry, which asserts that geometry is about the transport behavior of rigid   **241** rods. That geometry is about rigid rods can be refuted as follows. The world might have been purely gaseous, but surely even so we (perhaps as gaseous or disembodied persons) might have used geometry in explaining the laws of this gaseous world. Since there would have been no rigid rods we should not be using the geometry to explain the behavior under transport of rigid rods. By the same token, when geometry *is* applied to the behavior of rigid rods, it is better to say that the geometry *explains* this behavior than that it *describes* it. That is, the geometry has more content than the description of measurements with rigid rods, just as quantum mechanics has more content than we can get by adding together reports of what the experimenter sees when he looks at laboratory instruments.

Nevertheless there is a sense in which we can choose our geometry at will. Consider for example some semi-Euclidean Cartesian coordinates (x, y, z, t). That is we can envisage our Minkowski diagram as covered with a square mesh as in Figure 12. Now let us draw any mesh we like as in Figure 13.

Let the transition from Figure 12 to Figure 13 be according to the following equations, where f, g, h, j provide a one-one continuous mapping:

$$x' = f(x, y, z, t)$$
$$y' = g(x, y, z, t)$$
$$z' = h(x, y, z, t)$$
$$t' = j(x, y, z, t)$$

There are also functions f', g', h', j', such that:

$$x = f'(x', y', z', t')$$
$$y = g'(x', y', z', t')$$
$$z = h'(x', y', z', t')$$
$$t = j'(x', y', z', t')$$

Now if $Q(x, y, z, t) = 0$ is any law of nature in the original coordinates, we replace it with:

Space and time

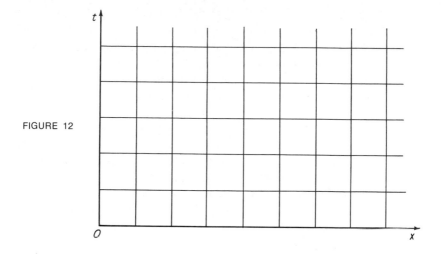

FIGURE 12

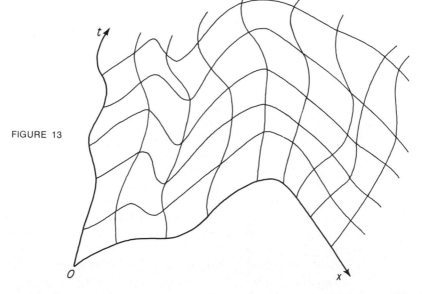

FIGURE 13

$$Q \quad \{f'(x', y', z', t'), \quad g'(x', y', z', t'), \quad h'(x', y', z', t'),$$
$$j'(x', y', z', t') \} = 0$$

In this way it is a simple matter to change our geometry and physics together so that the combination of the two remains essentially the same theory. It will be a consequence of the new physical theory and the new geometry that a rod which retains its length under transport (when length is measured in the old geometry) no longer retains a uniform length according to the metric of the new geometry. We may put this matter as follows: the congruence definitions of the new geometry are different from those of the old one.

For example we can easily modify our physical laws so that we go over from a Euclidean geometry (or rather a semi-Euclidean geochronometry) to a hyperbolic one. However the changes of our geometry which are permissible in this way are limited by an obvious requirement. It is necessary to retain the topology of the original geometry. Thus we can go over from a Euclidean to a hyperbolic space, because these possess the same topological structure: they are infinite in all directions. We can not go over from a Euclidean or hyperbolic space to a spherical or elliptical one, or vice-versa, since a spherical or elliptical space is finite but unbounded.

Suppose for example we map a spherical space onto a Euclidean one. Consider a light signal which circumnavigates the spherical space. This will be replaced by a light signal shooting off into infinite space followed by a light signal coming in from infinity from the opposite direction. To admit this would be, as Reichenbach remarked,[14] to tolerate causal anomalies.

For this reason Grünbaum regards the topological properties of space as intrinsic, whereas he regards the metrical properties as relative only to congruence conventions.[15] No doubt he is right in regarding the topological properties as more fundamental than the metrical ones, and perhaps it may even be that the physics of the future will be wholly topological and non-metrical. Nevertheless the standpoint of Chapters 3 and 5 may incline us to think of congruence definitions as not given *ab initio* but as deductions from our physics plus geometry. Why should we not take that combination of physics plus geometry which leads to the simplest formulation, and suppose, on grounds of simplicity, that this gives the correct picture of the world? Perhaps, however, this is putting too much weight on the principle of simplicity: Grünbaum would say that simplicity here is descriptive simplicity only, not inductive simplicity.

Suppose that space or space-time were made up of discrete lumps. Then we would not need the congruence definitions (or congruence theorems) of a geometry in order to assign length to an object. The length of an object could very naturally be defined as the number of lumps of space between its ends. Alternatively we could regard these lumps as points and define the length of anything as zero, using the criterion of modern measure theory, which assigns a measure zero to any finite set of points. Indeed if we used measure theory for our criterion of length any object would have zero length if space consisted of a merely denumerably infinite set of points. With spaces, which (in consequence of such things as the incommensurability of sides and hypotenuse of an isosceles right angle triangle) are held to contain a non-denumerable infinity of points, measure theory assigns non-zero length to an interval. The actual lengths which have to be assigned now depend on congruence rules or congruence theorems.

From an operational point of view we define "rigid" in terms of "not rigid". Thus clearly an india-rubber band is not rigid, because though its ends may coincide at one moment with the ends of a piece of iron or wood, they may also not so coincide, even though the rubber is taut. However iron and wood are approximately rigid, because if the ends coincide at one time they coincide at others. To a higher degree of approximation it may be **245** found that iron and wood are themselves "not rigid", since the wood may cease to coincide with the iron after it has been dampened. Again, pieces of iron and brass whose ends coincide at one temperature do not coincide at other temperatures. A more refined definition may be given in terms of iron and brass at a certain temperature (say at the freezing point of water). If the pieces of iron and brass (which are at this temperature) coincide at one place or time they will coincide at other places or times. Later on we can use our rough measures of length to construct laboratory instruments, such as spectrometers, and then we can use an even more refined standard of length, such as that of the wavelength of cesium light. Now we can set up correspondence rules between our relativistic geometry and our operational standards of length, and say that our operational standard and our geometrical one coincide in regions where there is not too strong a gravitational field.

Grünbaum regards the rough correspondence rules of which I have just spoken as *congruence definitions*. He then holds that geometry is an empirical science in the sense that a geometry is uniquely specified by the facts of the world together with our congruence definitions. If we like we can stipulate that the length of a rigid rod is some function $f(x, y, z, t)$ of its space-time position, in which case we go over to a different geometry, and that the g_{ik}'s in the formula $ds^2 = g_{ik} \, dx_i \, dx_k$ will be different. Nevertheless, Grünbaum would hold that it is not a different geometry in the sense that its physical meaning is different from that of the old one: the change in the congruence definitions and in the g_{ik}'s cancel one another out. In this way Grünbaum uses the case of physical geometry as a counter-example to the Duhemian thesis that a theory can be retained in the face of recalcitrant evidence provided that we make appropriate changes in our background assumptions. Grünbaum's reply[16] is that a *physical* geometry (i.e., the mathematical theory *together with* the congruence definitions) is uniquely determined by the empirical facts, at least if we can ignore the usual inductive risks of extrapolating from what we observe with a certain number of observations to what we would observe if we made indefinitely more observations. (This last qualification is unimportant, since it is hard to be Duhemian about "all ravens are black", where inductive risk occurs also.)

It is doubtful however, whether such an inductivist account of geometry will do when geometry is taken not as description of the transport behavior of rigid bodies, thought of commonsensically, but as *explanatory* of it. For example take the congruence rule: "The meter bar at Paris is the same length anywhere". This might be regarded as an analytic proposition, i.e., one which is true in virtue of linguistic conventions alone. But now that we have a standard of length based on the wavelength of cesium light the proposition about the meter rod in Paris becomes an obviously factual and no longer merely conventional one. Even neglecting this consideration, it is physically meaningful that the meter bar in Paris might double in length: as Hilary Putnam[17] has pointed out, from the point of view of quantum mechanics a spontaneous doubling in the length of a rigid rod is quite possible (though admittedly almost infinitely unlikely, so that we would never be justified in believing a report of such an alleged occurrence). Even the wavelength of cesium light is a standard of length only if we are in not too great a gravitational field. It can be seen, therefore, that a purely operational definition of length is foreign to modern science, and that what really happens is that the standard of length (the space-time metric tensor) is postulated within a theory, and the theory is loosely tied to experience by means of rough correspondence rules (and even these would be unnecessary in the case of a Feyerabendian consummation of science, in which our observational talk would all be done within the theoretical language itself).

One reason why Grünbaum appears to deny that   **247**

geometry is an explanatory theory analogous to electromagnetic theory, as an example, is that with a suitable transformation of the mathematical form of physical laws we can have (provided that we choose a geometry with the appropriate topology) whatever geometry we like. (Look at the replacement of the rectangular grid by the wavy one in Figures 12 and 13 above.) But, Putnam replies,[18] could we not remetrize many admittedly *physical* quantities just as well—for example replace pressure P by a remetrized $f(P)$? Where P occurred in a physical law f' (P) will now occur where f' is the inverse function of f. Does this mean that pressure also is "metrically amorphous"? If not, then a space-time interval can be regarded as a physical quantity just as much as can pressure.

It seems to me that we are getting into a morass which can be avoided only by *rejecting* Grünbaum's distinction between merely descriptive simplicity and what he calls "inductive" simplicity. In particular consider the law: "the world-line of a body not acted on by any (non-gravitational) forces, e.g., a light ray or a space-satellite, is a geodesic".[6] Under an arbitrary remetrization of space-time this would have to be replaced by something very much more complicated, and it would surely lose its explanatory force. For it would no longer appear as a maximum or minimum principle (analogous for example to Newton's first law of motion in classical physics) but as something messy and unbelievable save on the assumption that we have remetrized space-time in such a way as to *obscure* the manner in which space-time really exists. In which case can we not say that space-time *really is* such that for a free particle $\delta \int ds = 0$ (i.e., its world-line is a geodesic)?

Our picture then is of geometry as a physical hypothesis rather loosely tied to experience by correspond-

---

[6]A geodesic is either the shortest or longest distance between two points. Thus on the surface of the earth geodesics are great circles. Because g_{11}, g_{22} and g_{33} are negative geodesics in the space-time of relativity, they are *longest* distances.

ence rules which are *not* definitions and are *not* inviolable. In this respect it is no different from the theory, for example, that matter is composed of certain sorts of subatomic particles. It remains to say a few words relating geometry, as thus thought of, to geometry as it is thought of by pure mathematicians who study various kinds of spaces without worrying about whether they are physically realized.

We need to distinguish therefore *a priori* geometry (geometry as it presents itself to the pure mathematician) and physical geometry. Until the work of W. Bolyai and N. I. Lobachevski in the first half of the nineteenth century this distinction between pure and physical geometry was not understood, since it was believed that there was only one geometry, Euclidean geometry, and so a purely mathematical study of geometry could not fail to be applicable to actual space. However Bolyai and Lobachevski independently showed that it was possible to develop a geometry in which the axiom of parallels in Euclidean geometry is replaced by the axiom that through any point P not on a line L there is more than one parallel to L. (There are two lines through P which are called parallels to L, and moreover any of the infinite sheaf of lines between these parallels also does not intersect L.) By giving it an interpretation within Euclidean geometry, it is possible to show that the geometry of Bolyai and Lobachevski ("hyperbolic" geometry) is consistent if Euclidean geometry is. Words such as "straight line" are of course given a different meaning in the interpretation, but when we give these words the new Euclidean meanings we see that the axioms of hyperbolic geometry remain true.

Another way of denying the axiom of parallels is to say that there are *no* parallels to a given line through a point not on it. If the geometry is fully axiomatized, as by David Hilbert, there is now also a need for a consequential change in some of the purely topological axioms. Thus it will not be true that if B is between A and

C, then C is not between A and B. In this way we get elliptic geometry.

Hyperbolic and elliptic geometries are, like Euclidean geometry, geometries of constant curvature. Of course we are talking about three-dimensional spaces now, and the curvature of such spaces can not be visualized intuitively, as we can visualize the curved look of a sphere or hyperboloid. Curvature of space at a point P is given a purely mathematical definition. We can see how it works if we consider a two-dimensional case. Suppose that we draw a right angled triangle (whose sides are great circles) on the surface of a sphere. It will be discovered that Pythagoras' theorem is not obeyed. Thus the "curvature" of the surface of the sphere could be discovered by beings who lived only on the surface.

In the Euclidean case we have $ds^2 = dx^2 + dy^2$, where ds is the length of the hypotenuse of a small triangle whose sides have length dx and dy. In the most general case we have $ds^2 = g_{11}dx^2 + 2 g_{12} dx\, dy + g_{22}\, dy^2$. If it is a space of "variable curvature" g_{11}, g_{12} and g_{21} will be functions of x and y. The "curvature at a point" can be defined simply in terms of g_{11}, g_{12} and g_{22}, and is equal to the Gaussian curvature $\dfrac{1}{R_1 R_2}$ where R_1 and R_2 are the principal radii of curvature at the point. In the two-dimensional case R_1 and R_2 can themselves be visualized, but though this can not be done in the case of three or more dimensions, we can still define curvature in terms of g_{11}, g_{12}, etc. Thus in the four-dimensional case it is possible to define curvature in terms of the g_{11}, g_{12}, etc., which occur in the formula:

$$ds^2 = g_{11}\, dx^2 + g_{22}\, dy^2 + g_{33}\, dz^2 + g_{44}\, dt^2$$
$$+ 2 g_{12}\, dx\, dy + 2 g_{13}\, dx\, dz + 2 g_{14}\, dx\, dt$$
$$+ 2 g_{23}\, dy\, dz + 2 g_{24}\, dy\, dt + 2 g_{34}\, dz\, dt$$

Where the g's are functions of x, y, z, t we get the case of a space of variable curvature, which is needed by the general theory of relativity.

We noted that hyperbolic geometry can be shown to be consistent, if Euclidean geometry is, by interpreting it within Euclidean geometry. However if analysis, i.e., the mathematical theory of the real number, is assumed to be consistent, it is a simple matter to show the consistency of any geometry, whether Euclidean or non-Euclidean and whether of constant curvature or of variable curvature. Points are simply defined (to take the three-dimensional case) as triples of real numbers, planes as classes of triples of real numbers which satisfy equations of the first degree, lines as classes of triples of real numbers which satisfy pairs of equations of the first degree, and so on. The axioms of the geometry can be seen to be true under such a reinterpretation, and so the geometry must be consistent if analysis is.

In the case of an axiomatization of pure geometry, such as Hilbert's, it is commonly said that points, lines, and planes are "anything that satisfies the axioms". More precisely, Nagel[19] has characterized the axioms of pure geometry as "statement forms", that is, in the terminology of Chapter 2 above, sentence schemata. Thus on Nagel's view, the pure geometer shows merely that certain sentence schemata can be deduced from certain other schemata. This could be shown by expressing the axioms in the terminology of the predicate calculus and using only certain specific sentence letters instead of "point", "line", "plane", etc. It would then appear that so long as these sentence letters were not given an interpretation, the pure geometer would not be making any assertions and would have no subject matter.

However if the pure geometer does not wish to think of himself as without a subject matter, he can always give himself a subject matter which is independent of the nature of physical space by interpreting his schemata within the theory of the real number. Thus "is a point" in three-dimensional geometry will cease to be a mere schema (like "Fx") and will become the concrete predicate "is a triple of real numbers". The particular geometry is got by specifying the functions which correspond to the g's in the equation $ds^2 = \Sigma\, g_{ik}\, dx_i\, dx_k$.

In a geometrized physics, such as we saw was envisaged by J. A. Wheeler, space-time points are postulated as theoretical entities: they become the ultimate stuff of the world. Zeno once asked the question how dimensionless points could make up extended figures. Grünbaum has applied modern theory of dimension to solve this paradox.[20] According to the theory of dimension any finite or denumerable set of points has dimension zero, but a *non-denumerable* (continuous) set of points can have dimension one or greater than one. (Strictly speaking it is sets of points, not points, to which we ascribe dimensions, and so the term "dimensionless points" is not really meaningful. What is meant in talking of dimensionless points might be said better by talking of unit sets of points of dimension zero.)

Thus the question "What is geometry about?" may be answered in various ways. As it occurs in a geometrized physics geometry is about space-time points. In a particle physics making use entirely of a relational concept of space and time, geometry is incorporated in a physics which is about these particles alone, and relative positions come out as relations among these particles.[7] In the case of pure axiomatic geometry the axioms and theorems can be regarded merely as sentence schemata, but if it is wished to regard them as statements, they can be given an interpretation within the theory of the real number. Analytic geometry is either physical geometry (about postulated space-time points) or is pure geometry, in which case it is about sets of real numbers.

[7]For how to do this see W. V. Quine, *Word and Object*, section 52.[21]

SUGGESTIONS FOR FURTHER READING

A good account of the history of philosophical and scientific theories of space will be found in Max Jammer's *Concepts of Space*, revised edition (New York: Harper and Row, 1960). *The Philosophy of Space and Time* by Hans Reichenbach (New York: Dover, 1958), contains a useful discussion of non-Euclidean geometries and of space-time in special and general relativity. More recent discussions are those of Adolf Grünbaum, *Philosophical Problems of Space and Time* (New York: Alfred A. Knopf, 1963) and O. Costa de Beauregard, *La Notion de Temps, équivalence avec l'éspace* (Paris: Hermann, 1963). An even more recent work by Grünbaum, which could not be discussed in the present volume is his *Modern Science and Zeno's Paradoxes* (Middletown, Conn.: Wesleyan University Press, 1967). Somewhat dated but still useful popularizations of the theory of relativity will be found in E. Borel, *Space and Time* (New York: Dover, 1960), originally published in a French edition, 1922, and Sir Arthur Eddington, *Space, Time and Gravitation* (New York: Harper and Row, 1959), originally published by Cambridge University Press in 1920. Einstein's first paper on relativity, "On the Electrodynamics of Moving Bodies", and H. Minkowski's "Space and Time", made use of quite easy mathematics only, and can be found in *The Principle of Relativity, A Collection of Original Memoirs on the Special and General Theory of Relativity*, by H. A. Lorentz, A. Einstein, H. Minkowski and H. Weyl, with notes by A. Sommerfeld, and translated by W. Perrett and G. B. Jeffrey (London: Methuen, 1923, and in paperback, New York: Dover Books, 1952). A collection of readings on the philosophy of space and time, edited with an introduction by J. J. C. Smart, is *Problems of Space and Time* (New York: Macmillan, 1964). This contains a reprinting of Minkowski's paper, and also selections from Leibniz, Newton and Mach on absolute and relative theories of space. It also contains a useful paper by H. P. Robertson, "Geometry as a Branch of Physics"; part of Reichenbach's essay, "The Philosophical Significance of the Theory of Relativity"; and an extract from autobiographical notes by Einstein, all of which originally appeared in P. A. Schilpp (ed.), *Albert Einstein, Philosopher—Scientist* (La Salle, Ill.: Open Court, 1951, and paperback, New York: Harper and Row, 1959). Newton's theories of space and time were criticized by George Berkeley in the eighteenth century, in his *Principles of Philosophy*, sections 110–116 and his *De Motu*. An account of Berkeley as a precursor of Mach and Einstein is given in Chapter 6 of K. R. Popper's *Conjectures and Refutations* (London: Routledge and Kegan Paul, 1963, and New York: Basic Books, 1963). Leibniz's account of the relational theory of space and time is best got from *The Leibniz—Clarke Correspondence*, which has been edited by H. G. Alexander (Manchester: Manchester University Press, 1956, and New York: Barnes and Noble, 1964). Clarke was a supporter of Newton. Alexander's own introduction to this volume is of considerable interest.   **253**

Chapter 9 of Ernest Nagel's *Structure of Science* (New York: Harcourt, Brace and World, 1961), contains a discussion of alternative geometries, with an outline of the approach to a unified treatment of non-Euclidean geometries from the point of view of projective geometry. On this matter see Felix Klein, *Elementary Mathematics from an Advanced Standpoint*, translated from the third German edition by E. R. Hedrick and C. A. Noble (New York: Dover, 1939), Part 3, especially pp. 174–184.

On the clock paradox there is a very concise and lucid note by W. H. McCrea in *Discovery*, XVIII (February 1957), 56–58, and another lucid discussion is that on pp. 215–222 and 231–232 of G. J. Whitrow's *Natural Philosophy of Time* (London: Nelson, 1961, and paperback, New York: Harper and Row, 1963). A non-geometrical discussion is given by Adolf Grünbaum in his paper "The Clock Paradox in the Special Theory of Relativity", *Philosophy of Science*, XXI (1954), 249–253 and replies to discussions of this, *Philosophy of Science*, XXII (1955), 53, 233. On Zeno's metrical paradox of extension (the question of how to build up an extended space and time from unextended elements), see Chapter 6 of Grünbaum's *Philosophical Problems of Space and Time, op. cit.*, or his more detailed treatment in "A Consistent Conception of the Extended Linear Continuum as an Aggregate of Unextended Elements", *Philosophy of Science*, XIX (1952), 288–306 and in Chapter 3 of his book *Modern Science and Zeno's Paradoxes* (Middletown, Conn.: Wesleyan University Press, 1967). Hilary Putnam's paper "An Examination of Grünbaum's Philosophy of Geometry" in B. Baumrin (ed.), *Philosophy of Science, The Delaware Seminar*, Vol. 2, 1962–63 (New York: Interscience, 1963), pp. 204–255, is not always quite fair to Grünbaum, as when he criticizes Grünbaum's discussion of Zeno's metrical paradox of extension as though he were talking about Zeno's quite different paradoxes of motion, but as an independent discussion of the philosophy of space it is very valuable. Grünbaum's reply to Putnam's paper will be found in the forthcoming volume of *Boston Studies in the Philosophy of Science* and Grünbaum's forthcoming book, *Geometry and Chronometry in Philosophical Perspective* (Minneapolis: University of Minnesota Press).

An excellent popular account of questions of symmetry in physics (including the downfall of parity) can be found in Martin Gardner's witty book *The Ambidextrous Universe* (New York: Basic Books, 1964). See also Eugene P. Wigner, "Violations of Symmetry in Physics", *Scientific American*, CCXIII (December 1965), 28–36.

8

Direction
in time

The supposed passage of time

In the last chapter we adopted the point of view that the universe is a four-dimensional space-time manifold. Present, past, and future are all equally real. When we say that an event is in the future we are saying that it is later than our utterance, when we say that it is present we are saying that it is simultaneous with our utterance, and when we say that it is past we are saying that it is earlier than our utterance. The present, of course, partakes of the relativity of simultaneity, unless as seems plausible, we interpret presentness as simultaneity to an utterance relative to the system in which the utterer is at rest. However these refinements do not matter much. "Present", "past", and "future" are terms of our ordinary language, and science can get on much better without them. An objectionable feature of the sentences "E is present", "E is past", and "E is future", is that they are context dependent: their truth values depend on the times of their utterance. For scientific purposes "E is simultaneous with E_0", where E_0 is some reference event, does much better. Or better still, *"E* is at *t"* where *t* is the time coordinate of *E*. Within scientific theory we of course use "is" in a tenseless sense: "the eclipse of the moon is at *t"*, when said earlier or later than *t*, of course does not mean that the eclipse of the moon is at *that time* at *t*.

We do indeed have a feeling that the concept of the present is metaphysically important; it seems to be the crest of the wave on which we (like surfers) are being rushed forward into the future. Such metaphysical feelings are very confused: it is nonsense to say that we are rushing into the future; no wave can flow upwards through space-time, since time is already there in space-time. We talk of motion through space, and from the point of view of space-time this is just a matter of relative inclinations of world-lines, since my motion relative to you is just the rate of change of the distance between us with respect to time. There is clearly no room in the space-time picture for movement *through* space-time.[1]

Since movement is change of space with respect to time, what would movement through time be? Change of time with respect to what? Our feeling that we are moving through time[2] is therefore a sort of metaphysical illusion based on confusion of thought. At first sight it might seem to be explained simply by the fact that our stock of memories is always increasing, for example that five minutes from now we shall have more memories than we have now. If we identify ourselves with our stock of memories we perhaps get the feeling of being continually elongated in the time direction. This, how-ever, will not do. If we have more memories five min-utes hence than we have now, why do we not get the feeling of shrinking into the past just as easily as that of elongating into the future? Again, consider a very old

---

[1]For a clear statement of this point see Moritz Schlick, *Philosophy of Nature*, Chapter 7.[1]

[2]Or that future events are coming towards us.

man, whose memories are fading. May not his stock of memories actually be *decreasing* in size, as the acquisition of new ones is more than outweighed by the loss of old ones? The explanation of our confused feeling that we advance through time can not be simply that we have *more* memories at t_2 than we have at t_1 (where t_2 is later than t_1). The following suggestion may provide the answer. It is that at t_2 we have memories of various events E_1, E_2, E_3, . . . , and some of these events are themselves rememberings of other events in the set. Now suppose that E_1, E_2, E_3, . . . are related by a triadic relation of betweenness, so that if E_k is between E_h and E_l, E_h is not between E_k and E_l, and E_l is not between E_h and E_k. We can thus arrange E_1, E_2, E_3, . . . in an *order*, but this contains no intrinsic directionality. Let us, however, arbitrarily take one such direction so that the direction from E_n to E_{n+1} is the positive direction. We may find that we have chosen the direction so that if E_q is a remembering of E_p, the direction from E_p to E_q is always positive. Then our arbitrarily defined positive direction will have turned out to be the same as that from earlier to later. Now the mere fact that we are aware of earlier and later does not explain our subjective sense of progress through time. After all, we can distinguish north and south without feeling that one day we shall be Eskimos! Grünbaum, as I understand him, has suggested that our feeling of progress through time comes from the directionality imposed by the fact that our rememberings include rememberings of rememberings, and this imposes a directionality (from event remembered to remembering of it to the remembering of remembering of it) which possesses an obvious asymmetry.[3]

[3] I base the above remarks on some suggestions in p. 325 of Adolf Grünbaum's *Philosophical Problems of Space and Time*,[2] and the slightly fuller statement on p. 663 of Grünbaum's paper "Carnap's views on the Foundations of Geometry",[3] where Grünbaum says: "The flux of time consists in the *instantaneous awareness* of both the temporal order *and* the *diversity* of the membership of the set of remembered (recorded) or forgotten events, awarenesses in each of which the instant of its own occurrence constitutes a *distinguished element*".

Whether the above mentioned ideas are correct or not, it would seem at any rate that our confused idea of time flow has something to do with the asymmetry inherent in memory: that memories are of events which occur earlier than the memories, not later than them. That memories are of earlier events is a special case of a very general phenomenon, which is that of the asymmetry of records or traces. Thus today a tape recorder can have on its tape a record of yesterday's philosophy meeting, but it can not have one of tomorrow's meeting. Today's footprint among the rose bushes can be a record of last week's burglary, but not of next week's one. A fossil in the rocks may constitute a trace of an animal that lived a hundred million years ago, but there is nothing in the rocks to tell us about future species. Memories themselves consist of certain physical traces in the brain.[4] Can we find what is common to all cases of records or traces, whether brain traces, tape recordings, footprints, fossils, or anything else, and which explains why they give more or less reliable knowledge of earlier occurrences, not of later ones? The epistemological asymmetry seems to be a sign of a widespread physical asymmetry in the universe, or at the least, in our part of it.

It is true of course that we know a good deal about the future. An astronomer can predict the positions of the planets, and, rather less surely, we can predict storms from a weather report in the newspaper, and from a crack in a girder we can predict the collapse of a bridge. These cases of prediction are those which are subsumable under the "covering law" model (see Chapter 3), and in the case of prediction from laws there is indeed a symmetry between past and future. The way in which an astronomer predicts the position of Jupiter six months hence is no different from the way

[4]I write as a materialist. Even the psychophysical dualist would probably agree that if memories are not physical traces they depend on them, and so the issue of materialism as against other mind-body theories is not important here.

in which he retrodicts the position of Jupiter six months
ago. It will appear shortly that our knowledge of the
past through traces is rather different from retrodiction
by means of laws, but even should this not be conceded
it must surely be admitted that we can have very much
more extensive knowledge of the past in a way in which
we can not have detailed knowledge of the future, and
there must be some asymmetry in the universe, or at
least in our part of it, which will explain this familiar
fact.

Temporal asymmetry and statistical mechanics

Where does this temporal asymmetry come from? It
might be suggested that the asymmetry comes from the
laws of physics. This seems unlikely. The laws of classical mechanics and electrodynamics are time symmetrical: that is, if some function of $+t$ is a solution to them,
so is the same function of $-t$. (This is because their time
derivatives are all of the second order.) This feature of
classical mechanics is still preserved in ordinary quantum mechanics. (It is true that Schrödinger's equation
contains a first order time derivative, but this is multiplied by the square root of minus one. If we eliminated
the square root of minus one, we should have to square
the first order time derivative, and this shows that time
symmetry is still preserved in Schrödinger's equation.)
Phenomenological thermodynamics is of course not time
symmetrical, but we have rejected the claim that this
is a fundamentally correct theory. Consider, for example, the phenomenological "law" that a body sliding over a rough surface will slow down by friction. It
never happens in our experience that the reverse phenomenon happens: a body at rest on a rough surface
begins to move and gradually increases its velocity.
However this is not because it is contrary to the laws of
nature but because it is very unlikely. Imagine molecules of the rough surface coming out to hit molecules of   **259**

the sliding object, and molecules of the sliding object coming out to hit molecules of the rough surface. Reverse all these velocities and you get the case of the object at rest beginning to move, with a cooling down of the surface and the object.

A qualification may need to be made to the assertion that the fundamental laws of nature are time symmetrical. An experiment by J. H. Christenson, J. W. Cronin, V. L. Fitch, and R. Turlay,[4] reported in 1964, does suggest a possible violation of time symmetry (though there is still a symmetry if we reverse not just time alone but charge and parity as well). However I gather that it is not absolutely certain that the only good way to explain this experimental result is by postulating a violation of time symmetry. Moreover it is hard to see how such a very recondite violation of time symmetry could have much to do with the very obvious temporal asymmetry of records or traces with which we are concerned in this chapter.

Consider a pack of cards which is initially arranged in suits. Let us suppose that the cards are indestructible and are shuffled by an immortal shuffler. If the shuffling goes on long enough (an extraordinarily long time, of course) the pack of cards will come back again to its initial state of being ordered in suits. Indeed the shuffling will bring the cards back to the initial state over and over again, and eventually it will even be the case that the cards will return to the orderly state from a very disorderly state through precisely the reverse sequence of those intermediate steps which took the cards from their orderly to their well shuffled state. Over infinite time a particular piece of shuffling is no more nor less probable than the exact mirror image in time of this particular piece of shuffling. The reason why we think of shuffling as an irreversible process is simply because if we start from an arrangement in suits and shuffle for some specified time it is almost certain that the cards will end up in a "well shuffled" state. And this is because the number of states which we are willing to call "shuffled" is incomparably greater than the number of states which we are willing to call "ordered in suits".

Consider now a container which contains two gases in separate compartments separated by a wall. If we remove the containing wall the gases will mix. We can be quite sure of this, because the number of sub-microscopically distinct states of the two gases which count as "mixed" states is vastly greater than the number of sub-microscopically distinct states which count as "unmixed".

Suppose that we have n molecules of one gas in part A of the container and n' molecules of the other gas in part B of the container. Let us divide up each compartment into m small cells. Then, treating each molecule as distinguishable from every other, there are $m^n \cdot m^{n'}$ different configurations. When the barrier is removed there are $2m$ positions available to each molecule, and so the number of different configurations rises to $(2m)^n \cdot (2m)^{n'}$ which is greater by a factor of $2^n \cdot 2^{n'}$. No wonder mixed states of the gases are incomparably more common than are unmixed states. However this does not mean that any *one* "mixed" sub-microscopically distinct configuration is any the more probable than is any *one* "unmixed" configuration.

In statistical mechanics the sub-microscopic state of a gas depends not only on the positions of molecules but also on their momenta. (Sometimes their angular momenta of rotation and other parameters may also need to be discussed, but we shall here discuss only their translational momenta.) Consider n molecules. We can envisage a six-dimensional space giving the kth molecule a position $(x_k, y_k, z_k, p_{xk}, p_{yk}, p_{zk})$, where (x_k, y_k, z_k) are its spatial coordinates and (p_{xk}, p_{yk}, p_{zk}) are its components of momentum. Then instead of considering n molecules in the six-dimensional space we can consider one representative particle in a $6n$-dimensional space. This useful fiction is called a phase space. The principle of conservation of energy implies that the particle will trace out a path on a $(6n - 1)$-dimensional hypersurface in the phase space. Suppose we divide up this hypersurface into a large number of arbitrarily small cells. Then except for exceptional initial conditions the representative particle will eventually pass through every one of these cells. This is the "ergodic theorem". A case of exceptional initial conditions for which this theorem would not hold is one in which all molecules are in a rectangular container from whose walls they are reflected perfectly elastically, and all their motions are parallel to the sides of the box and they are never on collision courses with one another. Such a case could not occur in nature.

The probability of a state in which all the molecules of a gas have the positions $q_1, q_2, \ldots q_n$ and velocities $v_1, v_2, \ldots v_n$ respectively can be shown to be equal to the probability for positions $q_1, q_2, \ldots q_n$ (as before) together with the opposite velocities $-v_1, -v_2, \ldots -v_n$. This seems to have the paradoxical consequence, to which J. Loschmidt[5] drew attention, that mixing processes should be as common in a thermodynamically closed and finite system as are unmixing processes. A partial solution to this paradox lies in the reflection that any small closed (or almost closed) systems which we observe do not remain closed (or almost closed) systems for very long, and so theorems about what happens over a very long time can not apply. Nevertheless, there does remain a problem, to be considered later, as to why if we consider a large ensemble of systems over a short time (instead of one system over a long time) we do not find mixing and unmixing processes to be equally common.

More light can be shed on Loschmidt's paradox if we make a certain contrary-to-fact assumption. Let us suppose that the universe is a closed finite system of perfectly elastic Newtonian particles and that it is neither expanding nor contracting. We can ensure its closedness and finitude by assuming that these particles exist in a finite but unbounded elliptic space.[5] In such a case Loschmidt's paradox would be realized, and any evolutions of this universe would eventually be followed by precisely the reverse devolutions. (Or precisely enough, in the sense that however small the cells into which we subdivided phase space, the "representative point" of the system would eventually pass through the same sequence of cells in phase space in the reverse order. "Eventually" here of course refers to an almost inconceivably long time, even by comparison with the whole period of evolution of our galactic system.) For example, if our universe were a finite nonexpanding one of the sort entertained in our supposition, people just like us, far in the future, would be performing exactly the same actions, and having exactly the same sensory stimuli, except backwards in time.[6] It is worth pointing out, however, that such people would not feel any different. Since, according to our direction of earlier and later, the memory traces in brains in the time-reversed era would occur before the events of which they were traces, their concepts of earlier and later would also be the reverse of ours, and time for them would seem to go in the reverse direction from that in which it seems to go for us. There would therefore be a complete mirror image symmetry in time not only in the world at large but also in subjective experience: to people in a time reversed era it would still seem that

---

[5]S. Toulmin, in his contribution to *Metaphysical Beliefs*,[6] has made what seems to be an unjustified objection to treating the universe as a thermodynamically closed system. He says that a thermodynamically closed system is one which is isolated from outside influences, but that there can be no outside in the case of the universe. Toulmin's argument appears to depend partly on his contention that it is *meaningless* to talk of the surroundings of the universe. It seems to me that to talk of the surroundings of the universe is contradictory rather than meaningless. Since the negation of a contradiction is a truth, we can truly say that the universe has no surroundings. If we define "system S is isolated from its surroundings" as "there are no surroundings of S which causally influence S" then, trivially, S is isolated when it has no surroundings at all.

[6]In fact an infinite number of times, both in the same temporal direction and in the reverse direction.

the memory followed the remembered event, and the wound would still follow the blow.[7]

With respect to our actual universe we can not assume that it is finite (though it may be) nor that it is *not* expanding, since the red shifts observed in distant galaxies very strongly suggest that the universe *is* expanding. Cosmological thermodynamics is thus a difficult and questionable subject. Let us consider the question of the apparent temporal asymmetry of that space-time region of the universe in which we find ourselves and which we can easily observe. How is it that within this region at least there seems to be an asymmetry about traces, for example that there can be photographs or magnetic tapes of earlier events but not of later ones? Let us consider the thermodynamic characteristics of such things.

Suppose that we have an unbalanced die, with the probabilities for faces 1, 2, 3, 4, 5, 6 respectively p_1, p_2, p_3, p_4, p_5, p_6. Clearly $p_1 + p_2 + p_3 + p_4 + p_5 + p_6 = 1$. Let us suppose that we know these probabilities and are told that the die will be thrown on a certain occasion. How uncertain are we of the outcome? Suppose $p_6 = 0.99$ and that $p_1 = p_2 = p_3 = p_4 = p_5 = .002$. In this case we can be almost certain that a 6 will be thrown. There is thus very little uncertainty in the outcome to be dispelled by an actual throw, since in most cases the outcome of the throw will simply confirm our expectation. Intuitively it seems plausible to say that the maximum uncertainty to be dispelled by an actual throw occurs when $p_1 = p_2 = p_3 = p_4 = p_5 = p_6 = \frac{1}{6}$. Consider then this definition of the "information" (due to C. E. Shannon[8]) to be conveyed by an actual throw

$$H = -\sum_1^6 p_i \log p_i$$

In the case where the p_i are all equal to $\frac{1}{6}$ this comes

---

[7]F. H. Bradley considered that in a universe in which time direction was reversed, "Death would come before birth, the blow would follow the wound, and all must seem irrational".[7]

to $-\frac{1}{6} \log \frac{1}{6}$. (Note that $\log \frac{1}{6}$ is negative and so $- \log \frac{1}{6}$ is positive.) When there is no uncertainty in the outcome $H = 0$. Where the p_i are very unequal H is near to 0. For example, as p_6 approaches 1, the quantity H approaches 0, and we can also say that $H = 0$ for the case where $p_6 = 1$ and $p_1 = p_2 = p_3 = p_4 = p_5 = 0$, even though $\sum_1^6 p_i \log p_i$ is indeterminate in this case. It can be suspected already that H provides a good measure of something like information, for in the case where $p_6 = 1$ there is no uncertainty to be dispelled, and hence no information to be gained, by a throw of the die. In general if the probabilities of n alternative events are p_1, $p_2, \ldots p_n$, then the information to be gained by observing which one of them actually occurs is given by

$$H = - \sum_{i=1}^{n} p_i \log p_i.$$

Now recall the notion of phase space in statistical mechanics and let the p_i be the probability of the representative particle being in the ith cell of phase space. It can be seen that H as defined above becomes a maximum where the p_i are all equal. This is also the case in which the entropy is a maximum. In fact H as defined above is just minus one times Boltzmann's quantity H, and it is equivalent to entropy as defined by Boltzmann. Boltzmann's H theorem asserts that in a closed system his H decreases, which comes to much the same as to say that the entropy increases. Indeed sometimes entropy is simply *defined* as $\sum_{i=1}^{n} p_i \log p_i$ (or, better, by making the cells of phase space infinitely small, as $\int F \log F d\omega$ where F is a function which determines the probability of finding a molecule very close to a certain point of phase space).

This connection between information as defined in information theory and entropy as defined in statistical mechanics has given rise to one of the exciting ideas of recent science (though one to be handled cautiously), and it becomes at once more plausible that the information content of such things as photographs and magnetic tapes may have something to do with their low entropy as physical systems.

This may be so, even though it is the case that the term "information" in information theory is a technical one, which is used in a sense which is rather different from the ordinary one. Let us briefly examine some of the differences.

If we take the logarithms in the formula $H = -\sum_{i=1}^{n} p_i \log$

p_i to the base two, our unit of information (called a "bit", short for "binary digit") corresponds to the case where $H = -(\frac{1}{2} \log \frac{1}{2} + \frac{1}{2} \log \frac{1}{2})$, since this is equal to one when our logarithms are taken to the base two.

Suppose now that we have (as is of course possible) an alphabet consisting solely of 0's and 1's. Let it be an empirical fact that the frequency of 0's in a long piece of discourse is $\frac{1}{2}$, and similarly for the 1's. Let it also be the case, as is unlikely with any actual alphabet that the probability of a 0 or a 1 occurring is quite independent of what symbols have preceded it. (An extreme case which shows that this kind of assumption is not possible in English, is that the probability of "u" following "q" is very near to 1, whereas the frequency of u's in any long piece of discourse is rather small, and not at all close to 1.) Information theory can of course deal with cases in which the probability of a symbol occurring depends on the probabilities of those that have gone before (Markoff processes), but here, for mathematical simplicity, we are considering a sequence of 0's and 1's which are such that the probability of a 0 or a 1 occurring is always $\frac{1}{2}$, even relative to whatever other symbols have already occurred. I must stress that this is here meant as merely a simplifying expository device, since in any actual language rules of spelling and of syntax, as well as most probably of semantics too, would prevent the probability of a given symbol occurring from being independent of its place in the sequence of symbols. (Any actual language must contain a good deal of "redundancy", in the information theory sense of this word.)

With the above assumption then, consider a sequence of n 0's and 1's which are transmitted by some signaling system. This conveys n bits of information in the sense that n bits of uncertainty as to what will be sent are resolved by the signal as it is received. Let us suppose now that the sender and the receiver use the above binary code to send information in the *ordinary* sense of the word, i.e., what we shall call "semantic information", in the following way. Suppose that there are 100 squash[8] matches being played, in every case between well matched teams, so that in every case the recipient of the message is quite uncertain of the outcome, in the sense that he is inclined to give a probability of $\frac{1}{2}$ to either team winning. The sender and the recipient of the message each have a numbered list of the contests, and the convention is that if the nth digit transmitted is a "0" this signifies that the home team has won, and if it is a "1" it signifies that the away team has won. In this case we can equate the measure of the "semantic information" with the "information theory" information: the uncertainty as to what sequence of "0" and "1" will be sent is n bits, and so is the uncertainty as to the outcome of the n contests. In general, however, we can not equate semantic information with information theory information. This is partly because in general there is no simple correlation between the probability of, say, the word "blue" being sent and the probability of the thing of which the word is being predicated being blue. Questions of redundancy also complicate this issue. But the chief reasons why there is usually no simple relation between "information theory" information and "semantic" information are the following two. (1) It is not easy

[8] I have chosen squash rather than another game because I wish for simplicity to avoid the possibility of ties.

to give a definition of semantic information, except on certain artificial assumptions, which suppose a language whose propositions are then either atomic or their truth functions.[9] (2) Suppose that in a particular tractable case, such as the above one of the squash matches, we have the convention that the $(m + 1)$th digit gives the result of the mth match, and that the first digit is reserved for telling us whether or not *all* the home teams won. If all the home teams did win, then the first digit would give us n bits of semantic information and only 1 bit of "information theory" information. For the information theory information was calculated on the assumption that the probability of a "0" or a "1" is always $\frac{1}{2}$, even though, once we know the semantic rule, we can see that this is not true of the first digit.

In spite of the above, it is surely still true that in any signaling system, if no information theory information is sent — if the channel just emits "noise" — then no semantic information is sent in the channel. (Of course this may *indirectly* provide us with information about the channel, and even about the sender. If we observe artillery shells falling near a radio station which is about to begin operating, and nothing is subsequently heard in our earphones but sundry crackles, we suspect that the radio station has been knocked out.)

In information theory we are generally concerned with what Reichenbach has called "macroentropy".[10] In statistical mechanics, which we may call "microstatistics", we are concerned with the statistical distributions of the positions and momenta of molecules, but in macrostatistics we are concerned with the statistical distributions of the properties of macroscopic things. For example the objects of our macrostatistics may be grains of sand on a beach. From what we know of the probabilities, a fairly smooth stretch of beach is very much more probable than is a stretch of sand containing

[9]A definition of semantic information relative to a rather simple language has been given by Y. Bar-Hillel and R. Carnap.[9]

a footprint. That is, save on the assumption of the inter-action of a man walking on the beach with the sand of the beach, an indentation of the beach with the shape of a footprint is most improbable. Wind and weather, op-erating by chance, might scoop out such a shape, but it is most unlikely. For this reason the presence of a foot-print is a reliable indicator of the interaction of the beach with an outside system. We can say that the mac-roentropy of the beach has been decreased. It is the decrease of the macroentropy which makes the foot-print a reliable indicator, and not the decrease of mi-croentropy, even though in this case it is plausible to suppose that the microentropy has indeed been de-creased. (The microentropy of the total system, beach plus pedestrian, will of course have increased, and any reduction of the microentropy of the beach will be at the cost of a more than compensatory increase of en-tropy in the walker's body. Until he can acquire energy from his next meal every fresh step depletes his stored up energy and results in an increase of entropy in his body.)

To see clearly that it is the decrease of macroentropy, not necessarily of microentropy, which makes a system into a record, consider the case of a photographic re-production of a printed page. When a photon hits a photographic plate it blackens it slightly. This is because the light energy loosens the chemical bond in a silver bromide molecule in the emulsion, leading to an in-crease of entropy. We need not worry, however, about the full chemical details (e.g., whether or not there is an increase of entropy in the blackened regions of the plate, after the further chemical process of fixing) be-cause if (let us suppose) blackening corresponds to a change of entropy in one direction, then whitening cor-responds to a change of entropy the other way. Now since a page of black letters on white conveys the same information as white on black (it has the same macroen-tropy) it is quite clear that a decrease of macroentropy **269** could just as well correspond to an increase of microentropy as to a decrease of it.

The above point can be made clear by means of Figure 14. Here we have a sequence of areas of high microentropy (disordered regions) interspersed with occasional areas of low microentropy (highly ordered regions), which perhaps function as dots and dashes of Morse code. This can convey a signal neither better nor worse than the case of Figure 15, which is like Figure 14, except that where there are regions of high entropy in the one figure there are regions of low entropy in the other, and vice-versa. The ordered and disordered regions might be magnetized and unmagnetized regions of a tape, for example.

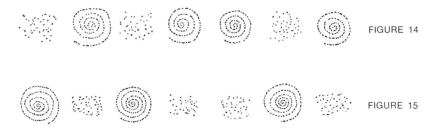

FIGURE 14

FIGURE 15

Nevertheless it probably remains true that in nearly all cases of *natural* records (e.g., footprints, fossils), systems with low macroentropy also in fact are systems of low microentropy. For a tendency to high microentropy is the norm, and it is usually low microentropy which makes a system stand out from its surroundings as evidence of interaction between the system which contains it and some outside system (e.g., between the beach and a pedestrian).

A footprint in the sand will tend to increase its entropy until its entropy is once more characteristic of the wider system of which it is a part. In some cases, how-

ever, a subsystem of lower entropy will remain in equilibrium until such time as it loses its individuality as a
system: consider a magnetized tape which loses practically none of its magnetism until such time as the tape
happens to be destroyed. But whether it possesses increasing entropy or whether it remains in thermodynamic equilibrium, the subsystem in question remains
in a lower entropy state as compared with what we
should expect if we compared it with its surroundings.
(It is necessary to use this rather cumbersome way of
expressing the matter: it will not do to say "its entropy
is lower than that of its surroundings", since entropy
depends on mass, and a small subsystem therefore
usually has less entropy than the rest of a large system of which it forms part.)

A system which is temporarily (or, as Grünbaum has
pointed out,[11] *indefinitely*, if it is in equilibrium) of
lower entropy than would be expected when we compare it with its surroundings is the sort of system which
Reichenbach[12] called a *branch* system. Reichenbach
thought of such systems as branching off from the entropy curve of the universe as a whole. He asserted the
hypothesis that the directions from lower to higher entropy of the subsystems is in almost all cases the same
as the direction from lower to higher entropy of the
whole universe. His actual formulation was defective
through failing to take account of the matter discussed
in the parenthetical sentence at the end of the previous
paragraph. This however, is easily fixed up in the
aforesaid manner, but his remarks have a further de-
fect. Why bring the entropy of the whole universe into
it? We know very little about the entropy of the whole
universe, and moreover it is not evident that entropy
can be meaningfully defined for the universe as a whole
if the universe is an infinite system, as is supposed in
some cosmological hypotheses. This reference to the
entropy curve of the universe is not essential however,
and Grünbaum has replaced Reichenbach's hypothesis   **271**

with the hypothesis, which constitutes a generalization from what we observe as *de facto* the case around us, that almost all such systems run from lower to higher entropy (unless they are in equilibrium) in the same direction as one another. This avoids the questionable reference to the universe as a whole. We can then define the direction from earlier to later as the direction from lower to higher entropy of most branch systems.

If we define the direction from earlier to later in this way, the proposition that nearly all branch systems increase their entropy becomes true by definition, but nevertheless it is not trivially so. It depends on the fact that nearly all branch systems run the same way. Moreover it leaves room for the assertion that a particular system increases its entropy to be an empirical one.

Of course this definition of the direction from earlier to later is not a prerequisite for learning our ordinary use of words like "earlier" and "later". It is obvious that children learn words like "earlier" and "later" long before they know the meanings of words like "entropy". This is because they presumably learn the words by something approaching an ostensive definition: in an idealized situation we could imagine getting a child and, showing an orange briefly, then an apple, and saying things like "orange earlier, apple later". However if our hypothesis is correct, that memory traces in the brain are subsystems of temporarily lower entropy than is characteristic of their surroundings, then the physical possibility of such ostensive learning of the words "earlier" and "later" implies the correctness of the presupposition of our physical definition of time direction, namely the presupposition that nearly all branch systems run in the same direction. It follows from the above that attempts to treat the "earlier-later" relation as an indefinable one (on the grounds, admittedly true ones, that children do not learn to use the words "earlier" and "later" by means of verbal definitions) conceal the physical basis of the directionality of this relation.[10]

It is true, of course, that we could define an *ordering* relation of "earlier" and "later" even in a temporally symmetrical universe. We could fix on two arbitrary events E_1 and E_2 and make the following stipulations. If an event A is between E_1 and E_2 then it is later than E_1 and earlier than E_2. If it is not between E_1 and E_2 but E_2 is between E_1 and A, then A is later than both E_1 and E_2. If A is not between E_1 and E_2 but E_1 is between A and E_2, then A is earlier than both E_1 and E_2. (Here we have made the assumption that events can be ordered[11] in a topologically open time: like a line which is infinite in both directions. For a closed time, such as might conceivably be postulated by some cosmologists, a rather more complicated definition would be needed.) The point is, however, that such a definition of "earlier" and "later" for a temporally symmetrical universe would be arbitrary: it would not matter whether we chose our events E_1 and E_2 so that the direction of positive time went in the direction AB (where A and B are two definite events) or so that it went in the direction BA. We would be giving an arbitrary direction to time, just as we might arbitrarily draw a spatial axis either in the direction from south to north or in the direction from north to south.

The definition of the direction from earlier to later in terms of the direction of entropy increase of most branch systems is not an arbitrary one, as would be that in terms of the direction from one to the other of two arbitrarily chosen events. The direction does corre-

[10]There therefore seems to me to be something which could at least be misleading in Max Black's contention in his essay "The 'Direction' of Time"[13] that whether one event is earlier than another depends on these events alone. However I am not sure whether I actually disagree with Black, especially in view of his cautious final paragraph.

[11]Grünbaum calls the ordering relation of betweenness for a topologically open time "o-betweenness".[14]

spond to something in the texture of the universe, or at least of that part of it with which we are acquainted.

We might ask what sort of fact it is that the vast majority of branch systems in our experience run from lower to higher entropy (unless they are in equilibrium) in the same temporal direction. Grünbaum regards it as a nomologically contingent one, or, in other words, as something which does not follow from the laws of nature alone. It is just a fact[15] which seems to be suggested by the sample of branch systems which we observe in the universe around us. This nomologically contingent fact can be expressed as a postulate[16] about the randomness of the distribution of the micro-states corresponding to a given macro-state. Suppose that the macro-state we are concerned with consists of milk above tea in a cup. This is exemplified every time someone pours milk into his tea. The various micro-states corresponding to the macroscopically indistinguishable states "milk above tea" are distributed in a random manner, so that practically none of them are those rare states which would not quickly lead to a mingling of the milk with the tea.

Suppose, however, that there are two distinct portions of the universe for each of which the above randomization postulate holds. Let us suppose that "the direction of time", i.e., the direction in which most branch systems increase their entropy, is opposite for the two systems. If the two parts of the universe interacted we would have difficulty in envisaging the situation, since this would upset our randomization assumption. Let us consider, however, that these two parts of the universe interacted hardly at all, but that there was a very occasional chance interaction. Here we would have a case similar to that envisaged by Norbert Wiener.[17] Suppose that a stone is hurled by someone A in the first part into the other part, where, according to A, B catches it. But since B takes the direction of time in the opposite sense to A he will regard himself as throwing the stone and will say that it is he who throws it and A who catches it.

Suppose that we find a copy of the Bible lying on the lawn outside our house. As we look at it we see that it suddenly takes off into the air and disappears into the depths of space. Such an occurrence would be physically[12] possible: all the molecules in the earth might happen to rise upwards at the same moment, thus imparting their kinetic energy to the Bible and expelling it into space. However such an occurrence would be so unlikely that we might prefer the hypothesis that the Bible had been hurled into our world by some missionary in a time reversed world.

The above fantastic story suggests at least that the hypothesis of temporally reversed but simultaneous regions of the universe need not be devoid of the possibility of an empirical test. However the probability of such a case would seem to be almost infinitely unlikely. It would demand a partitioning of phase space for the whole universe into two distinct parts, which would mean that the entropy of the combined universe would be much higher than would be at all probable. (As against the case of entropy increases, through infinite time, of a finite but unbounded nonexpanding universe, where, as we have seen, periods of increase and decrease of entropy, relative to an arbitrarily chosen direction of positive time, would be equally common.)

We have been attempting to relate the temporal asymmetry of at least a large cosmic region of the universe which surrounds us, to considerations of entropy and statistical mechanics. Let us see how these statistical considerations tie up, if at all, with two other features which some writers have considered to be the

[12]Actually this is not correct unless we imagine the occurrence to occur on a planet of very low mass and without an atmosphere. Otherwise there would not be enough energy in the part of the lawn underneath the Bible. But such considerations do not matter here, where our illustration is obviously a fantastic one, and if we like we can make similar fantastic assumptions about the mass of our planet.

basis of the temporal asymmetry of the world. There is (1) the principle of retarded waves, and (2) the fact of the expansion of the universe.

The principle of retarded waves

We noted earlier that the equations of electromagnetism are temporally symmetrical in the sense that if $f(t)$ is a solution of them so is $f(-t)$. For example a spherical light wave emerging from a point source is no more nor less consistent with Maxwell's equations than is a spherical light wave coming in from infinity and contracting to a point sink. The former case is that of a retarded wave, and the latter that of an advanced wave. When we calculate the electric potential ϕ at a point P and a time t due to a varying charge ρ at a distance r from P, we do so on the basis of the value of ρ at a time $t - \dfrac{r}{c}$ (i.e., at a time at which a departing light signal from the charge will reach P at the time t) and not at the time $t + \dfrac{r}{c}$, which would equally furnish a solution of Maxwell's equations.[18] This is called taking the *retarded* potential. If we calculated the potential on the basis of ρ at $t + \dfrac{r}{c}$ this would be taking the advanced potential. The "retarded" solution gives us the case of a wave emitted from the varying charge, whereas the "advanced" solution would give us a wave coming in to the charge ρ and causing it to vary. The principle of retarded waves then is just this: we find lots of cases in which apparently waves are emitted from sources and go off to infinity, but none in which waves come in from infinity to sinks. There are of course waves which come in to sinks and which can be regarded, when we discuss radio receiving aerials, for example, as "advanced" waves, but these all are themselves also "retarded" waves coming from some source, e.g., some transmitting aerial.

Is this principle of retarded waves independent of the principle of increase of entropy? If it were the case that a spherically contracting wave were decreasing its entropy, whereas a spherically expanding wave were increasing its entropy, then the principle of retarded waves would be simply a special case of the entropic criterion of temporal direction. However the usual definition of entropy in statistical mechanics depends on a finitude of phase space, and can not be applied to the case of a spatially infinite system. Statistical mechanics makes use of the quasi-ergodic hypothesis that the representative particle in phase space passes arbitrarily near to every point of phase space, and it is hard to see how this could be made plausible in the case of an infinite system. It is an open question whether a suitable substitute for the quasi-ergodic hypothesis and perhaps a plausible redefinition of entropy is possible, which would enable statistical mechanics to cover cases of processes in infinite space, and which would show retarded waves as cases of increasing entropy and advanced waves as cases of decreasing entropy.

O. Costa de Beauregard[19] has argued for the equivalence of the two principles (of increasing entropy and of retarded waves) by means of a consideration of scattering phenomena. Stating what I take to be his argument in my own way, it comes to the following consideration. Suppose that a coherent optical wave is scattered by reflection at a grating or a mirror. The reflected wave is an incoherent one. If we were to reverse the process (take the advanced instead of the retarded solutions) we should have the very unlikely case of a number of incoherent waves producing, on reflection, a coherent one. So the matter of taking the retarded solution is the same as the matter of not expecting the unlikely to happen, that is, it is equivalent to the principle of increase of entropy. De Beauregard points out that even when in statistical mechanics we consider a number of particles, these must be thought of in terms of wave mechanics as wave phenomena, and the principle of increasing entropy turns out to be a scattering phenomenon, just as in the optical case, and the principle of increase of entropy turns out to be equivalent once more to the principle of retarded waves. If de Beauregard is correct, then Popper, who based temporal asymmetry on the prevalence in our experience of expanding waves, rather than of contracting waves, was not giving a distinct alternative to the statistical approach to the problem of temporal asymmetry.[20]

Temporal asymmetry and the expansion of the universe

On the average, distant galaxies appear to be receding from us. This is deduced from the shift towards the red of certain recognizable lines in their spectra, which is most plausibly interpreted as being a Doppler shift due to recession in the line of sight. Approximately, the velocity of recession is proportional to the distance from us. (This linear relationship may not be quite correct, however, since recent observations have suggested a certain departure from the linear law in the case of very distant galaxies.) It must not be thought, however, that this recession of the galaxies is particularly a recession from our own one. If there is a general expansion of the universe, each galaxy will be the center of a recession from it, the recession being approximately proportional to distance. An illustration, once given by Eddington,[21] is a good one here. He was thinking in terms of a finite but unbounded spherical space, the three-dimensional analogue of the surface of a sphere. Consider then a rubber balloon, on which are inscribed a number of small dots, the dots being equally spaced all over the balloon. As the balloon is inflated, any two dots will move apart, the velocity of recession being proportional to their distance apart. The same phenomenon would clearly also be observed if there were a general expansion of an infinite space. We are not at present concerned, therefore, whether our cosmological theory postulates a finite but unbounded universe (as with the Einstein universe) or an infinite one (as with steady-state theories).

If we interpret the red shift, then, as evidence that the universe is expanding in the above mentioned manner, we get a built in criterion for the direction of our time axis. That is, the direction of positive time is that in accordance with which we say that the universe is expanding: if we took the direction of time in the opposite way (i.e., in commonsense terms, from future to past instead of from past to future) we should say that the universe is contracting. In other words the direction of positive time is that in accordance with which we should say that the universe is expanding.

If we took the direction of positive time in the opposite way from what we do at present, this would yield a merely conventionally different description of the facts in question. (There is a stronger sense in which we might speak of a contracting universe, namely that in which we should have to report the observation not of red shifts but of blue shifts.) After the merely conventional change of time direction, red shifts of course still exist, but they are spoken of in the following way. When we reverse the time axis, we must speak not of a photon leaving the distant galaxy and impinging on the photographic plate in our telescope, but of the photon leaving the photographic plate, passing through the telescope and setting off into space, eventually being absorbed by an atom on the distant galaxy. Due to the fact that (as we must now say) we and the galaxy are approaching one another, the photon increases in energy and is able to hop into an atom with an absorption of energy which is greater than that of the emission of the photon by the atom in the photographic plate. Contrast this with the idea of a *genuine* contraction of the universe, that is a   **279** contraction in the sense that the galaxies did not show red shifts but blue ones. (We shall see that the case of blue shifts presents physical problems: to say the least, a universe showing blue shifts will probably turn out to be uncomfortably hot!)

Some writers, including T. Gold, have tried to show that the expansion of the universe is the fundamental asymmetry and that the thermodynamic asymmetry, discussed earlier in this chapter, is a mere corollary of the cosmological asymmetry of expansion. Gold has given a striking example with which to support his view.[22] This example must be understood in the light of a well known consideration in cosmology, Olbers' paradox.

Early in the nineteenth century the astronomer Olbers considered the possibility that the stars were distributed on the average in a uniform manner throughout space, which naturally at that date he assumed to be Euclidean. (Today we would say "galaxies" or "clusters of galaxies" instead of "stars", but the argument would not be affected by the change.) Consider a thin spherical shell whose center is the earth and whose radius is r. The number of stars in the shell will be proportional to r^2. The intensity of light reaching us from each star in the shell will be proportional to $\frac{1}{r^2}$. Hence the amount of light reaching us from any distant shell of a certain thickness is proportional to $r^2 \bullet \frac{1}{r^2}$, that is, to a constant, and hence is independent of the radius of the shell. Indeed the assumption that space is Euclidean is not essential to the above argument, since if we reject this assumption, the argument would merely involve the replacing of r^2 and $\frac{1}{r^2}$ by $f(r)$ and $\frac{1}{f(r)}$ in the above argument.[23] It would seem to follow, then, integrating r from zero to infinity, that the amount of light reaching us will be infinite in amount.[13] Even at night the sky should be infinitely bright. This conclusion does indeed need to be modified in the light of the consideration that very far distant stars would be obscured by nearer stars, just as far distant trees in a forest can not be seen because they are blocked out by nearer trees. However the light from the far away stars would heat up the nearer stars and so increase the radiation which they would produce on their own account. It appears that when these considerations are taken into account it turns out that the night sky, though not infinitely bright, ought to be very bright indeed. Indeed assuming a large scale thermodynamic equilibrium it is clear that there should be no difference in apparent brightness between the nearer stars and the spaces of the sky between them.

The conclusion of Olbers' argument is of course paradoxical. So far from frizzling in intense heat from the sky we are (fortunately) quite cool, and when we look up at the sky at night we see not a blaze of light but a soothing darkness. The familiar fact that the sky is dark at night shows that there must be something wrong with one of Olbers' assumptions. One concealed assumption which Olbers made is that if the stars are everywhere of the same intrinsic brightness then the light reaching us from a given star will be on the average proportional to the inverse square of its distance from us. (We need not question here his assumption of Euclidean space.) However due to the fact of the red shift, which implies a loss of energy in the quanta of radiation reaching us, this simple application of the inverse square law will not do. Because of the red shift, distant shells of a given thickness will contribute less radiation to the total reaching

[13]This is easiest to envisage on the assumption of a topologically open space, Euclidean or hyperbolic. Nevertheless, the integration from zero to infinity could still be done on the assumption that space is spherical, since light could have traveled around and around the universe any number of times, assuming a steady-state theory. However the assumption of a steady-state is probably not compatible with that of a spherical universe.

us than will nearer shells. Indeed very distant galaxies would have a velocity of recession greater than the velocity of light,[14] and no radiation from them could reach us.

The expansion of the universe therefore explains why the sky is dark at night and why the universe at large constitutes a "nonreflecting sink for radiation". Gold suggests that this is the ultimate fact behind the "arrow of time". In the first part of this chapter we considered the approach from the point of view of thermodynamics, and of traces and records as branch systems whose entropy is temporarily lower than normal. (Whether microentropy or macroentropy is in question here is a further complication, but in most natural systems, as opposed to artificial signaling devices, we may plausibly assume that lower macroentropy involves lower microentropy.) Gold suggests that we should look deeper, and in effect his position is that it is the expansion of the universe which explains the formation of branch systems. Quite apart from any intrinsic interest which this suggestion may or may not have, a discussion of it provides an instructive way of raising some of the relevant philosophical issues. Gold gives a fanciful but nevertheless instructive example of a branch system which depends for its existence on the fact that the universe constitutes a nonreflecting sink for radiation. [24] Suppose, he says, that we could put a star inside an insulating box, so that no heat could leave the box or enter it from outside. After a sufficiently long time thermodynamical equilibrium will be attained: exactly as much radiation will be returning to the star after reflection from the sides of the box as will be emitted from the star. Within the box, time's arrow will then have been lost: on the average there will be no distinction between the processes that go on in the box and the reverse

[14]There is no conflict with the special theory of relativity here, since we are in the realm of the general theory and relativistic cosmology. It is still not the case that we are asserting that any signal or causal influence could be propagated with a local velocity greater than that of light.

processes. Gold now considers what will happen if we for a moment open a small window in a side of the box. While the window is open, radiation will stream out from the box, and so when the window is closed again the contents of the box will no longer be in a state of statistical equilibrium. There will now be a period of time during which there will be a continuous change of the entropy of the system consisting of the contents of the box (both matter and radiation). Until equilibrium is once more achieved there will be an arrow of time defined by the direction in which the entropy of the contents of the box is increasing. We can see that the momentary opening of the window of the box turns the system into a branch system, in Reichenbach's sense. Suppose however that the universe had not constituted a sink for radiation, so that when the window was opened exactly as much radiation came in through the window as escaped out of it. In this case there would be no lowering of entropy. Hence the system contained in the box becomes a branch system when the window is opened because the universe at large constitutes a sink for radiation. The universe constitutes a sink for radiation because it is expanding. It is therefore tempting to suppose that if we probe more deeply we shall find that it is the expansion of the universe which accounts for the "arrow of time", (or in other words the temporal asymmetry which we noted at the beginning of this chapter).

Indeed Gold rejects the statistical explanation of the arrow of time. He says: "Surely the fact that we had to deal with the problem in statistical terms rather than compute in detail the behaviour of all the constituent parts of our system, that constituted merely a lack of precision; surely it is not by rejecting information about our system that we can make it reveal to us the sense of time which it would otherwise not show".[25] But do we need to "reject information" before we can accept the statistical explanation? A statistical property (e.g., the average height of the students in a university) can be described and understood even though we have detailed knowledge of the heights of the individual students. Similarly consider n molecules (to be thought of as Newtonian particles) moving in a random way within a cylinder furnished with a piston. Let the piston be pulled back, doubling the volume of the cylinder. Statistics will tell us that it is almost certain that very soon about $\frac{n}{2}$ molecules will be in the original volume of the cylinder, and about $\frac{n}{2}$ will be in the new volume furnished by the withdrawing of the piston. One such occurrence is shown in Figure 16 below. The configuration (a) is followed by the configuration (b). Now reverse all the velocities in (b) so as to produce (c). (c) will develop into (d), which is the same as (a) but with velocities reversed.

Now it is quite untrue that a complete knowledge of the microstates (a), (b), (c), and (d) (as by a Laplacean superhuman calculator) would destroy our appreciation of the statistical difference implicit in the above states of

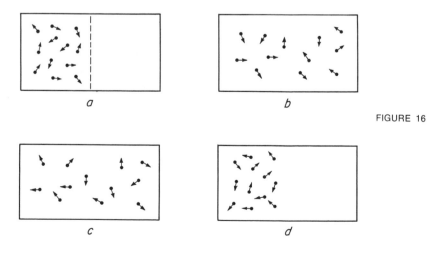

FIGURE 16

affairs. The Laplacean calculator would see that arbitrarily small displacements of the directions or magnitudes of the velocities in (a) will still lead to a uniform distribution in (b), whereas small arbitrary changes in the velocities in (c) will prevent the emergence of a state like (d) in which all the molecules are segregated in one half of the cylinder. I thus find Gold's objection to the statistical approach to the problem of temporal asymmetry quite unconvincing. We do not need to reject knowledge about the details of a system before we can appreciate the relevant statistical properties of the system.

Nor am I convinced by Gold's contention that the statistical account of temporal asymmetry depends importantly on the fact that the universe is expanding. No doubt if we are looking for a temporally asymmetrical feature of the universe we can find it at once in the fact of expansion itself. But how does this help to shed light on the statistical features which give rise to records and traces, and thereby to our subjective feeling of the passage of time? Gold's example does show how in one type of case the existence of a branch system depends on the universe being a sink for radiation. But (a) it is not clear that his account is sufficient to explain all branch systems or (b) that it is necessary even for the type of case he envisages.[15]

(a) Branch systems could surely arise in a wide variety of possible universes, some of which would be finite and nonexpanding. Consider the contrary-to-fact supposition of a finite universe which was made on p. 262 above. If we assume that the total mass-energy of a finite nonexpanding unbounded universe (with a three-dimensional spherical geometry) is constant, then the

[15]In the above discussion I have been relying on two papers published by Gold in 1958 and 1962. Gold has recently published another very readable paper "Cosmic Processes and the Nature of Time",[26] in which, so far as I can see, he presents the same sort of view, relating the statistical basis of the "arrow of time" to the expansion of the universe, though there are some novel features. In this latter paper, however, he does not make use of the thought experiment of the star in the box. In any case this paper reached me too late to be discussed in the present volume.

sky in such a universe could be dark at night. It is true that energy might circumnavigate space, but none of it can have done so too often if we take it that the universe is not in thermodynamical equilibrium and is not too far removed from a "beginning" when all or nearly all the mass-energy was in the form of mass. If there had been no evidence of expansion and if the cosmological evidence had led us to postulate such a finite nonexpanding universe, then we would have to take it that we were in one of the rare epochs of thermodynamical disequilibrium. (If the universe were in thermodynamical equilibrium there should be no difference in brightness between the stars and the rest of the sky.) Eventually such a finite nonexpanding universe will reach a state of equilibrium: enough mass would have been converted into radiation for the density of the mass-energy to be the same everywhere. Later on there would ensue temporary downgrades of the total entropy curve of the universe and eventually the universe would go through a process which was the reverse of our cosmic era of upgrade. Of course sentient beings who existed in this era of downgrade would feel that time was going the other way, and so they would regard this period of downgrade and of large scale absorption of radiation quite correctly from their point of view as a period of upgrade and of large scale emission of radiation. Perhaps indeed this last consideration shows the connection between the statistical criterion of the "arrow of time" and the principle of retarded waves as in effect used by Popper. However it is hard to see exactly what to say in the case of our actual universe, whose thermodynamics are more obscure than is the case with a finite nonexpanding universe.

Since there could be branch systems, in Reichenbach's sense, even in our hypothetical finite but unbounded nonexpanding (and noncontracting) universe, it would seem that the directionality in time which is apparent to us from the fact that traces are of earlier,

not of later, events, and which presumably gives rise to
our subjective sense of the direction of time, could exist
in the absence of the directionality manifested by the
expansion of the universe. In using his example in the
way he does, Gold would appear to be illegitimately
generalizing from a special case. Would not Gold's example of the star in the box show the same directionality even though the universe were *contracting*? In a
contracting universe Olbers' paradox would work the
other way. If we had blue shifts instead of red shifts (as
would be the case with a contracting universe), opening
the window in the box would still produce thermodynamical disequilibrium which would gradually disap-
pear, though in this case the disequilibrium would be
produced by radiation streaming in through the window, instead of by radiation streaming out. The progress of the system towards disequilibrium would define
exactly the same time direction as in the case of the
expanding universe.

Of course there are difficulties in the notion of a contracting universe (with blue shifts). The reasoning of
Olbers' paradox suggests that such a universe might be
(to say the least) uncomfortably hot. To avoid this we
might suppose, perhaps, that the contraction had not
been going on for too long, so that very distant objects,
which are seen very far in the past, would not show
blue shifts. At any rate it does not follow that in a contracting universe "time would run the other way".[16] Not
at any rate if "contracting universe" is here used in the
physically significant sense of "universe showing blue
shifts". The equilibrium of a system can be disturbed
just as much by radiation getting in as by radiation getting out. Of course, as has already been remarked, in
the physically nonsignificant sense we can regard our
own universe as a contracting one, simply by taking our

---

[16]See a paper "Physics and Cosmology", by H. Bondi.[27] The whole of this
beautifully written and witty paper is of interest for the general concerns of this
chapter.

direction of positive time in the opposite direction from the normal one. Then this would be a contracting universe showing red shifts, due to the emergence of photons *from* our eyes and photographic plates and being absorbed by the galaxies. This is just an alternative description of our own universe.

What about an oscillating universe in which the time direction as determined by traces was always in phase with the time direction as determined by the criterion of expansion? What would be of interest would be some way of showing that these two criteria might always coincide. It is hard to tell what would happen in an oscillating universe, since its thermodynamics is very obscure.[28]

On the whole, it would seem that it is the statistical solution of the problem of temporal asymmetry that is probably the most philosophically significant. It explains the epistemological asymmetry which is exemplified by the asymmetry of memories and traces, and thereby also explains our subjective illusion of the one way flow of time.

SUGGESTIONS FOR FURTHER READING

The question of temporal asymmetry provides the main theme of H. Reichenbach, *The Direction of Time* (Los Angeles: University of California Press, 1956); of Part II of Adolf Grünbaum, *Philosophical Problems of Space and Time* (New York: Alfred A. Knopf, 1963); of O. Costa de Beauregard, *Le Second Principe de la Science du Temps* (Paris: Editions du Seuil, 1963); and of O. Costa de Beauregard, "Irreversibility Problems" in Y. Bar-Hillel (ed.), *Logic, Methodology and Philosophy of Science* (Amsterdam: North-Holland, 1965), pp. 313–342, with which should be compared H. Mehlberg, "Space, Time, Relativity", *ibid.*, pp. 363–380, especially pp. 373–374. See also Grünbaum's paper "Popper on Irreversibility" in Mario Bunge (ed.), *The Critical Approach to Science and Philosophy, In Honor of Karl Popper* (New York: Free Press, 1964), pp. 316–331. A quite different point of view from that of the above works and of the present chapter can be observed in Max Black, *Models and Metaphors* (Ithaca, N. Y.: Cornell University Press, 1962), Chapter 10.

See also L. Boltzmann, "On Certain Questions of the Theory of Gases", *Nature*, LI (1895), 413–415; E. Schrödinger, "Irreversibility", *Proceedings of the Royal Irish Academy*, LIII (1950), 189–195; N. Wiener, *Cybernetics*, second edition (Cambridge: M.I.T. Press, 1961), Chapter 1; and letters by K. R. Popper in *Nature*, LXXVII (1956), 538; LXXVIII (1956), 382; LXXIX (1957), 1297; and LXXXI (1958), 402–403. A highly mathematical discussion of the problem of irreversibility is N. G. Van Kampen, "Fundamental Problems in Statistical Mechanics of Irreversible Processes", in E. G. D. Cohen (ed.), *Fundamental Problems in Statistical Mechanics* (Amsterdam: North-Holland, 1962), pp. 173–202. An elementary account of H-theorem and entropy can be found in Chapter 2 of Richard Schlegel's *Time and the Physical World* (East Lansing: Michigan State University Press, 1961).

An introduction to information theory is given in Chapter 5 of Colin Cherry, *On Human Communication*, second edition (Cambridge: Massachusetts Institute of Technology Press, 1957), Chapter 6 contains warnings against confusion of the concept of information in Shannon's sense with the concept as it occurs in more ordinary senses of the word, and a discussion of Y. Bar-Hillel's and R. Carnap's approach to the theory of semantic information. See Y. Bar-Hillel and R. Carnap, "Semantic Information", *British Journal for the Philosophy of Science* (1953–54), 147–157; Y. Bar-Hillel, *Language and Information* (Reading, Mass.: Addison-Wesley, 1964), Part 4; and Rulon S. Wells, "A Measure of Subjective Information" in R. Jakobson (ed.), *Twelfth Symposium in Applied Mathematics* (Providence, R. I.: American Mathematical Society, 1961), pp. 237–244. For Shannon's information theory the main source is his series of papers reprinted in Claude E. Shannon and Warren Weaver, *The Mathematical Theory of Communication* (Urbana: University of Illinois Press, 1949).

The papers by T. Gold which were discussed in the text are "The Arrow of Time", in *La Structure et l'Evolution de l'Univers, Proceedings of the 11th Solvay Conference* (Brussels: R. Stoops, 1958) pp. 81–91, and "The Arrow of Time", *American Journal of Physics*, XXX (1961), 403–410. See also Gold's paper "Cosmic Processes and the Nature of Time" in R. G. Colodny (ed.), (Mind and Cosmos Pittsburgh: University of Pittsburgh Press, 1966), pp. 311–329.

On the expansion of the universe, see H. Bondi, *Cosmology*, second edition, (New York: Cambridge University Press, 1961). An exposition for the general reader may be found in H. Bondi, *The Universe at Large* (London: Heinemann, 1960), especially pp. 17–34.

9

Determinism, free will, and intelligence

Determinism and indeterminism

In the previous chapter we observed the philosophical relevance of statistical mechanics and of cosmology to the problem of "the direction of time". In this chapter we shall consider questions of determinism and indeterminism and their relevance to the question of free will.

As a preliminary definition of determinism we can use the following. To say that determinism is true is to say that from a knowledge of the positions and motions of all particles of the universe a certain time t_0 a sufficiently powerful calculator could deduce the positions and motions of all particles of the universe at any earlier or later time. For example consider the motions of the particles which make up my hand when signing a five dollar check to be paid as a donation to the University cricket club, instead of (as I might in a more unworthy frame of mind) when making the movements which constitute crumpling up the cricket club's letter (hinting at the desirability of a donation) and throwing the letter in the waste paper basket. According to determinism, a complete knowledge of the positions and motions of all particles in the universe would enable a sufficiently powerful calculator to deduce either the one set of movements or the other one.

This is essentially the definition of determinism which was given by Laplace,[1] and we can refer to the sufficiently powerful calculator of the previous paragraph as a Laplacean demon. Now let us consider one or two minor modifications of the definition.

Some people might object that it is not meaningful to talk of complete knowledge of the positions and motions of all particles in the universe if there are infinitely many of these. Whether this is the case or not, we can avoid this problem of whether the universe is infinite by remarking that in order to predict an occurrence at a point P at a time $t_0 + t$ the Laplacean demon would not need to consider events at a distance from P greater than ct, where c is the velocity of light. This is because the theory of relativity assures us that no causal influence can travel with a velocity greater than c.

Another objection to the definition of determinism given above is that it uses a counterfactual hypothetical. If there is in fact no Laplacean demon, then it becomes vacuously true that *if* there is a Laplacean demon then something or other is the case. This is so at any rate if we renounce the strong or subjunctive conditional. However we can avoid this objection by remarking that the Laplacean demon is merely a poetical fiction with which we make a purely *logical* point about a *scientific theory*. That is, instead of saying that the *world* is deterministic let us first of all say that a *theory* is deterministic. Classical mechanics is deterministic in the sense that the axioms and rules of the theory are such that from a complete specification of positions and motions of all particles in the universe at t_0 the positions and motions at $t_0 + t$ are deducible. "Deducible" itself looks questionably modal, but it is not really so because if we imagine the theory to be formalized, the arithmetization of metamathematics enables us to give a purely arithmetical definition of "deducible".[1] Even for unformalized theories the notion "deducible" loses its modal look if we express "*B* is deducible from *A*" in the form "*B follows from A*".

It seems then that we can make fairly precise what it means to say that a *theory* is deterministic. Thus few people would wish to dispute the contention that classical mechanics is a deterministic theory whereas modern quantum mechanics is indeterministic. It may now be objected that even though we can state clearly what it means for a *theory* to be deterministic or indeterministic, this does not help us to state a metaphysical thesis about the *world* being deterministic or indeterministic. However once we have a satisfactory account of what it means to say that a theory is deterministic, we can go on from there to say what it is for the world to be deterministic: if we believe a theory *T* to be the truth about the world, then we believe that the world is deterministic or indeterministic according as to whether *T* is deterministic or indeterministic. Thus in the nineteenth century, classical mechanics was believed to be true, and so the world was believed to be deterministic, whereas nowadays we believe quantum mechanics to be true and so we believe that the world is indeterministic. Of course quantum mechanics may come to be replaced by a deterministic theory, but until it is we must hold it to be most plausible that the world is not a fully deterministic one.

The above account of determinism is based on the notion of formal deducibility within a theory and it makes no essential reference to prediction. The story of what could be predicted by a Laplacean demon is now seen to be merely a poetical way of making the formal or syntactical point. It is therefore of no consequence to our definition that perhaps in practice such universal prediction is not possible. It is possible that in gaining

[1]See p. 32 above.

his information about the state of a system any actual (or physically realizable) predictor would so disturb the system as to upset his own predictions. K. R. Popper has argued[2] that even according to classical physics it is not always physically possible that a predictor could predict an event within some arbitrarily small margin of error. He considers the case in which two predictor mechanisms *A* and *B* interact strongly. (I here simplify Popper's account slightly, without, I hope, misrepresenting its essential features.)

Suppose that *A* is to predict the behavior of *B*, and that *B* is to predict the behavior of *A*. Then in this case both predictors interact with one another *strongly*. (These predictor mechanisms interact strongly simply because a small change in the state of that which is predicted causes a large change in the predictor: movement of a dial arm for example.) Now if *B* is to predict *A*, it needs to know its own state as determined by *A*. However if it seeks information about its own state, the recording of this information will once more alter its own state, and so *ad infinitum*.[2] That is, *B* can never achieve complete knowledge of its own present state and hence can never predict *A*, whose future state also depends partly on the present state of *B*.

In reply, G. F. Dear[4] has argued that though it is indeed impossible that we should have two predictors *A* and *B* totally predicting each other, it is nevertheless true that given any finite prediction task, say that of predicting the behavior of a *specified* predictor *A*, we can then go on to specify a faster working predictor *B* which would be able to predict the behavior of *A* up to any pre-assigned limit of accuracy. Let *B'* be the part of *B* which interacts with *A* (say measuring arms which "feel" the values of the relevant parameters of *A*) and let *B''* be the computing part of *B*. Suppose at time t_1 that *B'* is placed in contact with *A* and it needs Δt_a sec-

[2]See also the remark by G. Ryle in *The Concept of Mind*[3] about the impossibility of *self*-prediction.

onds to measure the values of the parameters of A. Then B' is withdrawn from A and takes Δt_b seconds to communicate its readings to B'' and B'' takes Δt_c seconds to compute the state of A at time t_2. If $t_2 - t_1 > \Delta t_a + \Delta t_b + \Delta t_c$, B will be able to predict a state of A later than its own act of prediction.

In any case it must be stressed that the definition of determinism, in terms of derivability within a theory and not in terms of physically possible predictions, which has been given above, seems to sidestep Popper's objection. Dear does in fact define what it is for the world to be deterministic *via* the notion of what it is for *theories* to be deterministic, and so without essential reference to the epistemic notion of predictions.[5] Hence even if his technical objection to Popper were to be doubted, his more purely philosophical objection would be unaffected. It would appear that Popper's characterization of determinism is too much an *epistemological* one. On our present account we can say that the world is deterministic or not according as to whether we believe that the true *theory* about the world is deterministic or not, and the account of whether a theory is deterministic or not is formal, and in the case of fully formalized theories is even syntactical, but it is not epistemological. Even if it should be shown that a deterministic theory, formally or syntactically characterized, implies the impossibility of certain prediction tasks, this would not by itself impugn the deterministic character of the world as defined by the theory in question.

We shall say, then, that it is reasonable to hold that the universe is deterministic or indeterministic according as to whether or not we believe the true theory about the world to be deterministic or indeterministic. We said that a theory is deterministic or otherwise according as to whether the state of the world at $t_0 + t$ is or is not deducible from a complete specification of its state at t_0. Actually this requirement needs to be relaxed

295

a bit. For example we would not regard Newtonian mechanics as indeterministic simply because the many body problem can not be solved analytically. We regard it as deterministic if we can get an approximation *to any assigned degree of* accuracy of the state of the world at $t_0 + t$.

By the above criterion it is clear enough that classical mechanics and electromagnetism are deterministic whereas contemporary quantum mechanics is indeterministic. Here "indeterministic" means simply "not deterministic according to the above definition of determinism". However there are possible modifications of our definition of determinism which nevertheless keep to what seems to me to be the spirit of determinism. For example, suppose that the state of the whole universe at any time t could be deduced from a specification of the positions and motions of all particles at *two* times t_1 and t_2, or perhaps again from n times $t_1, t_2 \ldots t_n$. Theories embodying such ideas would seem to have quite a good claim to the title "deterministic", though of course it is largely an arbitrary matter whether we apply it or not. Slightly more removed from Laplacean determinism is the following idea, which I noticed in an article by D. W. Sciama,[6] who acknowledges indebtedness to K. V. Roberts. According to it, boundary conditions at two times t_1 and t_2 enable us to deduce the state of things not at any time t whatever (say later than t_2) but at any time t which is *between* t_1 and t_2. By thus extending the definition of determinism, Sciama suggests that the correctness of quantum mechanics can be reconciled with determinism. Von Neumann has shown that existing quantum mechanics becomes inconsistent if one postulates "hidden variables" so as to turn it into a deterministic theory.[7] However Sciama says that in the present suggestion the "hidden variables . . . escape his ban because they refer to the future".[8]

Sciama's suggestion shows the sort of way in which scientists might feel inclined to modify the classical Laplacean definition of determinism, while nevertheless we might contend that their modified definition kept within the spirit of determinism. I am not competent to discuss whether quantum mechanics could indeed be made deterministic in the above mentioned way, and henceforth in this chapter we shall take it that determinism is defined in the normal way, by reference to the possibility of calculation from a specification of boundary conditions at any *one* time t_0 only. Let us adopt now the more orthodox position that there is no natural extension of the definition of determinism which will make quantum mechanics come out as deterministic. Let us say, then, that an event not deducible from appropriate boundary conditions together with the laws of nature occurs by pure chance. "Pure chance" here is simply the negation of "determinism".

If indeterminism is true, then some events occur by pure chance. Thus the emission of an alpha particle from a radioactive atom at a given moment of time is according to modern quantum mechanics a matter of pure chance: there is no previous state of the world which implies (*via* the laws of nature) that this event will occur at this time. It is important to distinguish "pure chance" from the ordinary concept of "chance" or "accident" which is quite compatible with determinism. Consider two events as follows. (1) At a particular time t a radium atom emits an alpha particle. (2) At a particular time t a man walking along a road is struck on the head by a falling branch. The first case is one of chance in the sense that, if modern quantum mechanics is to be believed, it is not deducible from any specification, however complete and precise, of some previous state of the universe. The second case on the other hand is one of chance in a sense which is perfectly compatible with determinism. There is no law of nature which relates walking along roads to being hit on the head by falling branches but nevertheless this particular occurrence would be deducible, if determinism were true, from a complete specification of the boundary conditions obtaining in a sufficiently large portion of the universe at some previous time. In commonsense (and less scientific) terms, an accident is the intersection of two causal chains. If the man's wife had spent slightly more or less time in kissing him good-by, or if the gust of wind which finally broke the branch had come rather sooner or later, then the man would not have suffered the blow on the head. This is not incompatible with the view that the wife's kissing the man good-by and the occurrence of the gust of wind were determined by a previous state of the universe.

Free will and determinism

Does pure chance imply free will, and does the absence of pure chance imply the absence of free will? That is, are free will and determinism incompatible? I wish to argue that the question of pure chance or determinism is irrelevant to the question of free will, though, so far from free will and determinism being incompatible with one another, a close approximation to determinism on the macro-level is required for free will.

Consider two decision making computers A and B. Suppose that they are designed to select candidates for a staff training course for some organization. (I do not wish to argue here that selection of candidates should at present be automated in this way: my illustration is here meant purely to illustrate a metaphysical point.) Into the inputs of the computers all available information is fed by means of punched cards. The information consists of detailed records of examination results, gradings of mental character (e.g., "honest", "moderately honest", etc., "bad tempered", "easy tempered", etc.) and in short all possible information which might be of interest to a human selector. The machines have been programmed in such a way that we would be happy with the candidates selected (e.g., none of them are too stupid, too dishonest, too bad tempered).

Suppose that there are 20 vacancies and that the computer selects 19 candidates first. For the 20th (and last) place there are two equally good candidates. This last candidate is then selected from the two possibilities by means of a randomizing device. Suppose that Smith and Jones are the two candidates between which, on the available criteria, the machine so far can not choose. The randomizing device is such that it gives a probability of $\frac{1}{2}$ of choosing each candidate. In the case of machine A the randomizer consists of a roulette wheel on which there is an electrical contact. If the wheel stops with "red" opposite a fixed contact it causes the machine to choose Smith, whereas if "black" is opposite the fixed contact Jones is chosen. In the case of machine B the randomizer consists of a Geiger counter near a small quantity of a radioactive substance such that there is a probability of $\frac{1}{2}$ of the Geiger counter being actuated in the nth second after the start of operation of the machine, where n is an odd number, and there is a probability of $\frac{1}{2}$ of it being actuated in the mth second where m is an even number. If the Geiger counter is actuated in an odd numbered second the machine chooses Smith, and if it is actuated in an even numbered second the machine chooses Jones. Let us suppose that in fact, in the case of each machine, Smith happens to be the candidate chosen.

The machine A as described above can be regarded as a deterministic machine, since its behavior can be described with a close enough approximation by means of classical physics. We may say that the choice by machine A of Smith as against Jones was a deterministic one, since with sufficient knowledge of the inputs to the machine and of the initial state and working of the machine the choice of Smith as against Jones could have been predicted. On the other hand the machine B is an indeterministic machine, since the choice of Smith depended on an indeterministic quantum mechanical effect.

Was the choice of Smith as made by machine A any more or less "rational" than the same choice as made by machine B? Surely not. Was the choice of Smith by B "more rational" than the choice of the first nineteen candidates, whose qualifications were such that no use of the randomizer was necessary in their case? We may say that the indeterministic machine B is neither more nor less "free" than is the deterministic machine A. For this reason I hold that the principle of quantum mechanical indeterminacy has nothing whatever to do with the problem of free will. Whether our brains are (near enough) deterministic machines or whether they contain "pure chance" randomizers, they are neither more nor less possessed of free will.

Some philosophers would object to my implicit assumption above that choice is a matter of a largely causal computation process. They would say that in free choice we act from reasons, not from causes, and they would say that acting from reasons is neither caused nor a matter of pure chance. I find this unintelligible. The machine which chose the twentieth man by a quantum mechanical randomizer did not do so on account of a cause, but did so by pure chance. It had no reason to choose the one candidate rather than another. On the other hand the machine in choosing the first nineteen candidates did behave in a deterministic way and could be said to have been caused to make the choices it did. It was programmed in such a way that its causes corresponded to reasons, for example it was programmed in such a way that it chose the most intelligent, sensible, etc., candidates, and so it was programmed to act in accordance with what we would call "good reasons". It acted from reasons precisely because it was caused.

300   It may be objected, however, that here is the trouble.

It was *programmed* to do so, whereas we act freely. In reply to this we may make two rejoinders. In the first place are we not ourselves "programmed"? That is, on account of our genetic endowment, together with certain environmental influences both when we were embryos and ever since, our brains have been caused to have a certain structure. They therefore compute in certain ways. People with certain brain structures will make certain choices, and people with other brain structures will make other choices. The second rejoinder is as follows. If the view that we are largely deterministic machines is taken to imply that we do not have free will, we may concede indeed that we also do not have free will in the sense which the objector has in mind. It is not clear, however, what this sense is: the free choice is supposed to be not deterministic and not a matter of pure chance in the way in which a quantum jump is supposed to be pure chance. It is supposed to be pure chance in the sense of "not being determined" but the suggestion is that it is also not merely random and is "acting from reasons". The previous paragraph suggests, however, that acting from reasons is not merely random precisely because it is also acting from causes.

It is possible that the plain man's concept of free will has inconsistent elements in it. He may demand of free will that it be both random and yet not random. If so, we should feel no compunction about denying the existence of free will in the plain man's sense. This does not mean, however, that we do not have at our disposal the means to make most of the contrasts which the plain man makes by asserting or denying free will. A determinist can still make the distinction between the condition of a man who goes for a walk because he wants to do so (being determined by his desire, which we may take to be a state of neural interconnections in his brain) and a man in a prison cell who does not go for a walk, even though he dearly desires to do so. (The latter man would be caused by the state of his brain to go for a walk but he is prevented from doing so by the bolts and bars of his cell.) Being caused by your internal state of desire in the former way is, *ceteris paribus*, pleasant, and being prevented by external constraints is, *ceteris paribus*, unpleasant. Similarly we do not deny that there is an important difference between doing a thing X, because we want to do it and have no conflicting desires, and the case where we do X because of some threat. A man who gives money to charity because he wishes to help that good cause acts in a way which is relatively pleasant. A man who hands over money in a police court because he has to pay a fine also in a sense does what he wants to do, but he wants to hand over the money only in the sense that he dislikes the alternative of going to prison even more. Once more the determinist can make the relevant distinction, and whether or not he does so by means of the words "free" and "unfree" is not very important.

What about the contrast between a psychopathic offender (say a kleptomaniac) and an ordinary criminal (say a burglar)? In both cases their desires cause the behavior. The plain man and the criminal law both tend to contrast the case of the kleptomaniac and the ordinary burglar by denying that the kleptomaniac was fully free. We can make the required contrast (which is all that the criminal law should need) by saying that the kleptomaniac is not easily caused by threats of punishment to act otherwise, whereas the ordinary burglar is amenable to threats. On account of this we can give a rational justification for treating kleptomaniacs differently from burglars, and we can do so without involving the questionable concept of free will. Once more we conclude that if the plain man's concept of free will is a denial both of determinism and of randomness, then its apparent inconsistency does not matter all that much, since we can nevertheless make most of the distinctions which the plain man wishes to make without its aid.

Now let us consider a piece of science fiction. Instead of having our brains "programmed" by our genes and environment let us suppose that they could be programmed (or reprogrammed) by means of a machine. Suppose that it were possible to change a person's whole character by applying a number of electrodes to his head, so that in some (at present technologically inconceivable) way the interconnections between his neurons (and possibly also whatever constitutes his memory store) are radically altered. Perhaps we could apply such a machine to a humanitarian poet and turn him into a diabolical technologist who is an able inventor of lethal weapons. It might be said that such a "reprogrammed" man, however little he was thwarting contrary desires, would not be free, and would merit neither praise nor blame for his activities. In reply to this we could contend that he would merit praise or blame exactly as much or as little as would an ordinary person (i.e., a person who had not had his brain changed in this way). If it were useful (for deterrent reasons) to punish the ordinary person, so would it be useful (for deterrent reasons) to punish the reprogrammed person. (I neglect here the possibility that in the fictional case better results might be achieved by punishing not the programmee but the programmer.) The only good reasons for punishment or reward, praise or blame, seem to me to be their social effects. A philosopher who thinks that it is not right to blame or punish an ordinary person, is surely forgetting that the ordinary person is also programmed by his heredity and environment. Such a philosopher may have the extraordinary idea, when thinking of a vicious murderer, that if *he* had had the murderer's bad brain and bad environment he would nevertheless have acted differently. I think that such a view is unintelligible.

My conclusion therefore is that even though the brain should be a deterministic mechanism, we are still able to make the important contrasts which we normally signalize by calling behavior either "free" or "unfree". It is a matter of somewhat arbitrary choice whether or not we say that the ordinary man's concept of free will is contrary to determinism, and that the view of the mind as a deterministic (or largely deterministic) machine implies that we have not got free will. A lot depends on what plain man we catch, and on whether or not we catch him in a metaphysical frame of mind. If we do say that the plain man's concept of free will is incompatible with determinism, then even so we can also say that our denial of free will does not have the startling consequences which it would have had if it had implied also the denial of the important contrasts which have been discussed above. Alternatively we can use "free" and "unfree" in order to make the above mentioned contrasts, in which case determinism is perfectly compatible with free will.

What has science to say about the question whether the brain is a deterministic machine? A good many philosophers have held that the indeterministic nature of quantum mechanics leaves a loophole for free will. Our discussion of free will should have shown what is wrong with this. It is abstractly possible that the brain might contain indeterministic trigger mechanisms, like the Geiger counter of machine B above. Nevertheless this would mean only that the brain contained an indeterministic randomizer: if it contained instead a deterministic randomizer like that of machine A how would this affect the question of its freedom? We must not entirely discount the possibility of very small events, possibly below the level of quantum mechanical uncertainty, which occur in the synaptic knobs of single neurons, being amplified by neuronal mechanisms so as to produce behavioral effects. No less a neurophysiologist than Sir John Eccles[9] has indeed proposed such a mechanism. Eccles thinks that in this way events in an immaterial mind can have effects on the brain. Many scientists would perhaps think that the idea of an imma-

304

terial mind produces more difficulties than it solves. For one thing the postulation of an immaterial mind seems to raise difficulties for the genetical theory of evolution by natural selection. It is not difficult to see in a general way how mutations in genes lead, *via* the biochemistry of embryology, to slightly differently convoluted brains, and hence ultimately to the sort of potentialities for behavior which leads us to say that an organism has a mind. But it is hard to see how the production of an immaterial mind could come to be reconciled with the chemical approach to genetics. Eccles regards the existence of the immaterial mind as vouched for by introspection, but we shall here avoid discussing this issue, which raises large and controversial questions in the philosophy of mind. Let us remark, however, that the postulation of an immaterial mind does not help to illuminate the problem of free will. For once more we can ask whether events in the immaterial mind are caused, or whether they are random, or supposing that they are neither caused nor random, we can ask what this third possibility consists in.

One difficulty which I think must arise for anyone who supposes that the brain can contain a mechanism which amplifies very small triggering events, or perhaps functions as a whole as such a mechanism, is that of how such events are not masked by "noise"[3] (in the information theory sense of the word). It is sometimes said that a single photon can affect the human retina, and this is no doubt true. It does not follow, however, that the signal-to-noise ratio in the optic nerve would be high enough for the working of the brain to be affected by a single photon striking the retina.

Following D. M. MacKay,[10] therefore, I would prefer to suggest that the brain can be treated as though determinism were true. Even a single neuron is a macroscopic object as far as quantum mechanics is

[3]Thus in an electrical transmission system the "noise" of the channel may be due to random motions of the electrons (mainly) in the circuit.

concerned. Moreover it is likely that the behavior of an animal depends on the mass behavior of very many neurons, and that what is important are the statistical characteristics of very large ensembles of neurons, and that any indeterminacy which was likely to show up only in the odd neuron or two would not affect matters.

Creativity and intelligence

Some readers may object to the description in the foregoing pages of machines *A* and *B*, "making choices" and "having reasons". Wittgensteinians may want to point out that the "language game" (as they might put it) which we play with words like "free" and "choice" is played in complex social situations, and that an isolated machine could not meaningfully be said to make choices or to have reasons. This objection does not seem to affect the metaphysical issues at stake: whether or not humans are involved in complex relationships with one another is independent of whether or not they should be thought of as deterministic mechanisms. Complex human relationships might be complex inter-mechanism relationships.

Sometimes it is objected that we can not think of the human brain in the sort of way in which we think of an artificial machine because the latter "will do only what it is programmed to do". It may be conceded that human beings are versatile in a way in which artificial machines are not: a man may be a first rate topologist, quite a good beer drinker and conversationalist, a moderate cricketer, and not a bad connoisseur of female beauty. Even if the technology of the future were to enable us to realize all these capabilities in a single machine, it would be hardly likely that anyone should wish to do so. Maybe universities would invest in topology machines and film studios in machines for assessing the pulchritude of girls, but who would want a combination of the two machines?

It is not surprising that human beings should have great versatility. This is just what one would expect of organisms which have evolved through natural selection instead of being artificially constructed for a specific purpose. This is the main truth which lies behind the dictum that machines will do only what they are programmed to do. One would hardly bother to equip a topology machine with photo-receptors, whereas a machine for assessing the beauty of girls would doubtless need photo-receptors with full color vision. Of course machines tend to be specialized. They are built for a purpose. Even so, this purpose can be a very general one, as is shown by the case of versatile, general purpose computers. Moreover, except on certain theistic assumptions, human beings have not been made for any purpose at all. This is because they have not been made, but have evolved. *A fortiori* they were not made for a purpose.

When we bear the above cautions in mind we can go on to say, without so much fear of being misunderstood, that human beings also will do only what they have been programmed to do. By their programs we here mean (a) the innate structures of their brains and (b) the total amounts of "information" (in the information theoretic sense of the word) which come into their brains from the environment, especially from their sense organs.

Possibly what is meant when it is said that machines will do only what they are programmed to do is that machines are not capable of original thought, as humans are. Now it is true that existing computers are mostly unintelligent or moronic. By this I mean that after they have engaged in n operations there is a rule which specifies uniquely what the $(n + 1)$th operation is to be. They are so built that they act in accordance with the appropriate rule. Compare this with a piece of intelligent thought involved in problem solving. Consider a student trying to prove a geometrical theorem. There is no rule to tell him what to do in searching for a proof, though he has probably learned a few dodges which *might* work. If he succeeds in proving the theorem, this will be because of fortunate guesswork. It is a matter of common observation that some people are able to make fortunate guesses of this sort more often than others are able to, and this shows that problem solving cannot be a question of mere luck. What this additional factor could be, however, is far from clear. If we could really answer this question we should know at least in theory how to make artificial intelligences. At least something like luck is involved; a schoolboy who wishes to prove a geometrical theorem has to cast about for his solution. It is not like an exercise in long division, where the schoolboy always has a rule telling him what the next step is, that is, where there is a decision procedure. (See pp. 29–30 above.)

Suppose that the schoolboy does guess the proof of the theorem. Then there are rules which tell him that he has the proof. If he could survey all possible arguments then his rules would enable him to select a proof of the theorem in question. The trouble, however, is that the set of all possible proofs (which is a subset of the set of all finite strings of symbols in his vocabulary) is infinite. Even if we were to make the (mathematically unjustifiable) assumption (a) that there is a proof of our putative theorem, and (b) that it is less than some number n symbols in length, the number of strings of symbols from which we should have to make our selection would be astronomical (since this number goes up not with n but as a^n where a is the number of symbols in the relevant vocabulary) and any routine selection by even the fastest computer would not be possible. Somehow the number has got to be reduced. We can rule out, for example, ungrammatical strings of symbols, strings of symbols with premises which have been shown already to be false, strings of symbols which consist of incorrect deductive steps and so on. The question still remains as to how this reduction could be achieved in practice, in a sufficiently short time.

If the above line of thought is correct, then intelligence (or even genius) is a matter of *being able to select*. Even writing a poem can unromantically be thought of as selecting one string of symbols from the set of all possible strings of a certain length. This is the point of view of W. Ross Ashby whose ideas about artificial intelligence lean heavily on the notion of selection. [11] However in a sense (as Ashby of course himself recognizes) the above remark is by itself rather trivial. Shakespeare could not have selected (say) a thousand word sonnet from (say) a vocabulary of 3,000 words by going through all possible combinations and selecting the best one from them. He would have had to go through 3000^{1000} possibilities. At the rate of one a second this would take him a very long time even compared with the history of the whole universe since the big bang (assuming the big bang theory to be true) when the primeval atom exploded. It would be a prohibitively long time, too, even if we changed the problem to the easier one of selecting any sonnet (not the *best* sonnet) and if we replaced Shakespeare by a computer which examined possibilities at the rate of one per millimicrosecond.

It is true, of course, that our figure of 3000^{1000} possibilities is an upper limit which could be reduced by various short cuts. Thus suppose that a computer had built into it a dictionary with words of the English language in its memory store, and the capacity to check whether the first five letters chosen (say) were all or the first part of an English word. Then if the putative sonnet began with *"axyba"*, all sequences of letters beginning with *"axyba"* could be rejected at once, without examining them individually. Further constraints could be put in by getting the machine to check whether short sequences of words could form part of a grammatical sentence or sequence of sentences, or in cases where rules of grammar are not effective, whether they follow

309

that part of the grammar which is effective. (Recall that to say that rules are effective is to say that there is a decision procedure for the problem of whether they apply in a given case. Note that if grammar rules turn out not to be effective, then the problem of the mechanization of grammar becomes a special case of the problem of mechanization of intelligence.)

One way in which exhaustive search might be reduced is by combining it with intelligent conjecture in the sort of way which can be illustrated by the following example. Suppose that we have to search for one out of all the sequences of 6 letters. We have to search for one out of 26^6 possible sequences. Suppose, however, that we have reason for thinking that the first three letters of our sequence come out of the first half of the alphabet, and that the second three letters come out of the second half of the alphabet. Then if our conjecture is correct (which of course it may well not be) we have 13^6 possibilities to search, instead of the vastly greater number 26^6. A combination of intelligent guesswork and exhaustive search may possibly be more powerful than either method on its own. We still, of course, are unclear as to what intelligent guesswork consists in. But the above example shows some analogy to the way in which a mathematician breaks up the problem of proving a theorem into that of proving a number of intermediate lemmas.

Let us consider a simple situation for which intelligence is required: discovery of proofs of theorems in sentential logic, from a certain set of axioms. It is not usual to present sentential logic in axiomatic form, since there is no need for this. Owing to the existence of a decision procedure (the method of truth tables) we can entirely dispense with the need to devise proofs. When Whitehead and Russell wrote the first edition of *Principia Mathematica*,[12] the method of truth tables was not known to them, and they used the axiomatic method and did need to exercise a modicum of intelligence in discovering whether or not schemata were valid formulae of sentential logic.

Consider the following four axioms[4] which are sufficient for sentential logic.

(1) $(p \lor p) \supset p$
(2) $p \supset (p \lor q)$
(3) $(p \lor q) \supset (q \lor p)$
(4) $(p \supset q) \supset [(r \lor p) \supset (r \lor q)]$

An axiomatic system also needs rules. The axioms are like initial positions of chessmen: we need rules to get the game moving. The present system requires two rules. (a) We have the rule of *detachment*. If we have proved a formula A and also a formula of the form $A \supset B$ then we may write down B as a theorem. (b) We have the rule of *substitution*. If A has been proved and if B results from A by substitution of a well formed formula for a sentence letter of A wherever it occurs in A, then we are allowed to assert B as a theorem. This rule presupposes a rigorous recursive definition of "well formed formula", which is easy to give but which I shall here omit. We need also the definitions of $A \supset B$ as $\sim A \lor B$, $A \bullet B$ as $\sim(\sim A \lor \sim B)$, and $A \equiv B$ as $(A \supset B) \bullet (B \supset A)$. All possible sequences of successive applications of these rules to the axioms result in an infinite number of possible proofs of theorems. How can we single out some proof of some particular theorem? Even if we could assume an upper bound to the length of our proof, exhaustive search would be quite impracticable, and we obviously can not rely on blind guesswork either. Intelligence seems to be needed — perhaps not very much intelligence but some at least. In fact Allen Newell, J. C. Shaw, and Herbert A. Simon have designed a machine with this much intelligence.[16]

<hr>

[4]These are those of Hilbert and Ackermann.[13] If the second one is changed to "$q \supset (p \lor q)$" we get four of Whitehead and Russell's five axioms.[14] (The other Whitehead and Russell axiom was shown by Bernays[15] to be redundant.)

Suppose that the machine is seeking for the proof of a theorem of the form $A \supset C$ and it already has, in its stock of axioms and already proved theorems, one of the form $A \supset B$. Then the machine will be able to prove $A \supset C$ if it can prove $B \supset C$. This is because the passage, by means of the axioms and rules of the system, from sentences of the forms $A \supset B$ and $B \supset C$ to one of the form $A \supset C$ is a subroutine of the machine. So if the machine has proved $A \supset B$ (or has it as an axiom) and if it has not succeeded by substitution or detachment to prove $A \supset C$ directly, it tries to prove $B \supset C$ instead. Similarly if it has $B \supset C$ but not $A \supset B$, and if it can not prove $A \supset C$ directly, it tries looking for a proof of $A \supset B$. These methods are called "chaining".

In applying the rule of substitution the machine will get nowhere if it simply substitutes well formed formulae taken at random for sentence letters taken at random. It needs to apply substitutions in sentences which are in a certain sense "similar" to the sentence to be proved. The machine has incorporated in it a routine which enables it to compute whether or not two expressions are similar in this sense. This is the *similarity test*. There is also a *matching process* which is designed so that, if possible, two given subexpressions are made identical.

How the above strategies work out can be illustrated by means of the following case.[17] The machine has been set to prove "$p \supset p$". It has already proved "$p \supset (p \lor p)$". It behaves as follows. It first tries to prove "$p \supset p$" by substitution but it can find no similar theorem (such as "$q \supset q$") in order to make a substitution. Next it tries detachment. It finds several theorems of the form "$(F) \supset (p \supset p)$". For example by substituting "$\sim p$" for "q" in "$p \supset (q \lor p)$" it gets "$p \supset (\sim p \lor p)$" and hence "$p \supset (p \supset p)$" from the definition (incorporated in its store) of "$(F) \supset (G)$" as "$\sim(F) \lor (G)$". However the only axiom or already proved theorem of the form "$F \supset (p \supset p)$" is "$p \supset (p \supset p)$". The application of the method of detachment therefore leads it to the search for a proof of "p". This of course does not lead anywhere, for "p" is not provable. After some abortive attempts to prove "p" it then switches to the chaining method. It searches for a theorem of the form "$p \supset (H)$" and immediately selects the axiom "$p \supset (p \lor p)$". This leads it to replace its original problem by the problem of proving "$(p \lor p) \supset p$". It checks through the axioms and theorems already proved and quickly uses axiom (1) to give the required result.

Newell, Shaw, and Simon report that in the initial experiment the machine (in fact a digital computer programmed to simulate the machine) proved most of the theorems of propositional logic which had been proved in *Principia Mathematica*. About half of these were proved in less than a minute and most of the rest were proved within five minutes. A few took 15–45 minutes. The times taken increased sharply (perhaps exponentially) with the number of steps in the proof. There were striking similarities between the behavior of the machine and that of a human problem solver. For example when one of the later theorems was presented to the machine *after* it had stored in its memory a number of the theorems which it had so far proved it succeeded in proving the new theorem very quickly, but when these other theorems were removed from its memory store it could not prove the later theorem at all. Similarly the machine was susceptible to hints: in other words presenting it with a suitable intermediate lemma, would enable it to go on to prove a theorem which previously it had not succeeded in proving.

It might be denied that the machine had even a rudimentary intelligence in that intelligence belonged rather to the designers of the machine, who devised the strategies of proof which were programmed into it. As against this, do not schoolmasters and parents program heuristic strategies into their students? Yet two boys in a geometry class may differ in intelligence insofar as one

can apply the heuristics and the other can not. It could
be argued, however, that even so there is a mystery:
how did the first man to apply the heuristics in question
come to get hold of them? *Ex hypothesi* he did not get
hints from some school teacher. There must be some
evolutionary explanation of the way in which proof
strategies such as those which Newell, Shaw, and Simon had to program into their machine come naturally
to the human brain. It does not seem too much to hope
that a plausible explanation can be devised: after all
one important part of the heuristics of the machine
which we have been discussing is the tendency to look
out for and to discover certain abstract similarities of
structure. This could possibly be based on the ability of
our brain to recognize certain *Gestalten*, and such an
ability quite clearly has considerable survival value.
Consider the necessity of recognizing the shape of some
predator. When we bear in mind the capacities of predators to appear from unexpected angles and even to
camouflage themselves, it may even be advantageous
that shape recognition should not be too routine a matter: but that sometimes "almost similar" shapes should
be assimilated and sometimes not. We get a situation
rather resembling that in which similar patterns of proof
are tried out, and in novel situations these should not be
too similar.

It is true that the problem solving ability of the Newell, Shaw, and Simon machine is modest. It is true also
that the ability of the machine to simulate a human
problem solver does not necessarily mean that it works
on the same principles as the human brain. (Similarity
of function does not imply similarity of structure.) In any
case there is a difference between the machine and the
human in that the machine works faster but the human
has a larger memory store. (One unsolved problem is
how the human can so quickly extract information from
his vast memory store. How is its vastness to be reconciled with its accessibility?) Nevertheless though simi-

larity of function does not imply similarity of structure, it can point this way, and knowledge of the structure of a machine may suggest interesting hypotheses about the possible actual working of the brain. It is most economical to suppose, for lack of further information, and other things (such as the so far ascertained facts of anatomy) being equal, that if only one way of doing a job is known then the brain very likely does the job in that way.

One important manifestation of intelligence is an ability to learn a language. Noam Chomsky has speculated[18] that without an innate tendency to form grammatical hypotheses we could never learn languages of the general grammatical type which Chomsky holds to be common to all human language. Learning the grammar of a language is in his view analogous to hypothesis formation in natural science, except that the general form of the hypothesis is built into us. He holds that it would be impossible for a child to learn how to talk by means of the sort of inductive learning process suggested by B. F. Skinner in his *Verbal Behavior*.[19] One difficulty which would beset us in trying to develop artificial intelligence is the problem of how to build into it the sort of linguistic skills which we human beings possess. If it involves incorporating an "innate" (or inbuilt) schema of the sort envisaged by Chomsky then this might be very difficult or even technically impossible. The brain is very complex and devising the required schema might be like cracking a difficult code. Even if these skeptical doubts about the prospects for artificial intelligence are justified, they do not of course imply that there is anything mystical or nonmechanistic about the brain. It is just that a certain complex structure may have developed through the evolution of the species, and it might be hard to reproduce it artificially, or even to discover its exact description. In any case these considerations suggest that the construction of an artificial intelligence which would be of much use would be a task of a different order of difficulty altogether from that of making the sort of intelligent proof-making machine which was discussed above.

Nevertheless such a simple machine has many salutary lessons to teach the philosopher. For one thing it gives the lie to the view that a machine will do only what it is programmed to do and that it can never surprise its designer. (Why this ever seemed a plausible thing to say is rather a mystery, since even motor cars and radios sometimes surprise their designers.) A good example of what in a human being would be regarded as a sign of intelligence and creativity is the following proof of the equality of the two base angles of an isosceles triangle. It is a neater and simpler proof than that which most humans know, and was produced by a machine for proving theorems in elementary geometry which was constructed by H. L. Gelernter.[20] The proof is mentioned in a paper by M. L. Minsky[21] and goes as follows:

Given that in $\triangle$ ABC, $A\,B = A\,C$.
To prove that angle B = angle C.

$$A\,B = A\,C \text{ (given)}$$
$$A\,C = A\,B \text{ (given)}$$
$$B\,C = C\,B \text{ (identity)}$$
$$\therefore \triangle\,A\,B\,C \equiv \triangle\,A\,C\,B$$
$$\therefore \text{ angle } B = \text{ angle } C.$$

This proof in fact surprises quite a number of people by its neatness. They do not expect the machine to have proved the theorem in this way, not having thought of this method themselves, and being disposed themselves to prove it by the clumsier method, usually taught in schools, of considering the triangles ABD, ACD, where D is the midpoint of BC. In this case, the success of the machine is due to the very simplicity of its heuristics. To show that the angles B and C are equal, the heuristics determine the search for possibly congruent triangles in which B and C are. The machine immediately selects triangles *ABC* and *ACB*. The human problem solver becomes easily confused in such a degenerate situation in which the triangles in question are in fact coincident. Minsky has suggested that when machines are made with more powerful heuristics, they too may become confused in the same sort of way as do human beings. The "superiority" of the simple geometry proving machine in devising an elegant proof of the equality of the angles of the isosceles triangle is hence rather an illusory one. Nevertheless this does not detract from the fact that the machine was able to do something rather good and surprising which its own designer might never have thought of.

Now is there a difference in degree only between the sort of creativeness manifested by the machine in devising the very beautiful proof of the equality of two angles of the isosceles triangle and the sort of creativeness which is manifested by the artist or the poet in devising beautiful structures of paint or of words? Or for that matter in the scientist devising a beautiful theory? It is premature to answer this question with any definiteness, but we can see the manner in which physiology, biology, and the study of artificial machines are coming together to weaken the hold of traditional philosophy of mind and to make a mechanistic approach to those problems seem to be more fruitful and more likely to be upheld by the progress of science.

It is sometimes held that developments in one special science, namely mathematical logic, show the impossibility of a mechanistic philosophy of mind. As was noted in Chapter 2, Gödel has shown that however many axioms we have for elementary number theory or any stronger theory such as set theory, from which elementary number theory can be derived, there must be a true sentence of elementary number theory which is not provable from these axioms. Some writers[22] have seen in this fact a limitation on machines which does not apply to the minds of human beings, because we can always convince ourselves that such unprovable formulae are true.

Consider an idealized computer of the following sort. It has a finite number of internal states. It has an infinite tape (or if you like, it can be provided with extensions to its tape whenever it gets to the end of the tape). The tape initially contains a finite sequence of symbols. We can regard blank squares adjacent to non-blank squares as containing a symbol, the null symbol. At any moment the machine scans a particular square on the tape. There is a finite set of rules of the forms "if the machine is in internal state q_k and scans symbol S_i then it moves into internal state q_l and prints symbol S_j" and "if the machine is in internal state q_k and scans symbol S_i it moves its scanner one square right [left]". Idealized machines of this sort are called "Turing machines". No actual computer is a Turing machine: actual computers, for example, wear out eventually and so can not perform calculations which may require an unlimited number of steps. Any actual digital computer, working well, will never be able to perform any calculation or prove any theorem which a corresponding Turing machine could not perform or prove given unlimited time. If we build heuristics into the machine, as in the simple logic proving machine which was discussed above, this will not enable the machine to do anything that the moronic Turing machine could not do given infinite time. Thus a Turing machine can be specified which will churn out all theorems of a formally axiomatized system. On the other hand, if the system has no decision procedure, it is mathematically impossible that there be a machine to churn out all non-theorems, because, if there were such a machine, we would have a decision procedure for whether a sentence was a theorem or not: simply to wait until either the theorem producing machine or the non-theorem producing machine churns out the sentence. When there is no decision procedure we can specify a theorem churning machine only. Suppose that

318

after a few million steps it still has not produced the sentence in question. Clearly we do not know whether this is because it never will do so or simply because it has not been operating long enough. Now a machine with inbuilt heuristics for proof within the formal system will perhaps simply produce by good luck a theorem which the moronic machine would produce *eventually*. If the moronic machine would never produce the theorem neither will the machine with inbuilt heuristics.

Consider a Turing machine which churns out theorems of a formal system for elementary number theory (or some stronger theory). Gödel's theorem assures us that if the system corresponding to the Turing machine is consistent, then there will be a sentence G which is neither provable nor disprovable by the machine. Now anti-mechanists argue as follows. Whatever the system and whatever the machine we, as human beings, can show that G is in fact true. Hence we can be sure that G is true even though G is an undecidable proposition of the system corresponding to a Turing machine which represents me in the sense of being able to prove all the theorems which I can prove, and it would therefore seem that this Turing machine would both be able to prove G and not be able to prove it. This leads by *reductio-ad-absurdum* to the proposition that there can be no Turing machine which represents me.

The flaw in the argument, as has been pointed out by Hilary Putnam,[23] lies in the fact that we do not know that G is unprovable. We know only that G is unprovable if the Turing machine which represents me is consistent. For what Gödel proved was not a theorem of the form:

$$G \text{ is unprovable}$$

but one of the form

$$\text{consis} \supset G \text{ is unprovable}$$

where "consis" is the metamathematical sentence as-   **319** serting the consistency of the system in question. Unless we can show consistency[5] we can not show the unprovability of G. Now is it likely that I would be able to prove the consistency of such a complicated machine as would replace me? (Even if transfinite methods[6] were allowed.) And if transfinite methods are not allowed it is mathematically impossible to prove the consistency of a system at least as strong as elementary number theory. (This is a corollary of Gödel's theorem itself.) Of course if the system is *inconsistent,* then G is certainly provable, because anything whatever (including both G and ~G) can be derived from a contradiction. See pp. 32–33.

Indeed it is surely quite unplausible that one could prove anything in detail about a Turing machine which represented me in the sense of being able to prove all the theorems which I could prove in the whole of my life, unless indeed we take into account inconsistent reasonings in my lifetime, in which case any inconsistent machine would trivially do the trick. Surely the argument gets its plausibility because we consider only the case of a Turing machine which represents me at some instant of my life, and then we forget that this Turing machine will almost certainly not represent me at any later instant, on account of the continuous stream of "information" coming into my brain. Indeed the intuitive "seeing" of the truth of a Gödelian sentence corresponds to an argument which if formalized would have to be done in a semantic metalanguage. Now in so far as we can do this, it would seem that our intuitive knowledge of the syntactical and semantical rules of the language we speak must come from our ability to make empirical hypotheses on the basis of our experience of the language we speak. On the basis of this experience we can presumably ascend also to the semantics of our semantic metalanguage, and so on *ad infinitum.* Thus in

[5]Actually, it will be recalled, Gödel used in his original paper the stronger requirement of ω-consistency, but it was shown by Rosser that the weaker requirement of consistency will do.

[6]As in Gentzen's proof of the consistency of elementary number theory. [24]

fact we may correspond instant by instant to ever more powerful Turing machines. There is nothing contrary to mechanism in this, but only the triviality that we are being continually "reprogrammed" as a result of experience of our own behavior, as well as all sorts of other things. Notice that in order to prove anything about a Turing machine which represented me at instant t we should have to discover what this was, presumably by discovering the details of my neural circuitry at t. Even if this piece of science fiction were allowed to pass muster, it would still be obvious that the very act of ascertaining this circuitry would change it, and so once we knew what Turing machine represented me at t I would no longer be represented by it. There is nothing in the mechanistic theory of mind which is in the least incompatible with this fact.

Purposive mechanisms

The proof-making mechanism which was discussed in the previous section provides a particular instance of a purposive or "goal seeking" mechanism. Purposive mechanisms may be of various degrees of complexity, and with varying degrees of subtlety in attaining their goals. At the lowest level we have such simple devices as a thermostat or the governor of a steam engine. In these cases a difference between the actual state of affairs and the goal (between the actual temperature and the required temperature) causes a change in the device which causes a change in the actual state of affairs in the direction of bringing it closer to the goal. Normally this compensatory action will overshoot the mark, causing a change in the reverse direction, so that what we actually get is a temperature or rate of revolution which oscillates slightly about the required one. Not much more complex are the mechanisms of tropisms, such as the mechanism which causes a moth to fly towards a light, or one of Grey Walter's mechanical "tortoises" to seek its battery re-charger. [25] Then we have mechanical maze runners which try out at random alternative courses of action until (perhaps) they succeed in running the maze, and, at a higher level of sophistication, maze runners which learn from experience in the sense that they do not any longer try out courses of action which have been unsuccessful. Compare also Grey Walter's "tortoise" modified with his auxiliary electronic conditioned reflex mechanism. Then again, we have mechanisms with inbuilt computers, typified by the predictor controlled antiaircraft gun. The predictor receives information by radar of the course of the target airplane, and computes the position in which the airplane will be by the time a shell can reach it, and causes the gun to fire at this computed position. Indeed in an age of automatically controlled missiles and space satellites, as well as automatic factories and oil refineries, it is becoming commonplace that mechanisms can take over many of the purposive activities of men, or can even do them better. These developments have surely done at least as much as any purely philosophical analysis to weaken the hold of the idea that in teleology there is anything mysterious or incompatible with mechanistic ideas.

It might be wondered whether the difference between purposive and nonpurposive mechanisms is a sharp one. Richard Taylor has recently[26] considered the cases of (1) a torpedo which is guided by sound waves from the propeller of a target ship so as to "home" on to the target, and (2) a bomb, connected to a ship by a rope, so that when the ship stops the bomb drifts on to the ship. If we call the first a purposive mechanism, why not the latter? And does not this suggest that the ascription of purposiveness to the automatic torpedo is as mistaken as would be the belief of a person who did not notice the rope on the bomb, and thought that the bomb was purposively seeking the target ship? Against Taylor, I would suggest that there are significant differences between the two cases. We might perhaps regard the ship and bomb *together* as an extremely simple purposive mechanism, but the bomb itself need contain no mechanism whatever. What is transmitted from the ship to the torpedo is information in the form of sound waves, but these sound waves do not themselves exert the force which moves the torpedo towards the predicted position of the ship. In the case of the bomb, however, the rope which perhaps might be said to transmit "information" about the ship is in fact the very same thing as that which moves the bomb. The ship-bomb system is an "energy-flow" system rather than an "information-flow" system.[27] It is this feature, surely, which would lead cyberneticians to regard the torpedo, and not the bomb, as a purposive mechanism.

The motions of the ship and of the bomb to which it is attached can be said to be "epistemically dependent" on one another, since there is a simple law which relates motion of ship and bomb. This notion of "epistemic dependence" is due to G. Sommerhoff,[28] who uses it to analyze the difference between cases of apparent purpose due to physical stability, like that in which a ball always returns to the center of a hemispherical bowl, and cases of goal directedness. Sommerhoff concedes that the notion of epistemic dependence and independence is not an absolute one, and so perhaps it must also be conceded that there is not an absolute or sharp distinction between purposive and non-purposive mechanisms. However I do not see why either opponents or proponents of the notion that some mechanisms can be purposive need hold that the distinction is a sharp one. Perhaps it is no more sharp than is the distinction between living and nonliving. Is a virus living matter or is it nonliving? Doubts about whether to call a virus "living" should not lead us to doubt whether a cat is a living thing. Analogously, doubts as whether to call the bomb arrangement a purposive mechanism should not necessarily lead us to doubt whether the self-guided torpedo is.

323

Another of Taylor's objections to the notion of a purposive mechanism is also instructive. He gives the example of an old lady who is employed to thread needles on an assembly line. She is quite skillful, and gets the thread through the eye of the needle most times. Later on, out of a grudge against her employer she misses the eye of the needle quite often. Suppose now that she is replaced by an automatic needle threading device. How would an engineer make an automatic needle threader that missed the thread often *on purpose*? Clearly it would be no good making a machine which missed the thread quite often. That would of course only be to make an inefficient needle threading mechanism.

Surely this does not show that the old woman is not a purposive mechanism. It merely shows that by heredity and environment she has come to have many purposes or goal seeking "programs". She is, for example, not only a needle threading mechanism, but a grudge paying out mechanism. (If circumstances had been different, and she had been her employer's tea maker, the latter circumstance might have led her to pay out the grudge differently, e.g., by making cold tea for her employer.) Since grudges can be paid out in so many ways a human-like grudge paying out mechanism would be much harder to make than a needle threading mechanism.

It is true that in the case of humans, at least, we seem to invent our own goals. This brings us back to the general question of creativity and intelligence. Nevertheless the inventing of new goals is not necessarily mysterious. There is a sense in which even quite a crude mechanism may set itself a goal unintended by its designer, as when the position mechanism of a space rocket locks onto the wrong bright star. It is also to be remembered that we do not cease to talk of purposiveness in humans when they do *not* invent their own goals. There is something profoundly unoriginal in most human purposes. Consider the common desire to marry and have children. Some people, unfortunately, lack the genes which would make them susceptible to social pressures in this direction, but most people have them, and surely we can regard the purposes of such people as programmed into them both genetically and environmentally. It should also be asked whether the appearance of even very original purposes does not come simply from original means of solving the problem of attaining more general and unoriginal purposes. Thus a desire to create a new type of mathematics might be programmed into a clever and potentially ambitious young mathematician by doting parents, excited schoolmasters, already ambitious friends, and so on. The purpose of creating *this* sort of mathematics is clearly a novel one, but the purpose of creating a new and beautiful theory need not be.

Far as we may be from an understanding of all but rather simple forms of problem solving, we are even farther from an understanding of the higher forms of creativity in science, literature, and so on. Nevertheless further attempts to theorize mechanistically about these activities will surely tend to bring about a change in the climate of opinion, in which we shall come to be dissatisfied with the idea that even genius is mysterious. After all, even the failures of mechanistic theories of mind are brave failures: the mystery monger does not lay himself open to possible failure, and hence real success is not possible for him either. Mechanistic theories of mind also give us an idea of what a real explanation looks like: a resort to vitalistic or spiritualistic ideas seems less attractive if we recognize that the proponents of such ideas have an obligation to show us in detail how their ideas can help us to explain human behavior: they should not merely hope to placate us with the vague suggestion that, after all, a ghost can do *anything*.[7] It is not much good replacing unsolved prob-

---

[7]After all, if a ghost can go through closed doors, it presumably can do anything else that we find mysterious, such as writing poems.

lems about the workings of mechanisms by unsolved problems about the workings of ghosts. Indeed, just as a Turing machine might be realized approximately by a piece of transistorized circuitry, so also it could be realized approximately by an angel working according to rigorous rules. Similarly even the problems of the spiritual might turn out to be cybernetic ones.[8]

In assessing the probability of future mechanistic explanations of human abilities we need to be aware of the possibility of a certain sort of fallacy. Suppose that we have gone 80 percent[9] of the way towards the fulfillment of some task (let us suppose fully automatic machine translation of Russian into English). Y. Bar-Hillel, in an instructive critique of the possibility of fully automatic high quality machine translation,[30] mentions the "80 percent fallacy", described by W. E. Bull, C. Africa, and D. Teichrow,[31] of supposing that it therefore follows that a quarter of the effort already expended will get us the rest of the way. Thus in the case of machine translation, it is already possible to produce machines which translate in such a way that an intelligent post editor can make a good translation from the translation made by the machine. However to make fully automatic high speed translation possible, there arise difficulties of a different order from those which have as yet been overcome. Bar-Hillel gives a very simple explanation of this. Suppose that an electronic computer is translating the English sentence "The box is in the pen" into a language which has different words for "pen" = "writing utensil" and "pen" = "enclosure". A human translator would unhesitatingly choose the latter meaning, because of his *knowledge* that boxes are rarely small enough to go inside fountain pens, but are commonly found inside playpens or sheep-pens. To

[8]For an amusing example to illustrate how basic ideas of cybernetics might be applied to the spiritual see W. Ross Ashby, *An Introduction to Cybernetics*,[29] 4/15.

[9]Of course, a precise percentage like "80 percent" is probably meaningless in such a context as this, but this point is not important to the present issue.

make such high quality translation feasible one would have to build not only the grammatical and semantical rules of languages into a computer but also encyclopedic knowledge, and would have to also solve the problem of quick information retrieval from such a large store. (This latter problem, indeed, constitutes one of the unsolved problems which beset a mechanistic explanation of human intelligence.)

Now corresponding to this "80 percent fallacy" in technology, there is the possibility of a "10 percent fallacy" in metaphysics. Because cybernetic thinking has provided explanations of some purposive and intelligent activities in human beings, it is natural to jump to the conclusion that it can explain all of them. Nevertheless, one perhaps may be less repentant about committing the "10 percent fallacy". For whereas in technology one can often give good scientific reasons why the last 20 percent or even 2 percent of a project may raise difficulties of a new order of magnitude, and so the 100 percent completion of the task may not be practicable; the 10 percent fallacy in metaphysics would be objectionable only if it could be shown that there was an alternative to mechanistic methods of explanation which was in any better case. Since no scientifically respectable alternative to mechanistic theories of mind has been produced, it is not obviously unreasonable to go on with the assumption that our success rate of 10 percent is only because we are not clever enough or that we do not yet know enough.

Psycholinguistics and the Kantian problem

Modern linguistics is perhaps second only to philosophy in its interdisciplinary ramifications, and it is no coincidence that some of its leading exponents, notably Chomsky, are very capable philosophers. Consider the part which the notion of recursiveness plays in Chomsky's work: his *Syntactic Structures*[32] has clear liaisons with mathematical logic. Problems of machine translation link the subject up with electronics and the theory of computers. Linguistics also links up with psychology, since it raises questions as to how children learn the grammar of a language, and whether this can be explained on the basis of orthodox learning theory. It of course also links up with the humanistic philosophical disciplines. It is a superb discipline therefore for one who wishes to straddle university departments, and perhaps is one which might help to break down what C. P. Snow[33] has called "The Two Cultures".[10]

Now the impact of linguistics on psychology is of particular philosophical interest on account of Chomsky's suggestion, referred to on p. 315 above, that there may be an innate schema in our brain structure which leads the child to hypothesize a particular type of grammar. This raises the similar question of the possible innateness of conceptual schemes: indeed the two questions are not wholly separable, since the grammar of our language reflects a conceptual scheme. The way in which a natural language tends to use nouns and adjectives, instead of quantifiers, variables, and predicates, as in an artificial language based on mathematical logic, clearly inclines us to a metaphysics of substance and changing qualities.[11] Immanuel Kant held that certain categories, such as of substance and cause, were inescapable. Modern science has certainly shown him to be wrong here by avoiding the use of these categories in fundamental theories, but perhaps it might be argued that we have to use commonsense language as a stepping stone to a more adequate scientific language. It is certainly hard to envisage in detail how a child might begin to learn a language embodying quantification theory and the concept of objects

---

[10]That is, the sciences on the one hand and the humanities on the other.
[11]P. F. Strawson[34] has argued on philosophical grounds for the indispensability of commonsense metaphysical categories.

as four-dimensional space-time solids, so that the child would talk at once of differences between instantaneous cross sections of rabbits instead of about rabbits changing. Now the question of how much our ordinary conceptual schemes depend on innate brain structure is what I call the Kantian problem, and it seems to me that it will be solved eventually by neurophysiology and psycholinguistics. Of course even if it should be shown that our ordinary conceptual scheme of substance and change is innate to us, this does not mean that it is necessarily a good one. It means that it has proved useful in the history of the race, not that it is metaphysically adequate. We noted in Chapter 3 that an incorrect theory can sometimes be more useful, practically, than a correct one.

SUGGESTIONS FOR FURTHER READING

The libertarian theory of free-will is perhaps best defended by C. A. Campbell in his "Is Free-Will a Pseudo-Problem?", *Mind*, LX (1951), 441–465. Further considerations on free-will, from the point of view of scientific plausibility, are given by J. J. C. Smart, "Philosophy and Scientific Plausibility", in Paul K. Feyerabend and Grover Maxwell (eds.), *Mind, Matter and Method, Essays in Philosophy and Science in Honor of Herbert Feigl* (Minneapolis: University of Minnesota Press, 1966), pp. 377–390. Many philosophers deny that there is any incompatibility between free-will and determinism. A beautiful article by R. E. Hobart (Dickinson S. Miller) is "Free-Will as involving Determinism and Inconceivable without It", *Mind*, XLIII (1934), 1–26.

On questions connected with the mechanization of intelligence, there are a number of useful articles in the National Physical Laboratory Symposium, *Mechanisation of Thought Processes* (London: Her Majesty's Stationery Office, 1959), and C. E. Shannon and J. McCarthy (eds.), *Automata Studies* (Princeton: Princeton University Press, 1956). See also the article "Artificial Intelligence" by Marvin L. Minsky, *Scientific American*, CCXV, 3 (September 1966), 246–260. Two very useful papers by Herbert A. Simon are "Thinking by Computers" in R. G. Colodny (ed.), *Mind and Cosmos* (Pittsburgh: University of Pittsburgh Press, 1966), pp. 3–21 and "Scientific Discovery and the Psychology of Problem Solving", *ibid.*, pp. 22–40. F. H. George, *The*

Brain as a Computer (New York: Pergamon Press, 1961) is a useful treatise. For a comparison between electronic computers and human brains see J. von Neumann, *The Computer and the Brain* (New Haven, Conn.: Yale University Press, 1958).

On purposive mechanisms see W. Ross Ashby, *Design for a Brain*, second edition (New York: Wiley, 1960, and paperback, New York: Barnes and Noble, 1960) and *Introduction to Cybernetics* (New York: Wiley, 1961 and paperback, 1963), G. Sommerhoff, *Analytical Biology* (London: Oxford University Press, 1950), and the discussion of teleological and causal chains in R. B. Braithwaite's *Scientific Explanation* (London: Cambridge University Press, 1953). See also J. J. C. Smart, "Causality and Human Behaviour", *Aristotelian Society Supplementary Volume*, XXXVIII (1964), 143–148, which is part of a symposium with D. W. Hamlyn. For arguments against the mechanistic point of view, see Richard Taylor, *Action and Purpose* (Englewood Cliffs, N.J.: Prentice-Hall, 1966), Chapter 15. A. R. Anderson (ed.), *Minds and Machines* (Englewood Cliffs, N. J.: Prentice-Hall, 1964) includes reprints of a number of articles, including the well known article "Computing Machinery and Intelligence" by A. M. Turing. J. von Neumann's "The General and Logical Theory of Automata", in L. A. Jeffress (ed.), *Cerebral Mechanisms in Behavior, The Hixon Symposium* (New York: Wiley, 1951), pp. 1–41, contains a discussion of an automaton capable of reproducing itself. P. Benacerraf, "God, the Devil, and Gödel", *Monist*, LI (1967), 9–32, is an excellent and witty discussion of arguments which try to use Gödel's theorem to refute mechanism. An interesting paper by Theodore Mischel, "Pragmatic Aspects of Explanation", *Philosophy of Science*, XXXIII (1966), 40–60, is of interest in that it relates a discussion of Feyerabend's theory of scientific explanation (see Chapter 3 above) to a discussion of the relation between mechanistic explanations and commonsense explanations in terms of purpose.

N. Chomsky's attitude to psycholinguistics comes out in his review of Skinner's *Verbal Behavior in Language*, XXXV (1959), 26–58. This review has been reprinted in J. A. Fodor and J. J. Katz (eds.), *The Structure of Language, Readings in the Philosophy of Language* (Englewood Cliffs, N.J.: Prentice-Hall, 1964) pp. 547–548. See also Noam Chomsky, "Recent Contributions to the Theory of Innate Ideas", *Synthèse*, XVII (1967), 2–11, Hilary Putnam, "The 'Innateness' Hypothesis and Explanatory Models in Linguistics", *ibid.*, 12–22, and Nelson Goodman, "The Epistemological Argument", *ibid.*, 23–28. On the "Kantian Problem" see the remark on p. 168 of J. J. C. Smart, "Conflicting Views about Explanation", in R. S. Cohen and M. W. Wartofsky (eds.), *Boston Studies in the Philosophy of Science*, Vol. II (New York: Humanities Press, 1965), and pp. 234–235 of P. K. Feyerabend's "Reply to Criticism" in the same volume. Feyerabend here draws attention to paragraph 58 (b) of Wilfrid Sellars' "Scientific Realism or Irenic Instrumentalism", *ibid.*, 171–204.

reference notes

chapter 1

1 · See the paper by J. Holland Rose, "Was the Failure of the Spanish Armada due to Storms?", *Proceedings of the British Academy*, XXII (1936), 207–244, especially p. 226. (There is a misprint in the second footnote, where "E. M. Smart" should be "W. M. Smart".)

2 · Israel Scheffler, *The Anatomy of Inquiry* (New York: Knopf, 1963), p. 5.

3 · Ibid., p. 6.

4 · See for example Noam Chomsky, *Syntactic Structures* (The Hague: Mouton, 1957).

5 · W. H. Watson, *On Understanding Science* (London: Cambridge University Press, 1938).

6 · Ibid., p. 8.

7 · Gilbert Ryle, *Dilemmas* (London: Cambridge University Press, 1954).

8 · L. Wittgenstein, *Tractatus Logico-Philosophicus*, trans. by D. F. Pears and B. F. McGuinness (London: Routledge & Kegan Paul, 1962).

9 · W. V. Quine, *Word and Object* (Cambridge: M. I. T. Press, 1960).

10 · Encyclopedia Britannica, 13th ed., XXI (1926), p. 441.

11 · See H. Feigl, *"De Principiis non Disputandum . . .?"*, in Max Black (ed.), *Philosophical Analysis* (Ithaca: Cornell University Press, 1950).

12 · Albert Einstein, "Autobiographical Notes", in P. A. Schilpp (ed.), *Albert Einstein: Philosopher-Scientist*, 2nd ed. (La Salle, Ill.: Open Court, 1951), especially p. 53.

chapter 2

1 · An account of Gödel's method of proving completeness can be found in D. Hilbert and W. Ackermann, *Principles of Mathematical Logic*, trans. by L. M. Hammond, G. G. Leckie, and F. Steinhardt, and ed. with notes by R. E. Luce (New York: Chelsea, 1950), pp. 92–101. A much simpler method of proving completeness of predicate logic is given in W. V. Quine, *Methods of Logic*, rev. ed. (New York: Holt, Rinehart & Winston, 1959), pp. 253–260.

2 · Alonzo Church, "A Note on the *Entscheidungsproblem*", *Journal of Symbolic Logic*, I (1936), 40–41, 101–102. This note is short but it depends on a good understanding of results about Church's so-called "Calculus of Lambda-Conversion". This is equivalent to the theory of computability (Turing machines); and a proof of Church's theorem from the latter point of view (which most readers will probably find more easily understandable) is found in Martin Davis (ed.), *Computability and Unsolvability* (New York: McGraw-Hill, 1958), Chapter 8, section 4. This section can not be understood by itself but rests on the results of the preceding part of the book.

3 · A. Tarski, *A Decision Method for Elementary Algebra and Geometry*, 2nd ed. (Berkeley and Los Angeles: RAND Corporation, 1951).

4 · Kurt Gödel, *The Consistency of the Axiom of Choice and the Generalized Continuum-Hypothesis with the Axioms of Set Theory* (Princeton: Princeton University Press, 1940).

5 · Paul J. Cohen, "The Independence of the Continuum Hypothesis", *Proceedings of the National Academy of Sciences (U.S.A.)*, L (1963), 1143–1148; and LI (1964), 105–110.

6 · A. Tarski, *"Der Wahrheitsbegriff in den formalisierten Sprachen"*, *Studia Philosophica*, I (1936), 261–405. English translation in A. Tarski, *Logic, Semantics, Metamathematics* (Oxford: Oxford University Press, 1956).

7 · See W. V. Quine, *Mathematical Logic*, rev. ed. (New York: Holt, Rinehart & Winston 1959), section 5.

8 · K. R. Popper, "The Propensity Interpretation of the Calculus of Probability, and the Quantum Theory", in S. Körner (ed.), *Observation and Interpretation in the Philosophy of Physics* (New York: Dover, 1962); and "The Propensity Interpretation of Probability", *British Journal for the Philosophy of Science*, X (1959), 25 – 42.

chapter **3**

1 · See the report in *Scientific American* (July 1965), p. 46.

2 · C. G. Hempel, *Aspects of Scientific Explanation and Other Essays in the Philosophy of Science* (New York: Free Press, 1965).

3 · Michael Scriven, "Explanations, Predictions and Laws", in H. Feigl and G. Maxwell (eds.), *Scientific Explanation, Space and Time, Minnesota Studies in the Philosophy of Science*, Vol. III (Minneapolis: University of Minnesota Press, 1962), pp. 170 – 230.

4 · Hempel, *op. cit.*

5 · Nelson Goodman, *Fact, Fiction and Forecast* (Cambridge: Harvard University Press, 1955), Chapter 3.

6 · A. J. Ayer, "Review of Ernest Nagel's *Structure of Science*", *Scientific American* (June 1961), 197 – 203.

7 · See Alan Moorehead, *The White Nile* (London: Hamish Hamilton, 1960), p. 47.

8 · W. Dray, *Laws and Explanation in History* (Oxford: Oxford University Press, 1957).

9 · Hempel, *op. cit.*, pp. 415 – 425.

10 · *Ibid.*, p. 421, footnote 14.

11 · See especially N. R. Campbell, *Physics, The Elements* (London: Cambridge University Press, 1920), reprinted as *Foundations of Science* (New York: Dover, 1957).

12 · Campbell, *Foundations of Science*, p. 123.

13 · *Ibid.*, p. 144.

14 · Hempel, *op. cit.*, pp. 430 – 431.

15 · G. Schlesinger, "What Is Science For?", *Australian Journal of Science*, XXVI (1963), 163 – 167.

16 · See especially P. K. Feyerabend, "Explanation, Reduction and Empiricism", in H. Feigl and G. Maxwell (eds.),

Scientific Explanation, Space and Time, Minnesota Studies in the Philosophy of Science, Vol. III (Minneapolis: University of Minnesota Press, 1962), pp. 28–97; "Reply to Criticism, Comments on Smart, Sellars and Putnam", in R. S. Cohen and M. W. Wartofsky (eds.), *Boston Studies in the Philosophy of Science*, Vol. II (New York: Humanities Press, 1965), pp. 223–261; and "Problems of Empiricism", in R. G. Colodny (ed.), *Beyond the Edge of Certainty* (Pittsburgh: University of Pittsburgh Press, 1965).

17 · J. Kemeny and P. Oppenheim, "On Reduction", *Philosophical Studies*, VII (1956), 6–19.

18 · Hempel, *op. cit.*, p. 347, footnote.

19 · Ernest Nagel, *The Structure of Science* (New York: Harcourt, Brace and World, 1961), Chapter 11.

20 · Hilary Putnam, "How Not to Talk about Meaning, Comments on J. J. C. Smart", in R. S. Cohen and M. W. Wartofsky (eds.), *Boston Studies in the Philosophy of Science*, Vol. II (New York: Humanities Press, 1965), pp. 205–222, see p. 207.

21 · See Wilfrid Sellars, *Science, Perception and Reality* (New York: Humanities Press, 1963), Chapter 4; and "Scientific Realism or Irenic Instrumentalism, Comments on J. J. C. Smart", in R. S. Cohen and M. W. Wartofsky (eds.), *Boston Studies in the Philosophy of Science*, Vol. II (New York: Humanities Press, 1965), pp. 171–204.

22 · See for example, Sir Arthur Eddington, *The Philosophy of Physical Science* (London: Cambridge University Press, 1939).

23 · Feyerabend, "Explanation, Reduction and Empiricism", *op. cit.*, p. 260, footnote 44.

24 · R. Carnap, "Testability and Meaning", *Philosophy of Science*, III (1936), 419–471; and IV (1937), 1–40.

25 · Feyerabend, "Explanation, Reduction and Empiricism", *op. cit.*, pp. 65–66.

26 · See A. Einstein, *Investigations on the Theory of the Brownian Movement*, trans. by A. D. Cooper, and ed. with notes By R. Fürth (New York: Dover, 1956).

27 · Feyerabend, "Explanation, Reduction and Empiricism", *op. cit.*, p. 37.

28 · Putnam, *op. cit.*, p. 210.

29 · See David Lewis, "An Argument for the Identity Theory", *Journal of Philosophy*, LXIII (1966), 17–25.

30 · E. B. Uvarov, D. R. Chapman, and Alan Isaacs, *A Dictionary of Science*, 3rd. ed. (Baltimore, Md.: Penguin Books, 1964).

31 · Feyerabend, "Reply to Criticism", *op. cit.*, p. 248; and "Problems of Empiricism", *op. cit.*, p. 256.

32 · See Putnam, *op. cit.*, p. 211.

33 · *Ibid.*, p. 216.

34 · Sir George Thomson, "Some Thoughts on the Scientific Method", in R. S. Cohen and M. W. Wartofsky (eds.) *Boston Studies in the Philosophy of Science,* Vol. II (New York: Humanities Press, 1965).

chapter **4**

1 · Robert R. Sokal, "The Future Systematics", in Charles A. Leone (ed.), *Taxonomic Biochemistry and Serology* (New York: Ronald Press, 1964); and "Numerical Taxonomy", *Scientific American* (December 1966), 106–116.

2 · See Michael Scriven, "Truisms as the Grounds for Historical Explanations", in P. Gardiner (ed.), *Theories of History* (New York: Free Press, 1959), pp. 443–475.

3 · See C. G. Hempel's reply to Scriven in connection with the case of the bridge which collapses because of metal fatigue in his *Aspects of Scientific Explanation and Other Essays in the Philosophy of Science* (New York: Free Press, 1965), p. 371.

4 · See R. A. Fisher, *The Genetical Theory of Natural Selection*, 2nd ed. (New York: Dover, 1958).

5 · See G. G. Simpson, *The Meaning of Evolution* (New York: Mentor Books, 1954), pp. 34–35.

6 · Michael Scriven, "Explanation and Prediction in Evolutionary Theory", *Science*, CXXX (1959), 477–482.

7 · On self-reproducing machines, see J. Von Neumann, "The General and Logical Theory of Automata", in L. A. Jefress (ed.), *Cerebral Mechanisms in Behavior*, The Hixon Symposium, (New York: Wiley, 1951) pp. 1–41.

8 · See W. T. Williams, "Problems of Alien Biology", *Humanist*, LXXIX (November 1964), 329–332.

9 · Ibid.

10 · L. J. Henderson, *The Fitness of the Environment* (New York: Macmillan, 1913).

11 · J. A. Deutsch, *The Structural Basis of Behavior* (London: Cambridge University Press, 1960).

12 · Jerry A. Fodor, "Explanations in Psychology", in Max Black (ed.), *Philosophy in America* (London: Allen & Unwin, 1965 and Ithaca: Cornell University Press, 1965), pp. 161–179.

13 · B. A. Farrell, "On the Limits of Experimental Psychology", *British Journal of Psychology*, LVI (1955), 165–177.

14 · Deutsch, *op. cit.*, p. 12, and Chapter 10.

15 · Ibid., pp. 14–15.

16 · Fodor, *op. cit.*

17 · Ibid., p. 179.

chapter **5**

1 · N. R. Campbell, *An Account of the Principles of Measurement and Calculation* (London: Longmans, Green, 1928); and *Foundations of Science* (New York: Dover, 1957).

2 · See Campbell, *Foundations of Science, op. cit.*, p. 271.

3 · Sir Arthur Eddington, *The Nature of the Physical World* (London: Dent, 1964), p. 245.

4 · See N. R. Campbell, "The Errors of Sir Arthur Eddington", *Philosophy*, VI (1931), 180–192.

5 · Michael Scriven, "The Key Property of Physical Laws — Inaccuracy", in H. Feigl and G. Maxwell (eds.), *Current Issues in the Philosophy of Science* (New York: Holt, Rinehart & Winston, 1961), pp. 91–101; see especially p. 101.

6 · Ibid.

7 · See H. Mehlberg's comments on Scriven's paper, also in H. Feigl and G. Maxwell (eds.), *Current Issues in the Philosophy of Science* (New York: Holt, Rinehart & Winston, 1961), pp. 102–103.

8 · M. Scriven, "Rejoinder to Mehlberg", in H. Feigl and G. Maxwell (eds.), *Current Issues in the Philosophy of Science* (New York: Holt, Rinehart & Winston, 1961), pp. 103–104.

9 · Ibid., p. 104.

10 · See especially, Bishop George Berkeley, *Principles of Human Knowledge*, especially sections 58–66 and sections 101–117; and his *De Motu*. See David M. Armstrong (ed.),

Berkeley's Philosophical Writings (New York: Collier, 1965).

11 · Ernst Mach, *Contributions towards the Analysis of Sensations* (Chicago: Open Court, 1897); and *The Science of Mechanics: a Critical and Historical Account of its Development*, trans. by Thomas J. McCormack, 6th ed., rev. (La Salle, Ill.: Open Court, 1960), especially pp. 577–595.

12 · Wilfrid Sellars, *Science, Perception and Reality* (London: Routledge & Kegan Paul, 1963), Chapter 3.

13 · See P. W. Bridgman, "Operational Analysis", *Philosophy of Science*, V (1938), 114–131, especially p. 114.

14 · P. W. Bridgman, "Einstein's Theories and the Operational Point of View", in P. A. Schilpp (ed.), *Albert Einstein: Philosopher-Scientist*, 2nd ed. (La Salle, Ill.: Open Court, 1951), pp. 333–354.

15 · Albert Einstein, "On the Electrodynamics of Moving Bodies", in *The Principle of Relativity, a Collection of Original Memoirs on the Special and General Theory of Relativity*, by H. A. Lorentz, A. Einstein, H. Minkowski, and H. Weyl, with notes by A. Sommerfeld, trans. by W. Perrett and G. B. Jeffrey (London: Methuen, 1923).

16 · See for example W. Rindler, *Special Relativity* (Edinburgh: Oliver and Boyd, 1960), p. 12.

17 · Albert Einstein, "Autobiographical Notes", in P. A. Schilpp (ed.), *Albert Einstein: Philosopher-Scientist*, 2nd ed. (La Salle, Ill.: Open Court, 1951). For his indebtedness to Hume and Mach see p. 53; for his later rejection of Mach's position see p. 21.

18 · As by N. R. Hanson. See his "Number Theory and Physical Theory: An Analogy", in R. S. Cohen and M. W. Wartofsky (eds.), *Boston Studies in the Philosophy of Science*, Vol. II (New York: Humanities Press, 1965).

19 · Gilbert Ryle, *The Concept of Mind* (New York: Barnes & Noble, 1949), pp. 120–125.

20 · Stephen Toulmin, *The Philosophy of Science* (London: Hutchinson, 1953).

21 · See F. P. Ramsey, *Foundations of Mathematics* (London: Kegan Paul, 1931), p. 231.

22 · See W. V. Quine, *Set Theory and its Logic* (Cambridge: Harvard University Press, 1963), pp. 257–258.

23 · William Craig, "On Axiomatizability within a System", *Journal of Symbolic Logic*, XVIII (1953), 30–32; and "Replacement of Auxiliary Expressions", *Philosophical Review*, LXV (1956), 38–55.

24 · See Marshall Spector, "Models and Theories", *British Journal for the Philosophy of Science*, XVI (1965), 121–142.

25 · C. G. Hempel, "The Theoretician's Dilemma", in H. Feigl, M. Scriven and G. Maxwell (eds.), *Scientific Explanation, Space and Time, Minnesota Studies in the Philosophy of Science*, Vol. II (Minneapolis: University of Minnesota Press, 1958), pp. 37–98, see p. 79.

26 · Grover Maxwell, "The Ontological Status of Theoretical Entities", in H. Feigl and G. Maxwell (eds.), *Scientific Explanation, Space and Time, Minnesota Studies in the Philosophy of Science*, Vol. III (Minneapolis: University of Minnesota Press, 1962), pp. 3–17, see p. 9.

27 · See P. K. Feyerabend, "Explanation, Reduction and Empiricism", in H. Feigl and G. Maxwell (eds.) *Scientific Explanation, Space and Time, Minnesota Studies in the Philosophy of Science* Vol. III (Minneapolis: University of Minnesota Press, 1962) pp. 28–97, see pp. 36–39.

28 · R. Carnap, "Testability and Meaning", *Philosophy of Science*, III (1936), 419–471; and IV (1937), 1–40.

29 · K. R. Popper, *Conjectures and Refutations* (London: Routledge & Kegan Paul, 1963), Chapter 3, especially pp. 111–114. Instrumentalism has also been criticized elsewhere in Popper's writings.

30 · P. K. Feyerabend, "Realism and Instrumentalism", in Mario Bunge (ed.), *The Critical Approach to Science and Philosophy* (New York: Free Press, 1964), pp. 280–308.

31 · See Bernard Mayo, "More about Theoretical Entities", *Penguin Science News*, No. 39 (February 1956), 42–55, especially the final paragraph.

32 · K. R. Popper, "The Propensity Interpretation of the Calculus of Probability, and the Quantum Theory", in S. Körner (ed.), *Observation and Interpretation in the Philosophy of Physics* (New York: Dover, 1962) pp. 65–70, and discussion on pp. 78–89.

33 · P. K. Feyerabend, "Problems of Microphysics", in R. G. Colodny (ed.), *Frontiers of Science and Philosophy* (Pittsburgh: University of Pittsburgh Press, 1962), see p. 200.

34 · H. Margenau, *The Nature of Physical Reality* (New York: McGraw-Hill, 1950), p. 435.

35 · H. Margenau, *Open Vistas* (New Haven, Conn.: Yale University Press, 1961), see p. 161.

36 · J. C. C. McKinsey, A. C. Sugar, and P. Suppes, "Axiomatic Foundations of Particle Mechanics", *Journal of Rational Mechanics and Analysis*, II (1953), 253–277.

37 · W. V. Quine, *Word and Object* (Cambridge: M. I. T. Press, 1959), Chapter 6, especially section 4–1; and "Three Grades of Modal Involvement", *Proceedings of XIth International Congress of Philosophy*, XIV (Brussels, 1953), 65–81, reprinted in W. V. Quine *The Ways of Paradox* (New York: Random House, 1966), pp. 156–174.

38 · See Rudolf Carnap's account of his modal logic in P. A. Schilpp (ed.), *The Philosophy of Rudolf Carnap* (La Salle, Ill.: Open Court, 1963), pp. 889–900; also his remarks on p. 63 of the same volume; and his *Meaning and Necessity* (Chicago: University of Chicago Press, 1949). Also see, for example, the symposium between Ruth Barcan Marcus and W. V. Quine, together with the subsequent discussion, in M. W. Wartofsky (ed.), *Boston Studies in the Philosophy of Science*, Vol. I (Dordrecht, Holland: D. Reidel, 1963), pp. 77–116. Quine's reply to Marcus has been reprinted in his *The Ways of Paradox* (New York: Random House, 1966), pp. 175–182.

chapter **6**

1 · See David Hume, *Treatise on Human Nature*, Book I, Part 3, section 6, and *Enquiry Concerning Human Understanding*, Section IV, Part 2.

2 · Max Black, *Problems of Analysis* (Ithaca: Cornell University Press, 1954), Chapter 11; and *Models and Metaphors* (Ithaca: Cornell University Press, 1962), Chapter 12.

3 · R. B. Braithwaite, *Scientific Explanation* (London: Cambridge University Press, 1953), Chapter 8.

4 · J. M. Keynes, *A Treatise on Probability* (London: Macmillan, 1921), Chapter 22.

5 · Paul Edwards, "Bertrand Russell's Doubts about Induction", in A. G. N. Flew (ed.), *Logic and Language, First Series* (Oxford: Blackwell, 1951), pp. 55–79. Edwards is commenting on Chapter 6 of Russell's *Problems of Philosophy* (Oxford: Oxford University Press, 1946).

6 · Edwards, *op. cit.*, p. 59.

7 · Herbert Feigl, *De Principiis Non Disputandum . . .?*", in Max Black (ed.), *Philosophical Analysis* (Ithaca: Cornell University Press, 1950), pp. 119–156.

8 · Hans Reichenbach, "On the Justification of Induction", *Journal of Philosophy*, XXXVII (1940), 97–103. See also section 39 of his *Experience and Prediction* (Chicago: University of Chicago Press, 1938).

9 · Antony Flew, "Is Pascal's Wager the Only Safe Bet?", *Rationalist Annual* (1960), 21–25.

10 · James Cargile, "Pascal's Wager", *Philosophy*, XLI (1966), 250–257.

11 · Isabel Creed, "The Justification of the Habit of Induction", *Journal of Philosophy*, XXXVII (1940), 85–97.

12 · Jerrold J. Katz, *The Problem of Induction and its Solution* (Chicago: University of Chicago Press, 1962).

13 · See in particular Wesley C. Salmon, "Inductive Inference", in Bernard Baumrin (ed.), *Philosophy of Science, The Delaware Seminar*, Vol. 2 (New York: Interscience Publishers, 1963), pp. 341–370; as well as his paper "Vindication of Induction", with comments by Stephen Barker, rejoinder by Salmon, and comments by Richard Rudner, in H. Feigl and G. Maxwell (eds.), *Current Issues in the Philosophy of Science* (New York: Holt, Rinehart & Winston, 1959), pp. 245–264.

14 · Stephen Barker, "Comment on 'Vindication of Induction'", in H. Feigl and G. Maxwell (eds.), *Current Issues in the Philosophy of Science* (New York: Holt, Rinehart & Winston, 1959).

15 · Nelson Goodman, *Fact, Fiction and Forecast* (Cambridge: Harvard University Press, 1955), Chapter 3.

16 · Wesley C. Salmon, "The Foundations of Scientific Inference", in R. G. Colodny (ed.), *Mind and Cosmos* (Pittsburgh: University of Pittsburgh Press, 1966), pp. 135–275. On the rejection of basic observation predicates see p. 157; for a reference to Ian Hacking see p. 239.

17 · Ian Hacking, "Salmon's Vindication of Induction", *Journal of Philosophy*, LXII (1965), 260–266.

18 · See Katz, *op. cit.*, p. 61.

19 · Wesley C. Salmon, "The Short Run", *Philosophy of Science*, XXII (1955), 214–221.

20 · Brian Ellis, "A Vindication of Scientific Inductive Practices", *American Philosophical Quarterly*, II (1965), 296–304.

21 · K. R. Popper, *Conjectures and Refutations* (London: Routledge & Kegan Paul, 1963), p. 47.

22 · Hilary Putnam, "'Degree of Confirmation' and Inductive Logic", in P. A. Schilpp (ed.), *The Philosophy of Rudolf Carnap* (La Salle, Ill.: Open Court, 1963), pp. 761–783, see especially pp. 770–777.

23 · R. B. Braithwaite, *op. cit.*

24 · Pierre Duhem, *The Aim and Structure of Physical Theory* (Princeton: Princeton University Press, 1954).

25 · Ellis, *op. cit.*, p. 304.

26 · See for example Popper's *Conjectures and Refutations, op. cit.*, Chapter 1, especially pp. 53–55.

27 · See Rudolf Carnap, *Logical Foundations of Probability*, 2nd ed. (Chicago: University of Chicago Press, 1962); and *The Continuum of Inductive Methods* (Chicago: University of Chicago Press, 1952). See also Carnap's account of his basic concepts of probability and induction on pp. 966–979 of his "Replies and Expositions", in P. A. Schilpp (ed.), *The Philosophy of Rudolf Carnap* (La Salle, Ill.: Open Court, 1963).

28 · Popper, *Conjectures and Refutations, op. cit.*, p. 35.

29 · K. R. Popper, *The Logic of Scientific Discovery* (London: Routledge & Kegan Paul, 1959), see pp. 375ff.

30 · Popper, *Conjectures and Refutations, op. cit.*, p. 242.

31 · Adolf Grünbaum, *Philosophical Problems of Space and Time* (New York: Knopf, 1963).

chapter **7**

1 · Bertrand Russell, *The Philosophy of Leibniz* (London: Allen & Unwin, 1900).

2 · The quotations in the text are from Florian Cajori's edition of *Sir Isaac Newton's Mathematical Principles of Natural Philosophy and His System of the World* (Berkeley: University of California Press, 1934).

3 · Ernst Mach, *The Science of Mechanics: A Critical and Historical Account of its Development*, trans. by Thomas J. McCormack, 6th ed., rev. (La Salle, Ill.: Open Court, 1960), especially Chapter 2, Section VI, nos. 2–6.

4 · Gilbert Ryle, "The Verification Principle", *Revue Internationale de Philosophie*, III–IV (1951), 243–250.

5 · Immanuel Kant, *Prolegomena to Any Future Metaphys-*

ics, trans. with introduction and notes, by P. G. Lucas (Manchester: Manchester University Press, 1953).

6 · Adolf Grünbaum, *Philosophical Problems of Space and Time* (New York: Knopf, 1963), pp. 386–397.

7 · H. Minkowski, "Space and Time", in *The Principle of Relativity, A Collection of Original Memoirs on the Special and General Theory of Relativity*, by H. A. Lorentz, A. Einstein, H. Minkowski, and H. Weyl, with notes by A. Sommerfeld, trans. by W. Perrett and G. B. Jeffrey (London: Methuen, 1923), pp. 73–91, see especially pp. 78–79.

8 · *Ibid.*, p. 75.

9 · See Moritz Schlick, *Philosophy of Nature*, trans. by Amethe von Zeppelin (New York: Philosophical Library, 1949), p. 43.

10 · See E. A. Milne and G. J. Whitrow, "On the so-called 'Clock-paradox' of Special Relativity", *Philosophical Magazine*, XL (1949), 1244–1249; and G. J. Whitrow, *The Natural Philosophy of Time* (London: Nelson, 1961), pp. 219–222.

11 · See Grünbaum, *op. cit.*, Chapter 14.

12 · *Ibid.*, p. 419.

13 · J. A. Wheeler, "Curved Empty Space-Time as the Building Material of the Physical World: an Assessment", in E. Nagel, P. Suppes, and A. Tarski (eds.), *Logic, Methodology and Philosophy of Science: Proceedings of the 1960 International Congress* (Stanford: Stanford University Press, 1962), pp. 361–374.

14 · Hans Reichenbach, *The Philosophy of Space and Time*, trans. by Maria Reichenbach and John Freund with Introductory Remarks by Rudolf Carnap (New York: Dover, 1958), section 12.

15 · See Grünbaum, *op. cit.*, p. 97.

16 · *Ibid.*, Chapter 4.

17 · Hilary Putnam, "An Examination of Grünbaum's Philosophy of Geometry", in B. Baumrin (ed.), *Philosophy of Science, The Delaware Seminar*, Vol. 2 (New York: Interscience, 1963), pp. 205–255.

18 · *Ibid.*, pp. 219–220.

19 · Ernest Nagel, *The Structure of Science* (New York: Harcourt, Brace & World, 1961), Chapter 9.

20 · Adolf Grünbaum, *op. cit.*, Chapter 6. Grünbaum has given a more extended treatment in his paper "A Consistent

Conception of the Extended Linear Continuum as an Aggregate of Unextended Elements", *Philosophy of Science*, XIX (1952), 288–306 and in Chapter 3 of his book *Modern Science and Zeno's Paradoxes* (Middletown, Conn.: Wesleyan University Press, 1967).

21 · W. V. Quine, *Word and Object* (Cambridge: M. I. T. Press, 1960).

chapter **8**

1 · Moritz Schlick, *Philosophy of Nature*, trans. by Amethe von Zeppelin (New York: Philosophical Library, 1949).

2 · Adolf Grünbaum, *Philosophical Problems of Space and Time* (New York: Knopf, 1963).

3 · Grünbaum, "Carnap's Views on the Foundations of Geometry", in P. A. Schilpp (ed.), *The Philosophy of Rudolf Carnap* (La Salle, Ill.: Open Court, 1963).

4 · J. H. Christenson, J. W. Cronin, V. L. Fitch, and R. Turlay, "Evidence for the 2π Decay of the K_2^0 Meson", *Physical Review Letters*, XIII (1964), 138–140.

5 · J. Loschmidt, "Über das Wärmegleichgewicht eines Systems von Körpern mit Rücksicht auf die Schwere", *Sitzungsberichte der Akademie der Wissenschaften in Wien* LXXIII (1876); and LXXV (1877).

6 · S. Toulmin, R. W. Hepburn, and A. MacIntyre, *Metaphysical Beliefs* (London: S. C. M. Press, 1957).

7 · F. H. Bradley, *Appearance and Reality*, 2nd ed. (Oxford: Oxford University Press, 1930), p. 190.

8 · Claude E. Shannon, "The Mathematical Theory of Communication", originally published in the *Bell System Technical Journal* XXVII (1948), 379–423 and 623–656; and reprinted in Claude E. Shannon and Warren Weaver, *The Mathematical Theory of Communication* (Urbana: University of Illinois Press, 1949).

9 · Y. Bar-Hillel and R. Carnap, "Semantic Information", *British Journal for the Philosophy of Science*, XIV (1953–1954), 147–157.

10 · Hans Reichenbach, *The Direction of Time* (Berkeley: University of California Press, 1956), pp. 156ff.

11 · A. Grünbaum, *Philosophical Problems of Space and Time, op. cit.*, p. 258.

12 · Reichenbach, *op. cit.*

13 · Max Black, *Models and Metaphor* (Ithaca: Cornell University Press, 1962), Chapter 10, "The 'Direction' of Time". See especially the bottom half of p. 191 of Black's essay.

14 · Grünbaum, *Philosophical Problems of Space and Time, op. cit.*, p. 195.

15 · See especially, Grünbaum *ibid.*, p. 258, bottom paragraph.

16 · *Ibid.*, p. 257.

17 · Norbert Wiener, *Cybernetics*, 2nd ed. (New York: Wiley, 1961).

18 · See, for example, Charles A. Coulson, *Electricity* (New York: Interscience, 1948), section 113.

19 · O. Costa de Beauregard, *Le Second Principe de la Science du Temps* (Paris: Editions du Seuil, 1963), pp. 33–37.

20 · K. R. Popper, Letters in *Nature*, CLXXVII (1956), 538; CLXVIII (1956), 382; LXXIX (1957), 1297; LXXXI (1958), 402–403. For criticisms of Popper see A. Grünbaum, "Popper on Irreversibility", in Mario Bunge (ed.), *The Critical Approach to Science and Philosophy, in Honor of Karl Popper* (New York: Free Press, 1964), pp. 316–331.

21 · Sir A. S. Eddington, *The Expanding Universe* (London: Cambridge University Press, 1933), p. 66.

22 · T. Gold, "The Arrow of Time" in *La Structure et l'Evolution de l'Univers, Proceedings of the 11th Solvay Conference* (Brussels: R. Stoops, 1958), 81–91; and another paper with the same title in *American Journal of Physics*, XXX (1962), 403–410.

23 · See H. Bondi, *Cosmology*, 2nd ed. (London: Cambridge University Press, 1960), p. 22.

24 · Gold, "The Arrow of Time", *op. cit.* (1958), p. 85.

25 · *Ibid.*p. 82.

26 · T. Gold, "Cosmic Processes and the Nature of Time", in R. G. Colodny (ed.), *Mind and Cosmos* (Pittsburgh: University of Pittsburgh Press, 1966), pp. 311–329.

27 · H. Bondi, "Physics and Cosmology", *The Observatory*, LXXXII (1962), 133–143.

28 · *Ibid.*, pp. 142–143.

chapter **9**

1 · Marquis P. S. de Laplace, *A Philosophical Essay on Probabilities*, trans. from the 6th French ed. by F. W. Truscott and F. L. Emory (New York: Dover, 1951), p. 4.

2 · K. R. Popper, "Indeterminism in Quantum Physics and in Classical Physics", *British Journal for the Philosophy of Science*, I (1950–1951), 117–133 and 173–195.

3 · G. Ryle, *The Concept of Mind* (New York: Barnes & Noble, 1949), pp. 76–81.

4 · G. F. Dear, "Determinism in Classical Physics", *British Journal for the Philosophy of Science*, XI (1960–61), 289–304.

5 · *Ibid.*, p. 293.

6 · D. W. Sciama, "Determinism and the Cosmos", in Sidney Hook (ed.), *Determinism and Freedom in the Age of Modern Science* (New York: Collier, 1961), pp. 90–91.

7 · J. von Neumann, *Mathematical Foundations of Quantum Mechanics*, trans. by R. T. Beyer (Princeton: Princeton University Press, 1955), Chapter 4, section 2.

8 · Sciama, *op. cit.*, p. 91.

9 · J. C. Eccles, "Hypotheses Relating to the Brain-Mind Problem", *Nature*, CLXVIII (1951), 53–56.

10 · D. M. MacKay, "Brain and Will", *Listener*, LVII (1957), 788–789.

11 · W. Ross Ashby, "Design for an Intelligence Amplifier", in C. E. Shannon and J. McCarthy (eds.), *Automata Studies*, *Annals of Mathematics Studies*, No. 34 (Princeton: Princeton University Press, 1956), pp. 215–234.

12 · Alfred North Whitehead and Bertrand Russell, *Principia Mathematica*, 1st ed. (Cambridge: Cambridge University Press, 1913).

13 · See D. Hilbert and W. Ackermann, *Principles of Mathematical Logic*, trans. by L. M. Hammond, G. G. Leckie, and F. Steinhardt, and ed. with notes by R. E. Luce (New York: Chelsea, 1950), p. 27.

14 · Alfred North Whitehead and Bertrand Russell, *Principia Mathematica*, 2nd ed. (London: Cambridge University Press, 1927), * 1.2 to * 1.6.

15 · P. Bernays, *"Axiomatische Untersuchung des Aussagenkalküls der Principia Mathematica"*, *Mathematische Zeitschrift*, XXV (1926), 305–320.

16 · A. Newell, J. C. Shaw, and H. A. Simon, "Theory of Human Problem Solving", *Psychological Review*, LXV (1958), 151–166.

17 · Newell, Shaw, and Simon, *op. cit.*, p. 158.

18 · Noam Chomsky, "Review of B. F. Skinner's *Verbal Behavior*", *Language*, XXXV (1959), 26–58. This review has been reprinted in Jerry A. Fodor and Jerrold J. Katz (eds.), *The Structure of Language, Readings in the Philosophy of Language* (Englewood Cliffs, N.J.: Prentice-Hall, 1964), pp. 547–578.

19 · B. F. Skinner, *Verbal Behavior* (New York: Appleton-Century-Crofts, 1957).

20 · H. L. Gelernter "Realisation of a Geometry Proving Machine", *Proceedings of the International Conference on Information Processing* (Paris: UNESCO House, 1959), pp. 273–282.

21 · Marvin L. Minsky, "Some Methods of Artificial Intelligence and Heuristic Programming", National Physical Laboratory Symposium on *Mechanisation of Thought Processes* (London: Her Majesty's Stationery Office, 1959), Vol. I, pp. 5–27.

22 · See, for example, J. R. Lucas, "Minds, Machines and Gödel", *Philosophy*, XXXVI (1961), 112–127. This has been reprinted in A. R. Anderson (ed.), *Minds and Machines* (Englewood Cliffs, N.J.: Prentice-Hall, 1964), 43–59.

23 · Hilary Putnam, "Minds and Machines", in Sidney Hook (ed.), *Dimensions of Mind* (New York: Collier, 1961), 138–164.

24 · G. Gentzen, "Die Widerspruchsfreiheit der reinen Zahlentheorie", *Mathematische Annalen*, CXII (1936), 493–565.

25 · W. Grey Walter, *The Living Brain* (London: Duckworth, 1953).

26 · Richard Taylor, *Action and Purpose* (Englewood Cliffs, N.J.: Prentice-Hall, 1966), Chapter 15.

27 · See the discussion of Taylor's example by D. M. Armstrong in his Critical Notice of Taylor's *Action and Purpose*,

Australasian Journal of Philosophy, XLIV (1966), 231–240, especially pp. 238–239.

28 · G. Sommerhoff, *Analytical Biology* (Oxford: Oxford University Press, 1950), pp. 85ff.

29 · W. Ross Ashby, *An Introduction to Cybernetics* (New York: Wiley, 1961).

30 · Y. Bar-Hillel, *Language and Information* (Reading, Mass.: Addison-Wesley, 1964), p. 179.

31 · W. E. Bull, C. Africa, and D. Teichrow, "Some Problems of the 'word'", in W. N. Locke and A. D. Booth (eds.), *Machine Translation* (Cambridge: Massachusetts Institute of Technology Press, 1955), pp. 86–103.

32 · N. Chomsky, *Syntactic Structures* (The Hague: Mouton, 1957).

33 · C. P. Snow, *The Two Cultures and the Scientific Revolution* (London: Cambridge University Press, 1959).

34 · P. F. Strawson, *Individuals* (London: Methuen, 1959).

Index

A

Absolute space, 207–218, 236
Absolute space-time, 216, 236–241
Absolute time, 209–210, 236
Achinstein, P., 89
Ackermann, W., 50, 311n
Adam, 110
Adams, J. C., 201
Advanced wave, 276
Africa, C., 326
Agassi, Joseph, 172
Alexander, H. Gavin, 171, 253
Algorithm, 29, 148–149
Analogy, 70–74
Analysis, 34–35, 251
Anderson, A. R., 330
A priori rule, 187
Aristotle, 161, 213
Armstrong, D. M., 347
Artificial intelligence, 308–317, 329–330
Ashby, W. Ross, 309, 326n, 330

Astronomy, 7, 91–92, 165–166, 195, 199, 258
Ayer, A. J., 64, 89

B

Bar-Hillel, Y., 268n, 288–289, 326
Barker, Stephen, 188, 203
Baumrin, B., 88–89, 204, 254
Beauregard, O. Costa de, 253, 277–278, 288
Behavior, 114–115
Bellarmine, Cardinal, 155
Benacerraf, P., 330
Bennett, Jonathan, 202
Bergmann, Gustav, 173
Berkeley, George, 137, 253
Bernays, P., 311n
Bit, 266–267
Black, Max, 119, 178, 204, 273n, 289
Bode's law, 64n
Bohr, Niels, 72–74
Boltzmann, L., 265, 289
Bolyai, W., 249
Bondi, H., 287, 289
Borel, E., 253
Born, Max, 172
Boyle's law, 71, 124, 128
Bradley, F. H., 264n
Braithwaite, R. B., 19, 120, 178, 330
Branch system, 271, 274, 282–283, 285–286
Brazil, 199
Bridgman, P. W., 139
Broad, C. D., 203
Brodbeck, M., 20, 89
Bromberger, Sylvian, 89
Brownian movement, 82–83
Bull, W. E., 326
Bunge, Mario, 120
Burks, A. W., 205

Butler, R. J., 205
Butts, Robert E., 89

C

Calibrated instruments, 130
Caloric theory, 193
Campbell, C. A., 329
Campbell, N. R., 71, 126–131, 171
Cargile, James, 184n
Carnap, Rudolf, 20, 51, 82n, 144n, 154, 165, 196–198, 205, 268n, 289
Chance, 297–298, 300
Cherry, Colin, 289
Chomsky, Noam, 10, 120, 315, 327–328, 330
Christenson, J. H., 260
Christianity, 184
Church, Alonzo, 29–30, 50
Churchman, C. W., 171
Clarke, Samuel, 252
Clock paradox, 228–235
Cohen, E. G. D., 289
Cohen, Paul J., 35
Cohen, R. S., 88, 330
Colodny, R. G., 20, 88–89, 204, 206, 289, 329
Completeness, 28
Computability, 50
Confirmation, 196–198
Congruence convention, 244–249
Conservation laws, 160–161
Context dependence, 37, 255
Continuum hypothesis, 35
Contrary to fact conditionals, 63
Convergent rule, 185, 187
Copenhagen interpretation, 17, 156–157, 159, 172
Copernicus, 151, 155–156
Correspondence rules, 77–78
Corroboration, 198–200
Cosmology, 92, 170, 216–217, 236–241, 264, 271, 280–283, 285–289
Counter-inductive policy, 185–186

Covering law model of explanation, 67–70, 258
Craig, William, 147, 149–152, 173
Creed, Isabel, 184n
Crommelin, A. C. D., 199
Crooked rule, 185, 137
Cronin, J. W., 260
Curvature, 238–241, 250
Cybernetics, 5, 321–327

D

Danto, A., 20, 172
Darwin, Charles, 101–102
Davidson, C., 199
Davis, Martin, 50
Dear, G. F., 294–295
Decision procedure, 29, 30, 51, 141n, 191n, 307, 310, 318
Democritus, 17
Denotation, 28
Derived magnitude, 127–128
Descartes, René, 208, 216, 239–241
Description, 31, 59
Determinism, 228–229, 291–305
Deutsch, J. A., 113n, 116–119
Dispositional property, 169–170, 173
Doppler effect, 220, 278
Dray, William, 67
Duhem, Pierre, 195, 200–202, 205, 246–247

E

Earth, 64n, 95–96, 212
Eccles, J. C., 304–305
Ecology, 107
Economics, 7
Eddington, A. S., 80, 130, 199, 253, 278
Edwards, Paul, 181–184, 203–204

Effective hypothesis, 193–195
Einstein, Albert, 18, 86, 133, 139–141, 198–199, 213, 221–222, 239, 253, 278
Electronics, 98–101, 112–114, 119, 172
Elementary number theory, 32–33, 148, 317, 320
Eliminative induction, 179–180
Ellis, Brian, 171, 191–193, 195, 204
Entropy, 77, 265–278
Enumeration, simple, 190, 192
Epistemic requirement, 67
Ergodic theorem, 262
Evolution, 55, 69, 95, 101–110, 119, 305, 314–315
Experimental laws, 121–123
Explanation sketch, 67, 69–70, 103
Extension, 28
Extensional context, 39–40, 164

F

Farrell, B. A., 115–117, 119
Feigl, Herbert, 16, 20, 88–89, 171–173, 183, 204
Feyerabend, P. K., 20, 77, 79-89, 144n, 154–156, 161–162, 171–172, 205, 247, 329–330
Fisher, R. A., 105n, 107
Fitch, V. L., 260
Flew, Antony, 89, 184n, 204
Fodor, J. A., 114, 119, 330
Foucault's pendulum, 212–213
Fourier, J. B. J., 72
Free will, 298, 300–305
Frequency, 43–48, 157
Fundamental magnitude, 126–130

G

Galilean transformation, 218–220, 222–223
Galileo, 59, 84–85, 155

Games, theory of, 7
Gardner, Martin, 254
Geiger counter, 299, 304
Gelernter, H. L., 316
Gentzen, G., 320n
Geodesic, 248
Geology, 7, 91
Geometrical optics, 79, 143
Geometry, 241–254, 307–308, 316–317
George, F. H., 329
Gibbs, J. W., 74
God, 101–102, 215–216
Gödel, Kurt, 28, 32–33, 35, 50, 148–150, 317, 319–320, 330
Gold, T., 280, 282–283, 285, 287, 289
Good, I. J., 51
Goodman, Nelson, 62, 188–189, 191, 205, 330
Greeks, 207
Grünbaum, A., 20, 201–202, 205, 221, 238–239, 244–248, 254–255, 257, 271, 273n, 274, 288
Guinea, Gulf of, 199

H

Hacking, Ian, 189n, 204
Hamblin, C. C., 31n
Hamlyn, D. W., 323
Hammond, L. M., 50
Hanson, N. R., 20, 172
Harlow, H. F., 120
Harré, R., 172
Harrod, R. F., 205
Hayek, F. A., 120
Hebb, D. O., 120
Hedrick, E. R, 254
Heisenberg, W., 12, 57, 160
Hempel, C. G., 20, 51, 57, 75, 152, 171, 206
Henderson, L. J., 111, 120
Heuristics, 313–314, 316–319
Hilbert, David, 5, 18, 140n, 249–251, 311n

Hobart, R. E., 329
Hospers, John, 89
H theorem, 265, 289
Hume, David, 5, 18, 140n, 176–182, 184, 189, 204

I

Idealism, 15, 130
Identity, 30
Indeterminism, 228, 292–293, 295–298, 300–301
Induction, 134, 175–200, 202–205, 231–232, 247, 315
Inertial system, 165–166, 211–216, 237
Inference ticket, 171
Information, 264–268, 289, 305, 307, 314, 320, 322–323, 326
Instance confirmation, 197
Instrumentalism, 135, 138, 141–144, 150–151, 171-172, 197, 200
Intelligence, 307–311, 313, 315–316, 324, 329–330
Intensional contexts, 39–40
Ives-Stilwell experiment, 220

J

Jakobson, R., 289
Jammer, Max, 253
Jeffress, L. A., 330
Jeffrey, G. B., 253
Jeffrey, Richard C., 205
Jupiter, 64n, 258–259

K

Kant, Immanuel, 18, 207, 217, 328-330
Katz, Jerrold J., 184, 202, 204, 330
Kelvin (Lord), 74
Kemeny, J. G., 79, 205

Kennedy-Thorndike experiment, 220–221
Keynes, J. M., 179–180, 203
Kleene, S. C., 50
Kneale, W., 51, 89, 203
Körner, S., 20

L

Lamarck, J. B. de, 102
Laplace, P. S. de, 284–285, 292–293, 296–297
Leckie, G. G., 50
Leibnitz, Gottfried von, 207, 215–216, 239–241, 253
Leverrier, U. J. J., 201
Levi, I., 204
Limited variety, 179–180, 203
Linguistics, 4, 9, 327–330
Lobachevski, Nikolai, 249
Logic: predicate, 26–31, 148; sentential, 23–26, 147
Lorentz, H. A., 220–221, 253
Lorentz transformation, 221–225
Loschmidt, J., 262-263
Lowinger, Armand, 205

M

McCarthy, J., 329
McCrea, W. H., 254
Mach, Ernst, 18, 137, 140n, 172, 213, 237, 239, 253
Machine translation, 326–328
MacKay, D. M., 305
McKinsey, J. C. C., 163
Macroentropy, 268–270, 282
Macro-phenomenalism, 144, 153–154
Magic, 16
Mainx, Felix, 120
Marcus, Ruth Barcan, 51

Margenau, H., 162, 163n, 172
Mars, 64n
Maxwell, Grover, 20, 88–89, 153, 171–173, 205, 329
Maxwell, James Clerk, 218, 220, 276
Mayo, Bernard, 338
Measure theory, 245
Measurement, 121–129, 171–172
Mehlberg, Henryk, 133
Mellor, D. H., 171
Memory, 256–258, 263–264, 288, 309, 313–314
Mercury, 64n, 83, 199, 201
Metalanguage, 38, 167–169, 320
Metalogic, 41
Metamathematics, 57, 168, 293, 319
Michelson-Morley experiment, 219–221
Miller, Dickinson S., 329
Minkowski, H., 221, 223, 225–226, 231, 234–235, 242, 253
Minski, M. L., 316–317, 329
Mischel, Theodore, 330
Mises, R. von, 51
Modal expressions, 40, 164–165, 292–293
Model, 151
Mohs' scale, 127n
Monads, 208–209
Morgenbesser, S., 20, 172

N

Nagel, Ernest, 20, 50–51, 79, 87n, 88–89, 120, 171, 173, 203, 205, 251, 254
Natural history, 91–98, 119
Neidorf, Robert, 173
Neptune, 64n
Neumann, J. von, 34, 296, 330
Newell, Allen, 311, 313–314
Newman, J. R., 50
Newton, Isaac, 9, 55, 59, 71, 79–80, 83, 86–89, 106–107, 132–134, 164–165, 166n, 179, 195, 201–202, 209–211, 213–217, 221–225, 239, 253, 284, 296
Newton's bucket, 211–213

Noble, C. A., 254
Non-Euclidean geometry, 18, 135, 249–251, 254

O

Observation sentences, 15, 136–137, 143–145, 150
Ohm's law, 121, 131
Olbers, H. W. M., 75, 280–281, 287
Oparin, A. I., 120
Operationism, 135, 138–144, 171, 215, 241
Oppenheim, P., 79
Ostensive predicates, 189

P

Paleontology, 103
Pap, A., 20, 173, 203
Parity, 217, 260
Partial explanation, 67-70, 113-119
Pascal, Blaise, 184
Passmore, J. A., 205
Past, present, and future, 255–256, 279
Pauli, W., 162
Phenomenalism, 135, 137–138, 151, 153, 154n, 156, 172
Phlogiston, 86
Plato, 207
Pluto, 64n
Pointer readings, 130
Popper, K. R., 20, 46–47, 51, 177, 192, 196–202, 205, 253, 278, 286,
    288–289, 295–296
Possibility, 43–44
Pragmatics, 57–58
Predicate logic, 26–31, 33, 35
Presley, C. F., 172
Principe, Gulf of Guinea, 199
Probability: frequency interpretation, 43–48, 51; metalinguistic in-
    terpretation, 41, 44–46; propensity interpretation, 46–49, 51, 160,
    177

Program, 301–303, 307, 312–314, 316, 321, 324–325
Progression, 34
Proof theory, 37
Psycholinguistics, 327, 329–330
Psychology, 112–119, 328
Ptolemaic hypothesis, 151, 155–156
Pure chance, 297–298, 300
Purposive mechanism, 114–116, 321–324, 330
Putnam, Hilary, 50, 84–85, 88, 172–173, 193, 196, 205, 247–248, 254, 319, 330
Pythagoras' theorem, 250

Q

Quantifiers, 26
Quantum mechanics, 47, 67, 72–75, 139, 155–163, 169, 242, 259–260, 293, 296–297, 300–301, 304
Quasar, 79
Quasi-ergodic hypothesis, 277
Quine, W. V., 31, 35, 38n, 49–51, 84, 164–165, 173, 202, 205, 252n

R

Ramsey sentence, 145–147
Rational belief, 45
Ratoosh, P., 171
Reasons, 300–301, 306
Records, 105, 258, 260, 270, 282, 285
Redescription, 70
Reichenbach, H., 20, 89, 173, 183, 193, 204, 244, 254, 268, 274, 283, 288
Relative space, 207–208, 214, 217, 253
Relative space-time, 237–241
Relative time, 210, 253
Relativity, 75, 79, 83, 132n, 133, 139–140, 166n, 216–239, 282n, 286
Retarded wave, 276–278
Riemann, G. F. B., 240
Roberts, K. V., 296

Robertson, H. P., 253
Rose, J. Holland, 331
Rosser, Barkley, 33n, 50, 320n
Routley, Richard, 166n
Russell, Bertrand, 35, 182, 203, 310, 311n
Ryle, Gilbert, 12–13, 48, 142, 171, 294

S

Salmon, Wesley, 185, 187–193, 204
Saturn, 64n
Scheffler, Israel, 8–10, 19
Schema, 24–28, 251
Schilpp, P. A., 51, 205, 253
Schlegel, Richard, 289
Schlick, Moritz, 256n
Schrödinger, E., 259, 289
Sciama, D. W., 296
Scope, 27
Scriven, Michael, 57, 68, 89, 106, 119, 131–133, 171, 173
Sellars, Wilfrid, 80n, 88, 138, 172–173, 330
Semantics, 33, 37–38, 57, 266, 320, 326
Sentential logic, 23–26, 310–313
Set theory, 33, 163, 317
Shakespeare, William, 309
Shannon, C. E., 264, 289, 329
Shapere, Dudley, 89
Shaw, J. C., 311, 313–314
Simon, Herbert A., 311, 313–314, 329
Skinner, B. F., 120, 319, 330
Smart, J. J. C., 20, 172–173, 253, 329–330
Smullyan, R., 50
Snell's law, 122
Sobral, Brazil, 199
Sokal, Robert R., 95n
Space, 207–218
Space-time, 241–248, 252–256
Spector, Marshall, 172
Statistical explanation, 65–66, 69, 102–103, 106

Statistical laws, 69, 177, 194n
Statistical mechanics, 77–79, 259–265, 275, 277
Statistical taxonomy, 95n
Steinhardt, F., 50
Stevens, S. S., 171
Stove, D. C., 205
Straight rule, 185, 187, 191
Stratification, 35
Strawson, P. F., 204, 328
Strong conditional, 164–165, 167–169, 292
Structural terms, 8–10
Subjunctive conditional, 167–168, 292
Sufficient reason, 215–216
Sugar, A. C., 163
Suppes, P., 163
Syntax, 32, 51, 57, 145, 168, 266, 293, 295, 320

T

Tarski, Alfred, 30, 37
Tautologous schema, 25–26
Taxonomy, 92–96
Taylor, Richard, 322, 324, 330
Teichrow, D., 326
Teleological explanation, 55, 100–102, 120
Temperature, 84–86
Thermodynamics, 14, 77–78, 82–83, 133, 217, 259–265, 271, 281–289
Thomson, G. P., 87
Thomson, Judith Jarvis, 205
Thomson, W., 74
Thornton, J. B., 172
Time, 207, 209–210
Topology, 235, 244, 248–249, 281n, 306–307
Toulmin, Stephen, 20, 119, 142–143, 171, 263n
Traces, 258–260, 263, 282, 285–286, 288
Truth, 36–37
Truth functions, 14, 268
Truth table, 24, 26
Turing, A. M., 50, 318–321, 326, 330

Turlay, R., 260
Turner, Merle B., 120
Type rules, 35

U

Uranus, 200–201
Urmson, J. O., 204

V

Valency, 153
Valid schema, 25–28
Validation, 16, 183, 189, 196
Van Kampen, N. G., 289
Van der Waals' equation, 124–125
Variable: bound, 26; free, 26
Venus, 64n, 211
Vindication, 16, 183–185, 189–190, 193–194, 203
Void, 207–208
Vulcan, 201

W

Wald, George, 120
Wallace, John R., 205
Walter, W. Grey, 321–322
Wartofsky, M. W., 51, 88, 330
Watkins, J. W. N., 205
Watson, W. H., 11, 14–16, 19
Weaver, Warren, 289
Wells, Rulon S., 289
Weyl, H., 253
Wheeler, J. A., 170, 216, 240–241, 252
Whitehead, A. N., 163n, 310, 310n

Wiener, Norbert, 274, 289
Wigner, Eugene P., 254
Will, F. L., 204
Williams, D. C., 204–205
Williams, W. T., 111, 120
Wisdom, J. O., 205
Witchcraft, 16
Wittgenstein, Ludwig, 9, 11–12, 18, 20, 120, 183, 306
Woodger, J. H., 120
Woolsey, C. N., 120
World line, 223, 225–226, 231, 235, 248, 256
Wright, G. H. von, 51, 203, 205

Z

Zeno, 252, 254
Zermelo, E., 34